TEACHER'S EDITION

P9-BYM-161

Common Core
Progress™
Mathematics

2

For additional online resources, access your state-specific Teacher Toolbox.
Go to **www.SadlierConnect.com** and enter the **Teacher's Access Code:**

State	Access Code	State	Access Code
Alabama	CCPM01AL23	Mississippi	CCPM28MS2S
Arizona	CCPM04AZ2O	Missouri	CCPM29MO24
Arkansas	CCPM05AR22	New Jersey	CCPM34NJ2A
California	CCPM06CA24	North Carolina	CCPM37NC2V
Colorado	CCPM08CO2W	Ohio	CCPM39OH2P
Connecticut	CCPM09CT2U	Oklahoma	CCPM40OI2
Florida	CCPM12FL29	Pennsylvania	CCPM42PA2K
Georgia	CCPM13GA2B	South Carolina	CCPM45SC2Y
Illinois	CCPM17IL2X	Tennessee	CCPM47TN2D
Kentucky	CCPM21KY2C	Texas	CCPM48TX2I
Louisiana	CCPM22LA2Z	Wisconsin	CCPM55WI22
Massachusetts	CCPM25MA2G	Other States	CCPMNA229Y
Michigan	CCPM26MI2L		

Sadlier School

TEACHER'S EDITION

Common Core
Progress™
Mathematics

Cover: *Series Design:* Studio Montage;
Title design: Quarasan, Inc.

Photo Credits: Cover: age fotostock/Zoonar/N Sorokin: *right*. Getty Images/Daryl Solomon: *top left*. Used under license from Shutterstock.com/RoboLab: *background*. Interior: Blend Images/Jose Luis Pelaez Inc: T3; Corbis/ Ocean: T15; Dreamstime.com/Nyul: T17; Yobro10: T9. Masterfile (Royalty Free Division): T12; Blend Images/ Radius Images: 144 *top*. Corbis/Blend Images/JGI/Jamie Grill: 54 *top*. Dreamstime.com/Viktor Gladkov: vi *top right*; Oleg Zhukov: 145. Getty Images/Mark Bowden: 246 *top*; John Lund/Sam Diephuis: 9; SelectStock: 8 *top*; Daryl Solomon: vi *center*. iStockphoto.com/busypix: 55. Used under license from Shutterstock.com/Cimpinski: 145 *inset*; elisekurenbina: vi *bottom left*; FocusDzign: vi *top left*; Jana Guothova: 8 *bottom*, 54 *bottom*, 144 *bottom*, 246 *bottom*; Ian 2010: vi *bottom right*; RoboLab: 1, vi *background*.

Illustrator Credit: Bob Holt

William H. Sadlier, Inc.
9 Pine Street
New York, NY 10005-4700

Printed in the United States of America.
ISBN: 978-1-4217-3162-9
1 2 3 4 5 6 7 8 9 WEBC 18 17 16 15 14

Common Core State Standards © 2010. National Governors Association Center for Best Practices and Council of Chief State School Officers. All rights reserved.

Contents

Access Your Digital Resources

Get Started

1. Go to www.SadlierConnect.com.

2. Log in

Don't have a username and password?
Self register! Teachers click "Get Started!" in
the Teacher Registration section.

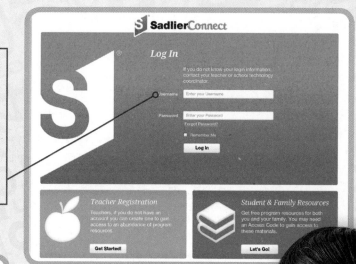

3. Select your program to begin accessing content.

With one username and password,
you now have access to all your
Sadlier Mathematics and English
Language Arts content.

Contents

continued on next page

Contents

continued on next page

Contents

Program Overview

Common Core Progress Mathematics is a streamlined, yet comprehensive K-8 supplemental mathematics program that follows the structure of the Common Core State Standards for Mathematics and integrates the Standards for Mathematical Practice into every lesson. The program systematically addresses all of the Common Core State Standards for Mathematics across the Domains: Operations and Algebraic Thinking, Number and Operations in Base Ten, Measurement and Data, and Geometry, which helps prepare students for the rigor of Common Core standardized assessments and enables them to develop key college and career readiness skills.

In *Common Core Progress*, students will:

- Build understanding of key mathematical concepts using multiple representations of a skill.

- Model mathematics with real-world problems to make sense of math and apply their knowledge.

- Share their thinking and reason mathematically while developing academic vocabulary.

- Use higher-level thinking skills and apply levels of Webb's Depth of Knowledge (DOK) with rigorous, cognitively-demanding independent practice items.

- Regularly use the Standards for Mathematical Practice so that they become habits of mind.

With the support of a comprehensive Teacher's Edition, teachers will be able to:

- Scaffold student learning with easy-to-use, comprehensive lesson plans.

- Use student assessment data, both observational and formal, to inform and redirect instruction.

- Understand the progression of Common Core Mathematics requirements across grade levels and tailor instruction to Common Core grade-level standards.

- Support diverse learners, including English language learners, struggling learners, and those needing extended learning opportunities.

- Access online and professional development resources to enhance instruction.

Founded on the Common Core Standards

Sadlier's *Common Core Progress Mathematics* was designed to effectively implement the three instructional shifts (focus, coherence, and rigor) that are necessary to teach the Common Core State Standards (CCSS) and fully addresses the shifts that were reorganized by Student Achievement Partners and the Publisher's Criteria to fall under rigor: fluency, deep understanding, application, and dual intensity.

Shifts in Mathematics Common Core Standards		
Shift	**Requirement**	**How Addressed in *Common Core Progress***
Focus	Class time and energy spent on a deeper focus on the key concepts as prioritized by the standards.	*Common Core Progress* is designed to focus on the major work of the grade per the CCSS.
Coherence	Learning within and across grade levels is carefully connected in order to build students' understanding.	Learning Progression charts that describe how the standards are developed across the grade levels are provided for each unit.
Rigor as Fluency	Students are expected to have speed and accuracy with simple calculations; teachers structure class or homework time for students to memorize through repetition.	Fluency Practice is provided (online) with references to the extra practice included at point of use in the Teacher's Edition.
Rigor as Deep Understanding	Students deeply understand and can operate easily within a math concept before moving on.	The structure of the lesson allows the student to develop a deep understanding of the concept being covered, with the Guided Instruction and Guided Practice portions of the lesson establishing the conceptual understanding.
Rigor as Application	Students use math and choose appropriate concept for application–not only when prompted.	While working independently on the independent practice and the performance tasks, students must determine which skills, strategies, and practices best serve to solve the problems and tasks at hand.
Rigor as Dual Intensity	Students are practicing and understanding with intensity.	As students work through the scaffolded Independent Practice exercises, teachers can gauge student understanding of the concepts by referencing the Common Error Analysis guidance provided in the Teacher's Edition. Through both direct instruction and practice students work toward a deep understanding of the concept.

Flexible Program Use

Common Core Progress fully aligns to the Common Core State Standards, serving as a flexible resource for supporting schools in meeting the full breadth and rigor of these standards. Lessons focus on the key concepts addressed in the Common Core and combine solid content with a pedagogically-sound lesson design that simplifies the instructional process.

Common Core Progress can be used as:

- Supplemental lessons to fill Common Core gaps in a current core Mathematics program.

- Targeted preparation materials for Common Core standardized assessments.

- Support for individual or small group instruction on a particular Common Core standard.

Diverse Grouping Models

The *Common Core Progress* program employs diverse grouping and instructional models to help teachers provide effective instruction in the Common Core State Standards.

Guided Instruction For standard instruction, the program uses **whole-class** instruction to provide direct skill instruction and think-aloud modeling while the students follow along with the teacher, helping students conceptualize skills and concepts through modeling and reasoning.

Guided Practice For scaffolded practice of the standard, students work through problems of increasing complexity, independently or in small groups, as the teacher circulates around the classroom to gauge understanding of the concepts and skill being learned.

Independent Practice For application of the standards, lessons offer independent practice requiring students to use their critical-thinking skills and apply their math knowledge.

Foundational Skill Support and Fluency Practice

Foundational skills lessons and fluency practice are provided in the following ways in *Common Core Progress*.

- A comprehensive Foundational Skills Handbook, located in the back of this guide as well as in the student edition, provides a review of *all* prerequisite mathematics needed to understand the concepts and skills of Grade 2.

- Fluency practice is available online providing students with the opportunity to build their skills of performing calculations and solving problems quickly and accurately in order to meet the grade level fluency expectations specified by the Common Core State Standards.

- Problem-Solving Model offers students a four-step model as an approach to solving problems.

Print Edition

Print Components

Student Worktext

Organized around the Common Core Domains, the standards-based instruction includes clearly-stated models, multiple representations of skills, a focus on the critical areas of each grade level, and connections between topics to meet all Common Core State Standards. ▶

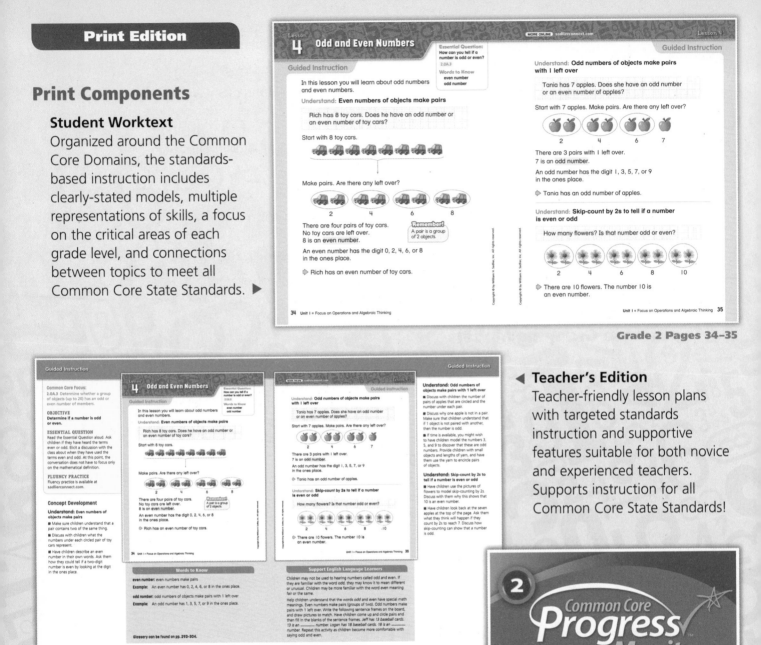

Grade 2 Pages 34–35

Grade 2 Teacher's Edition Pages 34–35

◀ Teacher's Edition

Teacher-friendly lesson plans with targeted standards instruction and supportive features suitable for both novice and experienced teachers. Supports instruction for all Common Core State Standards!

Progress Monitor

Four comprehensive Benchmark Assessments to identify instructional needs as benchmarked against the grade level's full set of Common Core State Standards. ▶

Grade 2 Progress Monitor

Digital Components

A rich array of online digital components supports program implementation and extends learning.

- **Home Connect Activities** support family member involvement and help create associations with math in real-world situations

- **Student Book Performance Tasks 1 and 2 Resources** allow students to apply their learning and provide teachers with robust evaluation support

- Downloadable **Unit Performance Tasks** provide practice opportunities for Performance Tasks related to the program's instructional units

- **Additional Practice** downloadables offer opportunities to augment program practice

- **Fluency Practice** downloadables provide opportunities for students to improve speed and accuracy with simple calculations

- **Teacher Resources**, such as a professional development training video support teachers in implementing the program

iProgress Monitor (Optional Purchase)

This dynamic online assessment system is available to help monitor student progress on the Common Core standards in real time and customize assignments based on individual needs through it's built-in test generator feature. See page T13 of this guide for more information.

Online State-Specific Teacher Toolbox

Tailored to your state, and to each grade level, K-8, the online State-Specific Teacher Toolbox has everything you need to seamlessly incorporate *Progress* into your core Math programs!

Find answers to critical questions on structure and pacing to assessment to professional development and much more! Learn how *Progress*...

- Relates to your state's Common Core **implementation plan**.

- Aligns with the **structure and pacing** of your state's model curriculum.

- Correlates to your **state's standards**.

- Supports your state's **assessment** plan.

- Helps to implement a **Common Core curriculum**.

- Provides embedded **Professional Development**.

Interactive Edition

The Interactive Edition of *Common Core Progress* is a web-based version of the complete program through **www.SadlierConnect.com**, with access to rich media and an abundance of resources for teachers, students, and parents.

Core Digital Components

Digital **Student Worktext** Digital version of the Student Worktext, accessible online to all students.

Digital **Teacher's Edition** Digital version of the Teacher's Edition, available 24/7 to teachers at home or at school without the need to carry a heavy text! Incorporates links to all online resources as well as iProgress Monitor.

Digital Components
Exclusive to the Interactive Edition!

- **Interactive Whiteboard Tools** provide support for teaching key skills and concepts.

- **Domain- and Lesson-Specific Videos** support student learning of Commom Core State Standards.

- **iProgress Monitor** gives students access to:
  - Independent Practice
  - Common Core Reviews
  - Performance Tasks

Plus, access program assessment in a digital format or build your own!

Plus all the Digital Components included with the Print Edition!

Common Core Progress contains many formative and summative assessment opportunities to help teachers gather evidence of students' progress toward mastering the Common Core State Standards and prepare for the new Common Core assessments.

Integrated, Ongoing Assessment Opportunities

Observational Assessment opportunities are a routine part of each Lesson Plan in the Teacher's Edition. Common Errors and Teaching Tips features at point of use help teachers identify student misconceptions and provide strategies for solutions. ▶

Teaching Tips

Item 16
Students may have difficulty solving the problem because they do not draw the array correctly. Provide grid paper for those who have difficulty aligning rows and columns.

Unit 2 Common Core Review

1. Write how many hundreds, tens, and ones. Then write the number.

_____ hundreds _____ tens _____ ones

2. Skip-count by 5s.

900, _____, 910, 915, _____, _____, 930, _____, 940

3. Skip-count by 10s.

265, _____, _____, 295, _____, _____, 325, _____, 345

Write the number and the expanded form for the number name.

4. one hundred thirty-nine _____ _____

5. six hundred eight _____ _____

Compare. Write >, <, or =.

6. 410 ◯ 401   7. 340 ◯ 434

136 Unit 2 ▪ Focus on Number and Operations in Base Ten

Grade 2 Page 136

◀ Unit **Common Core Reviews** assess the Common Core State Standards taught within the Unit and expose students to the question types that they might experience on the new Common Core assessments.

---

9. Which equations have a difference of 5?

A 15 − 10 = ▤ *and* 9 − 4 = ▤
B 15 − 10 = ▤ *and* 12 − 8 = ▤
C 9 − 4 = ▤ *and* 12 − 8 = ▤
D 15 − 10 = ▤, 9 − 4 = ▤, *and* 12 − 8 = ▤

10. Anne collected leaves. She put them into groups of 5.

How many leaves did Anne collect?

A 3   B 5   C 15   D 20

11. The clock shows the time that Lita's soccer practice starts.

At what time does Lita's soccer practice start?

A 4:10 P.M.
B 4:50 P.M.
C 5:50 P.M.
D 10:25 P.M.

Go on

8 Benchmark 1 ▪ Book A ▪ Progress Monitor

Grade 2 Progress Monitor Benchmark Assessment

◀ Benchmark Assessments in **Progress Monitor** (an optional purchase) provide four comprehensive assessments that can be administered periodically throughout the school year to evaluate students' knowledge and skill level relative to the grade level's set of Common Core State Standards.

Performance Tasks 1 and 2

provide benchmark Performance Tasks that parallel the tasks in standardized assessments to be used as guided practice opportunities. The tasks assess conceptual understanding of the content standards and show evidence of the Standards for Mathematical Practice through application, modeling, and written arguments. They are also available online at **www.SadlierConnect.com**. These Performance Tasks can also be used for mid-year and end-of-year assessment purposes. These Performance Tasks play a vital role in helping you determine if students are able to integrate the standards being taught and apply them in solving real-world problems. ▶

Grade 2 Pages 276–277

Performance Task 2

Summer Camp

1. Every morning the children at Blue Lake Camp work on craft projects. Terry drew this fish that he planned to carve from a piece of wood.

a. Estimate the length of Terry's fish drawing in centimeters.

The drawing is about _____ centimeters long. Talk about how you estimated the length.

b. Draw a fish that you would like to carve from a piece of wood. Estimate the length of your drawing in centimeters.

c. Use a centimeter ruler to measure Terry's fish. Then measure your fish to the nearest centimeter.

Terry's fish is _____ centimeters long.

My fish is _____ centimeters long.

d. Compare the lengths. Whose fish is longer? How much longer?

_____ fish is _____ centimeters _____ than _____ fish.

At the Camp Store

2. Keesha needs 56¢ to buy a marker.

a. Draw coins that Keesha could use to pay for the marker.

b. Draw a different group of coins that Keesha could use to pay for the marker.

c. Tell how you checked the value of your groups of coins.

276 Performance Task 2

Performance Task 2 277

Downloadable **Unit Performance Tasks**, available online at **www.SadlierConnect.com**, provide practice opportunities for students to solve real-world problems that integrate the standards within each Domain, connect to the Standards for Mathematical Practice, and often require students explain and justify their solutions.

iProgress Monitor (Optional Purchase)

Augment your assessment resources with customized assignments and test-building power!

- **Independent Practice, Unit Common Core Reviews, and Benchmark Assessment** items can be assigned to individual learners with reports that capture student progress. Includes additional items beyond those in the print program. Items can be accessed according to standard/lesson. Responses are automatically scored and reported in a grade book.

- The **Build a Test** feature enables teachers to customize assignments/assessments by a particular standard with items beyond those provided in the Student Worktext.

Student Worktext

With a full-color, engaging design the Student Worktext, also available in an ebook format, provides students with the opportunity to

- Develop proficiency in mathematics through the integration of the Common Core State Standards and the Standards for Mathematical Practice
- Build conceptual understanding of mathematical content following a gradual release of responsibility model of instruction
- Reason and communicate mathematically
- Develop mathematical arguments and model real world problems

Organized around the Common Core Domains, the lessons in the Student Worktext address all of the Common Core State Standards and focus on the major work of each grade level.

A Unit Introduction That Focuses on Standards

Grade 2 Page 54

Home Connect activities for each unit provide families a window into their child's learning and encourage them to take an active role.

Grade 2 Page 53

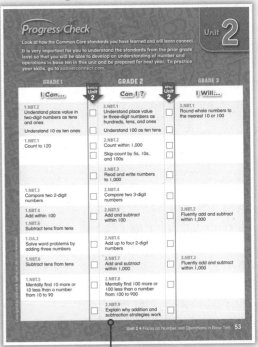

Progress Check at the beginning of each unit allows students to focus on the unit's key standards, self-assess before learning, and reflect on progress at the end of the unit.

Grade 2 Page 55

An **Essential Question** sets the focus and identifies the big idea for each unit, enhanced with vivid images featuring engaging and relevant content that helps students make connections between math and the real world.

Gradual Release of Responsibility

Each standard is taught using a gradual release of responsibility instructional model. By gradually decreasing the level of support within each lesson, students can develop the conceptual understanding necessary for solving complex problems and tasks independently.

This gradual release of responsibility instructional model starts with **Guided Instruction**, helping students conceptualize skills and concepts through modeling and reasoning. The Standards for Mathematical Practice (MP) are embedded in all instructional presentations.

Guided Instruction

The **Understand** instructional presentations break down the Common Core State Standards into simpler chunks of content to help students build their knowledge of the complete standard being addressed.

Each lesson begins with an **Essential Question** to prompt students' thinking and classroom discussion to help define the lesson objective.

Key **academic vocabulary** is highlighted and used strategically when teaching the lesson.

The **Connect** and **Understand** presentations, together, help build knowledge to answer the lesson's Essential Question.

Notes provided throughout the instruction provide scaffolding of concepts so students can go back and review each step.

Opportunities for classroom discussion integrate the Standards for Mathematical Practice and build student confidence with the new material being learned.

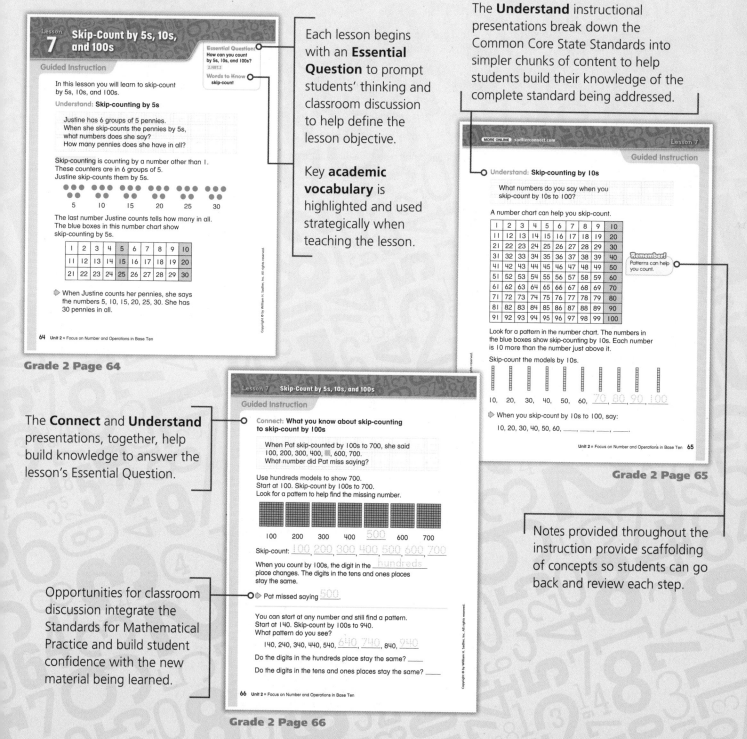

Grade 2 Page 64

Grade 2 Page 65

Grade 2 Page 66

T15

Gradual Release of Responsibility

The structure of the lesson continues the gradual release of responsibility model with **Guided Practice**, which allows the opportunity for students to work through problems with the teacher's supervision and assistance.

Guided Practice

Grade 2 Page 67

Scaffolding is gradually removed as students work through the problems on the page(s). This allows the students more independence in applying and developing strategies and skills necessary to solve the problems.

MORE ONLINE sadlierconnect.com

Lesson 7

Guided Practice

I. **What are the missing numbers?**

5, 10, 15, 20, ▢, 30, ▢, ▢

Step 1

Look for a pattern to find the first missing number.

The pattern shows skip-counting by what number? __5__

When you skip-count by 5, the ones digit is __0__ or ___.

What number comes before the first missing number? ___

The ones digit in the first missing number is ___.

What is the first missing number? ___

Step 2

Use the pattern to find the other missing numbers.

What is the ones digit in the missing number

that comes next after 30? ___

What is that missing number? ___

What is the last missing number? ___

The missing numbers are ___, ___, and ___.

👦 **Think•Pair•Share**

MP3 2. Lucy is number 114 in a line for a museum. Bill is 10 people behind Lucy in the line. Erica is 10 people behind Bill. What number is Erica? Talk about how you know.

Erica is number ___ in the line.

Unit 2 ▪ Focus on Number and Operat...

Think-Pair-Share opportunities encourage students to think independently about mathematics and then discuss, model, and explain their reasoning while learning from one another, serving to establish reliance on the Standards for Mathematical Practice.

👦 **Think•Pair•Share**

Gradual Release of Responsibility

The gradual release of responsibility model culminates with **Independent Practice**, which requires students to use their critical-thinking skills, apply their math knowledge, and respond to problems leveled to Webb's Depth of Knowledge. These Independent Practice pages can be used independently at home or in class.

Independent Practice

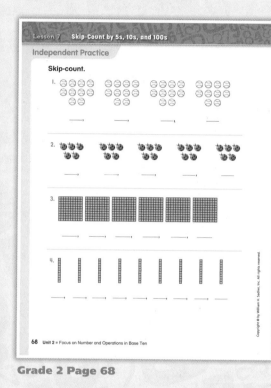

As the level of scaffolding decreases and students' knowledge and confidence with the material increases, the exercises become more difficult and require higher-order thinking as well as justification of answers.

Grade 2 Page 68

Lesson 7

Independent Practice

Write the missing numbers.

5. Skip-count by 5s.   5, 10, 15, ___, 25, ___, 35

6. Skip-count by 100s.   100, 200, ___, ___, 500, 600

7. Skip-count by 10s.   10, ___, 30, ___, ___, 60, 70

Circle the correct answer.

8. Linda skip-counted like this:
   100, 110, 120, 130, 140, 150, 160
   How did she skip-count?

   by 5s   by 10s   by 100s

9. Theo started at 300. He skip-counted by 100s. Which shows how Theo counted?

   300, 400, 500, 600, 700

   100, 200, 300, 400, 500

   300, 310, 320, 330, 340

10. See how Mia skip-counted.

   5, 10, 15, 20, 25, 30, ▨

   What was the last number she said?

   40

   35

   45

Grade 2 Page 69

Lesson 7   Skip-Count by 5s, 10s, and 100s

Independent Practice

11. Skip-count by 100s.
    250, 350, 450, ___, 650, ___, 850, ___

12. Skip-count by 10s.
    140, 150, 160, ___, 180, ___, 210, ___, ___

13. Skip-count by 5s.
    100, ___, 110, 115, ___, 125, 130, ___, ___, 145, ___

14. Skip-count by 100s.
    176, 276, ___, 476, ___, ___, 776, ___, ___

15. Skip-count by 10s.
    335, ___, ___, 365, ___, ___, 395, ___

16. Skip-count by 5s.
    580, ___, ___, 595, ___, ___, 610, 615, ___

17. Skip-count by 5s.
    470, ___, ___, 485, ___, 495, ___, ___, 510

Students have ample opportunities to model, reason, and justify their answers and apply all of the Standards for Mathematical Practice.

Grade 2 Page 70

Lesson 7

Independent Practice

18. Skip-count by 10s.
    380, ___, ___, 410, ___, ___, 440, 450, ___

Count by 1s to find the missing numbers.

19.

788	789			792	793
		797	798		
	803	804		806	

20.

612			615		617
		621	622	623	
626	627		629		

21. Suppose you are counting by 1s. What are the next five numbers that come just after 347?

    347, ___, ___, ___, ___, ___

22. Rita skip-counted: 215, 225, 235, 245, 255, 265, 275. She says she started at 215 and skip-counted by 5s. Thomas says she skip-counted by 10s. Who is right? Explain.

Grade 2 Page 71

Built-In Common Core Assessment Practice

Every unit concludes with a **Common Core Review** that provides practice with items similar to those students will encounter on Common Core standardized assessments. Covering all of the standards presented in the unit, the reviews allow teachers to monitor student progress and understanding of each standard.

Unit | Common Core Review

Write a related subtraction fact.

1. $8 + 6 = 14$

_____ − _____ = _____

2. $4 + 9 = 13$

_____ − _____ = _____

Circle the correct answers.

3. Circle all the even numbers.

12 13 15 17 18

4. Circle all the odd numbers.

4 6 7 8 9

Add or subtract.

5. $16 − 9 = $ _____

6. $8 + $ _____ $ = 11$

7. _____ $ − 5 = 8$

8. _____ $ + 9 = 17$

9. $15 − 6 = $ _____

10. $14 − $ _____ $ = 7$

11. _____ $ + 8 = 15$

12. $9 + 9 = $ _____

50 Unit 1 • Focus on Operations and Algebraic Thinking

Grade 2 Page 50

Unit | Common Core Review

13. Circle the correct equation to solve the problem.

Brady has 32 fewer marbles than Emma.
Emma has 63 marbles.
How many marbles does Brady have?

$63 + 32 = 95$ $63 − 32 = 31$ $95 − 32 = 63$

14. Draw a picture to model the problem.
Write a subtraction equation. Then solve the problem.

There were 29 acorns.
Molly took some of them.
Now there are 14 acorns.
How many acorns did Molly take?

_____ − _____ = _____

Molly took _____ acorns.

Write and solve an addition equation to solve the problem.

15. Antonio collects 16 pinecones on Friday and 20 on Saturday. How many pinecones does he collect in all?

_____ + _____ = _____

Antonio collects _____ pinecones in all.

16. Noah has 19 shells. Gia has some shells too. Together Noah and Gia have 31 shells. How many shells does Gia have?

_____ + 🔲 = _____

Gia has _____ shells.

Unit 1 • Focus on Operations and Algebraic Thinking 51

Grade 2 Page 51

Unit | Common Core Review

even number. Draw 2 equal groups that you are correct. Then write an equation to show your work.

10   9

_____ = _____

the rows. Complete the equation to tell y hearts in all.

$4 + 4 + 4 = $ _____

the array. Circle the equation that shows y flowers.

$5 + 5 + 5 = 15$

$4 + 4 + 4 + 4 = 16$

$5 + 5 + 5 + 5 = 20$

array with 2 rows and 3 counters in . Write two equations for the array. each equation shows.

erations and Algebraic Thinking

Grade 2 Page 52

Performance Task 1

Riding the Bus

1. Alice takes the bus to school with her mom. After they got on the bus one morning, Alice counted 36 people in all on the bus.

At the first stop, 3 people got on the bus.
At the second stop, some people got off the bus. Then there were 29 people on the bus.

a. How many people were on the bus after the first stop? Tell how you know.

b. How many people got off the bus after the second stop? Tell how you know.

140 Performance Task 1

Grade 2 Page 140

Performance Task 1

Bus Station

2. At Gate A, 4 rows of are buses are parked. There are 3 buses in each row.

At Gate B, there are 5 rows of buses with 2 buses in each row.

a. Draw an array to show the buses parked at each gate.

b. Write an addition equation for each array.

Gate A: _____

Gate B: _____

c. How many buses are parked at Gate A and Gate B in all? Write an addition equation to help you solve the problem.

_____ + _____ = _____

There are _____ buses parked at Gates A and B in all.

d. There are 17 buses parked in two rows at Gate C. Can you draw an array to show the buses parked at Gate C? Tell how you know.

Performance Task 1 141

Grade 2 Page 141

Performance Tasks provide opportunities for students to demonstrate their understanding of content standards and to show evidence of the Standards for Mathematical Practice through application, modeling, and written arguments.

Teacher's Edition

Teacher-friendly, easy-to-use lesson plans support teachers in providing systematic instruction, practice, and application of Common Core State Standards. The Teacher's Edition is also available in an eBook format.

At-a-Glance Unit Introduction Pages

Unit introduction pages, featuring student self-assessment, a home connection, a planner for understanding key concepts at a glance, and learning progressions provide an at-a-glance reference for busy educators!

Each unit begins with support for student self-assessment and connecting to home. The **Progress Check** provides students with a visual roadmap identifying how the Standards are developed and linked across grade levels, emphasizing coherence.

Home Connect activities for each unit encourage families to take an active role in their child's learning and connect math to real-world situations.

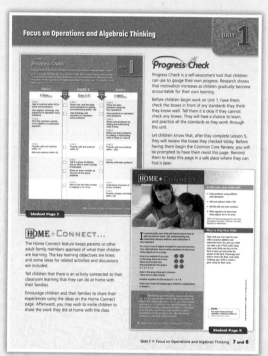

Grade 2 Teacher's Edition Pages 7 and 8

Unit Planner

The **Unit Planner** outlines everything a teacher needs to know to gather unit resources, and identify all lesson objectives, essential questions, and vocabulary.

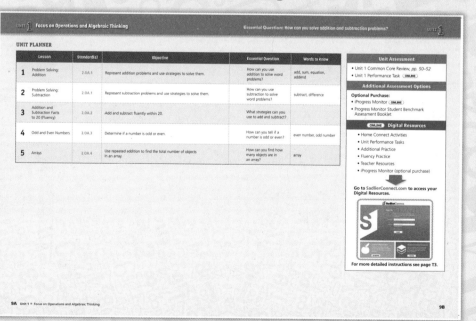

Grade 2 Teacher's Edition Pages 9A and 9B

Learning Progressions

Learning Progressions provide context and background knowledge for the Common Core State Standards by showing them what students learned in the previous grade and connections to what they will learn in the next grade, building coherence within and across grade levels.

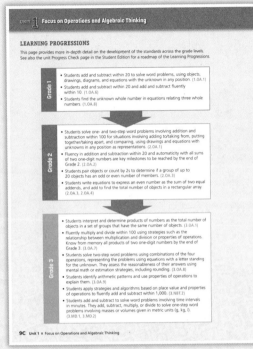

Grade 2 Teacher's Edition Page 9C

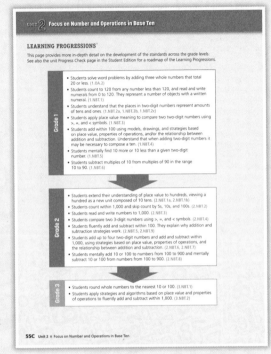

Grade 2 Teacher's Edition Page 55C

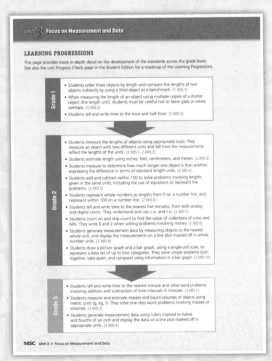

Grade 2 Teacher's Edition Page 145C

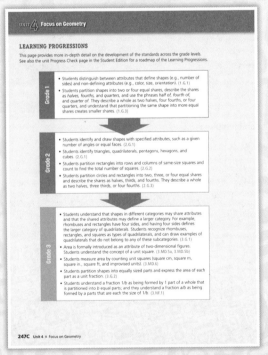

Grade 2 Teacher's Edition Page 247C

On-the-Spot Lesson Support Makes Teachers Common Core Experts!

Lesson plans feature instruction built around key standards cover ALL Common Core standards.

Guided Instruction

Clearly stated objectives provide the focus for each lesson.

Resources available to support all learners and encourage fluency practice are listed at point-of-use.

The standards are broken down to help students build the concept and gain full understanding.

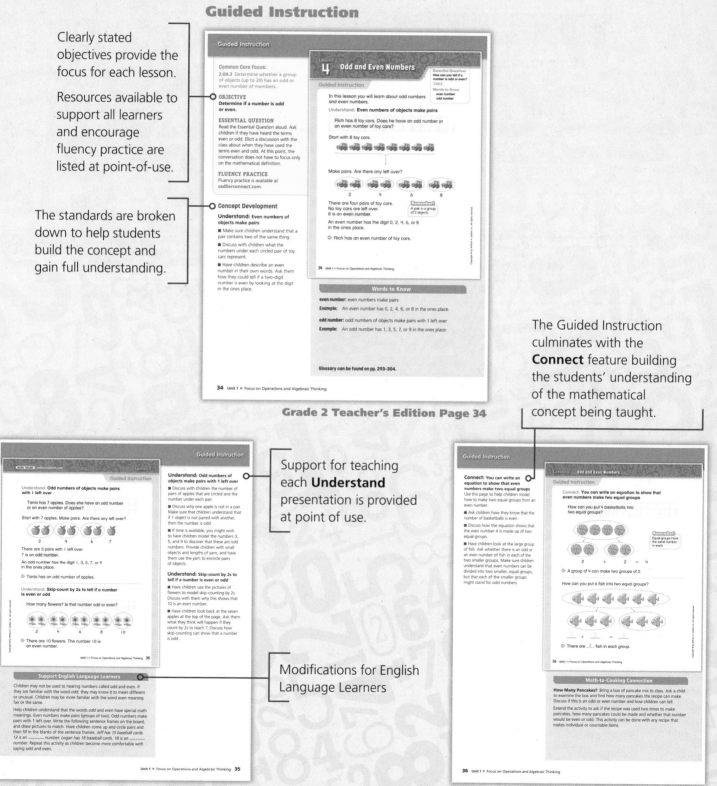

The Guided Instruction culminates with the **Connect** feature building the students' understanding of the mathematical concept being taught.

Grade 2 Teacher's Edition Page 34

Support for teaching each **Understand** presentation is provided at point of use.

Modifications for English Language Learners

Grade 2 Teacher's Edition Page 35

Grade 2 Teacher's Edition Page 36

Successive Increase of Student Responsibility Leads to Success

Guided Practice

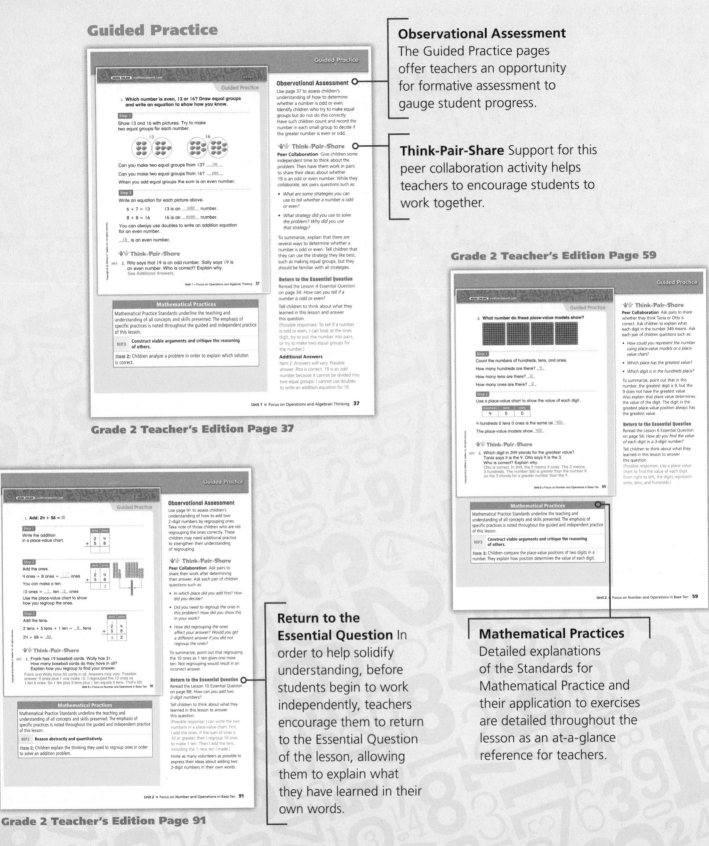

Grade 2 Teacher's Edition Page 37

Grade 2 Teacher's Edition Page 59

Grade 2 Teacher's Edition Page 91

Observational Assessment
The Guided Practice pages offer teachers an opportunity for formative assessment to gauge student progress.

Think-Pair-Share Support for this peer collaboration activity helps teachers to encourage students to work together.

Return to the Essential Question In order to help solidify understanding, before students begin to work independently, teachers encourage them to return to the Essential Question of the lesson, allowing them to explain what they have learned in their own words.

Mathematical Practices
Detailed explanations of the Standards for Mathematical Practice and their application to exercises are detailed throughout the lesson as an at-a-glance reference for teachers.

Scaffolded Practice Make Independent Application of Skills Accessible

Common Core Progress provides ample opportunity for rigorous independent practice allowing students to develop procedural fluency together with conceptual understanding.

Independent Practice

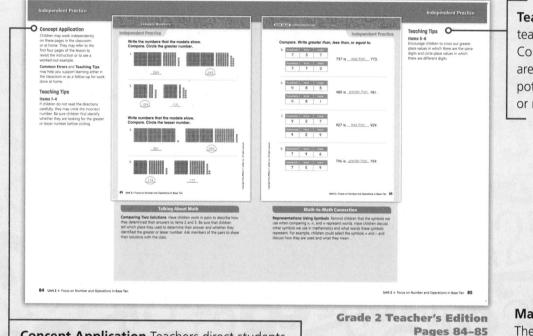

Teaching Tip Point-of-use teaching strategies and Common Error Analyses are provided help identify potential areas of confusion or misconceptions.

Grade 2 Teacher's Edition Pages 84–85

Concept Application Teachers direct students to work independently on increasingly cognitive demanding exercises and tasks.

Mathematical Practices Chart The Standards for Mathematical Practice are seamlessly correlated to items throughout the program.

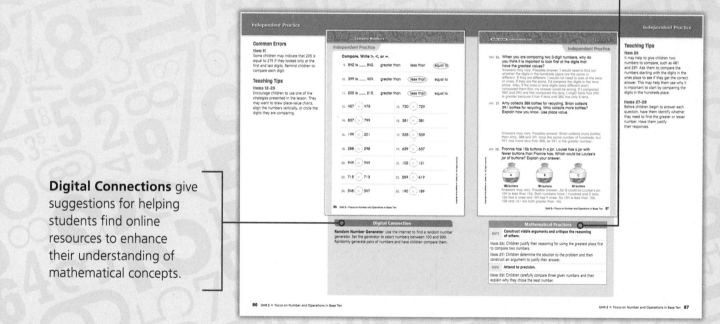

Digital Connections give suggestions for helping students find online resources to enhance their understanding of mathematical concepts.

Grade 2 Teacher's Edition Pages 86–87

Overview of the Teacher's Edition

Assessment Tools Make Grading Simple

Common Core Progress supports busy teachers by offering easy-to-use rubrics for grading and results charts that outline next steps after grading or assessment.

Grade 2 Teacher's Edition Pages 136–137

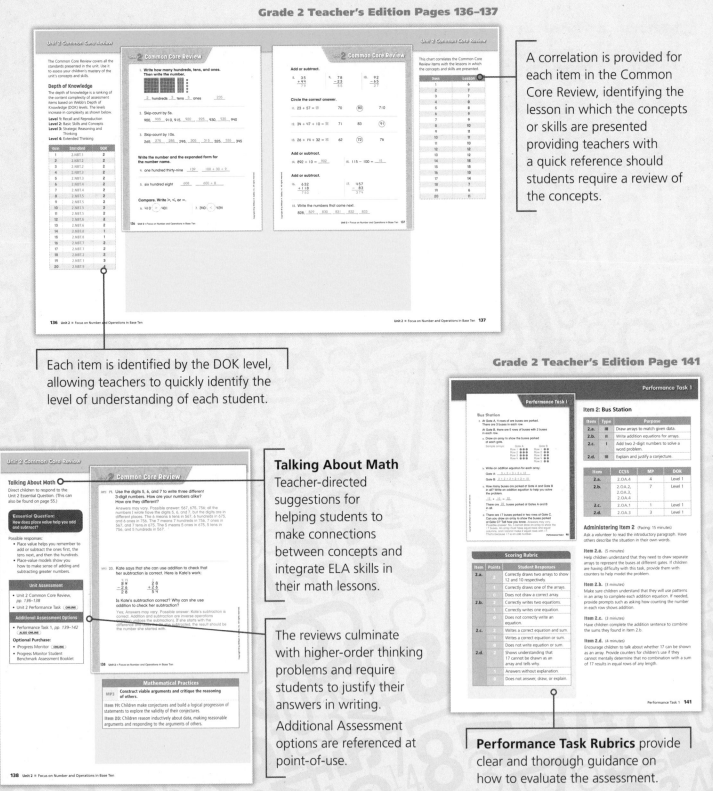

A correlation is provided for each item in the Common Core Review, identifying the lesson in which the concepts or skills are presented providing teachers with a quick reference should students require a review of the concepts.

Each item is identified by the DOK level, allowing teachers to quickly identify the level of understanding of each student.

Grade 2 Teacher's Edition Page 141

Talking About Math
Teacher-directed suggestions for helping students to make connections between concepts and integrate ELA skills in their math lessons.

The reviews culminate with higher-order thinking problems and require students to justify their answers in writing.

Additional Assessment options are referenced at point-of-use.

Performance Task Rubrics provide clear and thorough guidance on how to evaluate the assessment.

Grade 2 Teacher's Edition Page 138

T24

For more specific suggestions on planning and pacing, please see the Teacher Toolbox.

Weeks	Student Worktext	Online Resources to Enrich, Support, and Assess
1-5	Unit 1: Focus on Operations and Algebraic Thinking Lessons 1–5; pp. 10–49	Unit 1 Performance Task; Additional Practice; Fluency Practice; Teacher Resources Optional purchase: iProgress Monitor
6-15	Unit 2: Focus on Number and Operations in Base Ten Lessons 6–15; pp. 56–135	Unit 2 Performance Task; Additional Practice; Fluency Practice; Teacher Resources Optional purchase: iProgress Monitor
16	Performance Task 1 pp. 139–142	Performance Task 1
17-26	Unit 3: Focus on Measurement and Data Lessons 16–27; pp. 146–241	Unit 3 Performance Task; Additional Practice; Fluency Practice; Teacher Resources Optional purchase: iProgress Monitor
27-29	Unit 4: Geometry Lessons: 28–30; pp. 248–271	Unit 4 Performance Task; Additional Practice; Fluency Practice; Teacher Resources Optional purchase: iProgress Monitor
30	Performance Task 2 pp. 275–278	Performance Task 2

Suggested Pacing

To achieve optimum student results, it is suggested that *Common Core Progress* become an integral part of your math instruction. The multi-part lesson structure provides you with the flexibility you need in order to focus on a particular Common Core State Standard each day.

Suggested Timeline	Day 1	Day 2	Day 3	Day 4	Day 5
Lesson Structure	Guided Instruction	Guided Practice	Independent Practice	Independent Practice	• Additional Practice Online • iProgress Monitor Customized Assignments

Progress Monitor Student Benchmark Assessments, an optional purchase, is a workbook containing four comprehensive Benchmark Assessments that you may administer throughout the school year to track and assess students' mastery of the Common Core State Standards.

The lessons in this book are built upon the progression of the Grade 2 Common Core State Standards for Mathematics (CCSS). These Standards identify the mathematical concepts that students need to learn.

The focus of each *Common Core Progress* lesson is identified with a Common Core State Standard abbreviation without the topic label. For example, Grade 2 Lesson 1 focuses on Operations and Algebraic Thinking standard 1 and is referenced as 2.OA.1, not 2.OA.A.1. Note: Topic abbreviations are not used in these references.

Operations and Algebraic Thinking   2.OA

Represent and solve problems involving addition and subtraction.

2.OA.1   Use addition and subtraction within 100 to solve one- and two-step word problems involving situations of adding to, taking from, putting together, taking apart, and comparing, with unknowns in all positions, e.g., by using drawings and equations with a symbol for the unknown number to represent the problem.

Add and subtract within 20.

2.OA.2   Fluently add and subtract within 20 using mental strategies. By end of Grade 2, know from memory all sums of two one-digit numbers.

Work with equal groups of objects to gain foundations for multiplication.

2.OA.3   Determine whether a group of objects (up to 20) has an odd or even number of members, e.g., by pairing objects or counting them by 2s; write an equation to express an even number as a sum of two equal addends.

2.OA.4   Use addition to find the total number of objects arranged in rectangular arrays with up to 5 rows and up to 5 columns; write an equation to express the total as a sum of equal addends.

Number and Operations in Base Ten   2.NBT

Understand place value.

2.NBT.1   Understand that the three digits of a three-digit number represent amounts of hundreds, tens, and ones; e.g., 706 equals 7 hundreds, 0 tens, and 6 ones. Understand the following as special cases:

2.NBT.1a   100 can be thought of as a bundle of ten tens—called a "hundred."

2.NBT.1b   The numbers 100, 200, 300, 400, 500, 600, 700, 800, 900 refer to one, two, three, four, five, six, seven, eight, or nine hundreds (and 0 tens and 0 ones).

2.NBT.2   Count within 1000; skip-count by 5s, 10s, and 100s.

2.NBT.3   Read and write numbers to 1,000 using base-ten numerals, number names, and expanded form.

2.NBT.4   Compare two three-digit numbers based on meanings of the hundreds, tens, and ones digits, using >, =, and < symbols to record the results of comparisons.

Use place value understanding and properties of operations to add and subtract.

2.NBT.5   Fluently add and subtract within 100 using strategies based on place value, properties of operations, and/or the relationship between addition and subtraction.

2.NBT.6   Add up to four two-digit numbers using strategies based on place value and properties of operations.

2.NBT.7   Add and subtract within 1000, using concrete models or drawings and strategies based on place value, properties of operations, and/or the relationship between addition and subtraction; relate the strategy to a written method. Understand that in adding or subtracting three-digit numbers, one adds or subtracts hundreds and hundreds, tens and tens, ones and ones; and sometimes it is necessary to compose or decompose tens or hundreds.

2.NBT.8   Mentally add 10 or 100 to a given number 100–900, and mentally subtract 10 or 100 from a given number 100–900.

2.NBT.9   Explain why addition and subtraction strategies work, using place value and the properties of operations.

Measurement and Data   2.MD

Measure and estimate lengths in standard units.

2.MD.1 Measure the length of an object by selecting and using appropriate tools such as rulers, yardsticks, meter sticks, and measuring tapes.

2.MD.2 Measure the length of an object twice, using length units of different lengths for the two measurements; describe how the two measurements relate to the size of the unit chosen.

2.MD.3 Estimate lengths using units of inches, feet, centimeters, and meters.

2.MD.4 Measure to determine how much longer one object is than another, expressing the length difference in terms of a standard length unit.

Relate addition and subtraction to length.

2.MD.5 Use addition and subtraction within 100 to solve word problems involving lengths that are given in the same units, e.g., by using drawings (such as drawings of rulers) and equations with a symbol for the unknown number to represent the problem.

2.MD.6 Represent whole numbers as lengths from 0 on a number line diagram with equally spaced points corresponding to the numbers 0, 1, 2, . . ., and represent whole-number sums and differences within 100 on a number line diagram.

Work with time and money.

2.MD.7 Tell and write time from analog and digital clocks to the nearest five minutes, using a.m. and p.m.

2.MD.8 Solve word problems involving dollar bills, quarters, dimes, nickels, and pennies, using $ and ¢ symbols appropriately. *Example: If you have 2 dimes and 3 pennies, how many cents do you have?*

Represent and interpret data.

2.MD.9 Generate measurement data by measuring lengths of several objects to the nearest whole unit, or by making repeated measurements of the same object. Show the measurements by making a line plot, where the horizontal scale is marked off in whole-number units.

2.MD.10 Draw a picture graph and a bar graph (with single-unit scale) to represent a data set with up to four categories. Solve simple put together, take-apart, and compare problems using information presented in a bar graph.

Geometry 2.G

Reason with shapes and their attributes.

2.G.1   Recognize and draw shapes having specified attributes, such as a given number of angles or a given number of equal faces. Identify triangles, quadrilaterals, pentagons, hexagons, and cubes.

2.G.2   Partition a rectangle into rows and columns of same-size squares and count to find the total number of them.

2.G.3   Partition circles and rectangles into two, three, or four equal shares, describe the shares using the words *halves, thirds, half of, a third of,* etc., and describe the whole as two halves, three thirds, four fourths. Recognize that equal shares of identical wholes need not have the same shape.

The eight Standards for Mathematical Practice identified in the Common Core State Standards set the expectations for the ways students should approach the study of, and practice with, the subject of mathematics. These Mathematical Practices are fully embedded within the instruction and practice, labeled as MP , and encourage students to develop the habit of reliance on the practices when approaching problems.

Mathematical Practices in *Common Core Progress*

Additionally, the emphasis of specific practices is noted throughout the guided and independent practice of the lessons.

1. **Make sense of problems and persevere in solving them.**
   The Guided Instruction provided in the program offers stepped out approaches to solving problems, helping students develop strategies to use when approaching new problems.

2. **Reason abstractly and quantitatively.**
   Concepts are introduced using the Understand and Connect structure to help students break down the components of the standard and develop the reasoning skills necessary for deep conceptual understanding.

3. **Construct viable arguments and critique the reasoning of others.**
   Whether justifying their reasoning in writing or participating in group discussions about a Think-Pair-Share exercise, there are opportunities in every lesson for students to practice the skills of developing and defending mathematical arguments and communicating their ideas clearly.

4. **Model with mathematics.**
   In addition to the models of real world situations presented to the students throughout the program to introduce new concepts, students are encouraged to develop their own models when working through the exercises.

5. **Use appropriate tools strategically.**
   Having a solid understanding of the tools available and practicing with those tools during Guided Instruction and Guided Practice, fosters familiarity and fluency using the tools when working independently.

6. **Attend to precision.**
   Students are encouraged to be precise and accurate during each stage of the problem solving process, from using the correct vocabulary to communicate ideas to attending to the units used to express their answers.

7. **Look for and make use of structure.**
   Presenting concepts and skills in a way that reveals mathematical structures, allows students to seek out these patterns on their own.

8. **Look for and express regularity in repeated reasoning.**
   As students work through cognitively-demanding exercises they develop an awareness of repeated reasoning which promotes their ability to apply similar reasoning in real world situations.

Progress Check

Unit 1

Look at how the Common Core standards you have learned and will learn connect.

It is very important for you to understand the standards from the prior grade level so that you will be able to develop an understanding of operations and algebraic thinking in this unit and be prepared for next year. To practice your skills, go to sadlierconnect.com.

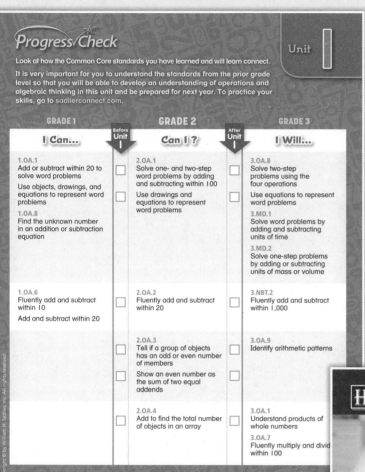

GRADE 1		GRADE 2		GRADE 3
I Can...	Before Unit 1	**Can I ?**	After Unit 1	**I Will...**
1.OA.1 Add or subtract within 20 to solve word problems — Use objects, drawings, and equations to represent word problems	☐	**2.OA.1** Solve one- and two-step word problems by adding and subtracting within 100 — Use drawings and equations to represent word problems	☐	**3.OA.8** Solve two-step problems using the four operations — Use equations to represent word problems
1.OA.8 Find the unknown number in an addition or subtraction equation	☐			**3.MD.1** Solve word problems by adding and subtracting units of time
				3.MD.2 Solve one-step problems by adding or subtracting units of mass or volume
1.OA.6 Fluently add and subtract within 10 — Add and subtract within 20	☐	**2.OA.2** Fluently add and subtract within 20	☐	**3.NBT.2** Fluently add and subtract within 1,000
		2.OA.3 Tell if a group of objects has an odd or even number of members — Show an even number as the sum of two equal addends	☐	**3.OA.9** Identify arithmetic patterns
		2.OA.4 Add to find the total number of objects in an array	☐	**3.OA.1** Understand products of whole numbers — **3.OA.7** Fluently multiply and divide within 100

Unit 1 ■ Focus on Operations and Algebraic Thinking

Student Page 7

Progress Check

Progress Check is a self-assessment tool that children can use to gauge their own progress. Research shows that motivation increases as children gradually become accountable for their own learning.

Before children begin work on Unit 1, have them check the boxes in front of any standards they think they know well. Tell them it is okay if they cannot check any boxes. They will have a chance to learn and practice all the standards as they work through this unit.

Let children know that, after they complete Lesson 5, they will review the boxes they checked today. Before having them begin the Common Core Review, you will be prompted to have them revisit this page. Remind them to keep this page in a safe place where they can find it later.

HOME◆CONNECT...

In this unit, your child will:

- Solve problems using addition and subtraction.
- Add and subtract within 100.
- Identify odd and even numbers.
- Write equations to show how many objects are in an array.

NOTE: All of these learning goals for your child are based on the Grade 2 Common Core State Standards for Mathematics.

Ways to Help Your Child

Flash cards are a fun way for your child to practice addition and subtraction facts. You and your child can make a set of flash cards using index cards. Write one fact on the front of each card and write the answer on the back. Encourage your child to review the flash cards daily. Challenge your child to create a game using the flash cards.

In second grade, your child will need to know how to add and subtract within 100. Understanding the relationship between addition and subtraction is very important.

An array is a set of objects arranged in rows and columns. Your child will learn how to write equations to show how many objects are in an array.

Here is an example of an array. In this array, there are 3 rows. There are 2 in each row. One equation for this array is $2 + 2 + 2 = 6$.

Also in this array, there are 2 columns. There are 3 in each column.

Another equation for this array is $3 + 3 = 6$.

Work with arrays will prepare your child for multiplication in Grade 3.

Activity: Your child will be asked to determine if a group of objects has an odd or even number of objects. Odd numbers end with 1, 3, 5, 7, or 9. Even numbers end with 0, 2, 4, 6, or 8. There are several strategies your child might use, such as make pairs of objects or skip-count by 2s. Ask your child if some of the numbers of objects encountered at home are odd or even. Then discuss the strategy he or she used to determine this.

ONLINE For more Home Connect activities, continue online at sadlierconnect.com

8 Unit 1 ■ Focus on Operations and Algebraic Thinking

Student Page 8

HOME◆CONNECT...

The Home Connect feature keeps parents or other adult family members apprised of what their children are learning. The key learning objectives are listed, and some ideas for related activities and discussions are included.

Tell children that there is an activity connected to their classroom learning that they can do at home with their families.

Encourage children and their families to share their experiences using the ideas on the Home Connect page. Afterward, you may wish to invite children to share the work they did at home with the class.

UNIT PLANNER

	Lesson	Standard(s)	Objective
1	Problem Solving: Addition	**2.OA.1**	Represent addition problems and use strategies to solve them.
2	Problem Solving: Subtraction	**2.OA.1**	Represent subtraction problems and use strategies to solve them.
3	Addition and Subtraction Facts to 20 (Fluency)	**2.OA.2**	Add and subtract fluently within 20.
4	Odd and Even Numbers	**2.OA.3**	Determine if a number is odd or even.
5	Arrays	**2.OA.4**	Use repeated addition to find the total number of objects in an array.

Essential Question	Words to Know
How can you use addition to solve word problems?	add, sum, equation, addend
How can you use subtraction to solve word problems?	subtract, difference
What strategies can you use to add and subtract?	
How can you tell if a number is odd or even?	even number, odd number
How can you find how many objects are in an array?	array

Unit Assessment

- Unit 1 Common Core Review, *pp. 50–52*
- Unit 1 Performance Task ONLINE

Additional Assessment Options

Optional Purchase:

- iProgress Monitor ONLINE
- Progress Monitor Student Benchmark Assessment Booklet

ONLINE Digital Resources

- Home Connect Activities
- Unit Performance Tasks
- Additional Practice
- Fluency Practice
- Teacher Resources
- iProgress Monitor (optional purchase)

Go to SadlierConnect.com to access your Digital Resources.

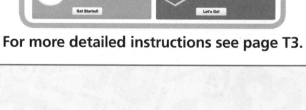

For more detailed instructions see page T3.

LEARNING PROGRESSIONS

This page provides more in-depth detail on the development of the standards across the grade levels. See also the unit Progress Check page in the Student Edition for a roadmap of the Learning Progressions.

Grade 1

- Students add and subtract within 20 to solve word problems, using objects, drawings, diagrams, and equations with the unknown in any position. (1.OA.1)
- Students add and subtract within 20 and add and subtract fluently within 10. (1.OA.6)
- Students find the unknown whole number in equations relating three whole numbers. (1.OA.8)

Grade 2

- Students solve one- and two-step word problems involving addition and subtraction within 100 for situations involving adding to/taking from, putting together/taking apart, and comparing, using drawings and equations with unknowns in any position as representations. (2.OA.1)
- Fluency in addition and subtraction within 20 and automaticity with all sums of two one-digit numbers are key milestones to be reached by the end of Grade 2. (2.OA.2)
- Students pair objects or count by 2s to determine if a group of up to 20 objects has an odd or even number of members. (2.OA.3)
- Students write equations to express an even number as the sum of two equal addends, and add to find the total number of objects in a rectangular array. (2.OA.3, 2.OA.4)

Grade 3

- Students interpret and determine products of numbers as the total number of objects in a set of groups that have the same number of objects. (3.OA.1)
- Fluently multiply and divide within 100 using strategies such as the relationship between multiplication and division or properties of operations. Know from memory all products of two one-digit numbers by the end of Grade 3. (3.OA.7)
- Students solve two-step word problems using combinations of the four operations, representing the problems using equations with a letter standing for the unknown. They assess the reasonableness of their answers using mental math or estimation strategies, including rounding. (3.OA.8)
- Students identify arithmetic patterns and use properties of operations to explain them. (3.OA.9)
- Students apply strategies and algorithms based on place value and properties of operations to fluently add and subtract within 1,000. (3.NBT.2)
- Students add and subtract to solve word problems involving time intervals in minutes. They add, subtract, multiply, or divide to solve one-step word problems involving masses or volumes given in metric units (g, kg, l). (3.MD.1, 3.MD.2)

Focus on Operations and Algebraic Thinking

Unit 1

Essential Question:
How can you
solve addition and
subtraction problems?

Unit 1 ▪ Focus on Operations and Algebraic Thinking 9

Essential Question:
How can you solve addition and
subtraction problems?

As children become involved with
the Essential Question they will use
addition and subtraction strategies,
drawings, patterns, and the relationship
between addition and subtraction to
solve problems.

Conversation Starters

Have children discuss the photograph.
Ask question such as: *How can you
describe the ways that the dolls are
arranged? How does the arrangement
make the dolls easy to count? Where
have you seen dolls or other collections
arranged in the same way?*

Ask children to compare the number of
dolls on each shelf. *What is the greatest
number of dolls shown on a shelf? Is
there more than one shelf that has this
number?* (The second shelf and the
bottom shelf each show the greatest
number, 11.) *How many dolls are on
the top and middle shelves in all? How
can you find out?* (I can count 3 dolls
on the top plus 9 dolls on the middle
shelf. That's 12 dolls in all.) *How many
more dolls are on the bottom shelf than
on the shelf just above it? How do you
know?* (There are 11 dolls on the bottom
shelf and 9 on the next-to-bottom shelf.
So there are 2 more on the bottom.)

Have children work together to describe
any patterns they see in the picture,
such as whether any row can be
counted by 2s or by 3s.

Activity

Materials: counters
Make counters available for children's use. Have pairs work
together to count the dolls on any two shelves in the picture. Direct one
partner to point to one doll on a shelf with each count and then write the
number at the end of the row. Then have pairs switch rolls to count the
dolls on another shelf and record the number.

Now have pairs take counters to model the dolls on each of the two
shelves they selected. Tell them to align the counters in two rows, to
represent each shelf of dolls they counted. Ask children to check that the
numbers of counters match the numbers they wrote for the shelves. Then
direct pairs to count to find how many dolls there are on their two shelves
in all. Call on them to explain their results.

Common Core Focus:

2.OA.1 Use addition and subtraction within 100 to solve one- and two-step word problems involving situations of adding to, taking from, putting together, taking apart, and comparing, with unknowns in all positions.

OBJECTIVE

Represent addition problems and use strategies to solve them.

ESSENTIAL QUESTION

Read the Essential Question to the class. Review the concept of addition. Make sure children understand that addition involves the joining of two or more groups. Briefly review strategies they have learned for adding.

PREREQUISITE SKILLS

Use Foundational Skills Handbook page 279, *Addition Problems,* to review how to solve situational addition problems.

FLUENCY PRACTICE

Fluency practice is available at **sadlierconnect.com**.

Concept Development

Understand: Use drawings and equations to solve addition word problems

■ In this lesson, children use information from the problems to form equations. These equations contain a symbol to stand for an unknown quantity. Children use different strategies to solve for the unknown.

■ Ask children to share different strategies that they could use to determine the sum of 8 and 11. Examples they may share are counting on 8 from 11, using cubes to represent the addends, and applying their knowledge of addition facts.

Lesson 1

Problem Solving: Addition

Essential Question:
How can you use addition to solve word problems?
2.OA.1

Words to Know
add
sum
equation
addend

In this lesson you will learn different ways to solve addition word problems.

Understand: Use drawings and equations to solve addition word problems

> There are 8 frogs sitting on a log.
> Then 11 more frogs jump onto the log.
> How many frogs are on the log in all?

You want to find how many frogs in all. You need to add the numbers.

Draw a picture to help you find the sum.

◼ frogs in all	
8 frogs	11 frogs

Write an equation. An equation is a number sentence with an equal sign.

$8 + 11 = ◼$

8 frogs and 11 more frogs is 19 frogs in all.

$8 + 11 = 19$

▷ There are 19 frogs in all.

Words to Know

add: to find how many in all

Example: $3 + 2 = 5$

sum: the answer in addition

Example: $4 + 3 = 7$
                        ↑
                       sum

Glossary can be found on pp. 293–304.

Lesson 1

Guided Instruction

Understand: Write an equation to solve an addition word problem

> Joanne has a sticker album. She has 15 baseball stickers and 20 football stickers. How many stickers does Joanne have in her album?

You are putting two groups together.

One group has 15 baseball stickers.
The other group has 20 football stickers.

Add to find how many stickers Joanne has in her album.

Write an addition equation.
Use the numbers you know.
Use ▨ for the number you do not know.

$$15 + 20 = ▨$$

Remember!
You can use a picture to help find the sum.

◄──────── ▨ stickers in all ────────►
15 baseball stickers	20 football stickers

$$15 + 20 = \underline{35}$$

▷ Joanne has __35__ stickers in her album.

Unit 1 ■ Focus on Operations and Algebraic Thinking **11**

Words to Know

equation: a number sentence with an equal sign

Example: 5 + 6 = 11   8 − 6 = 2

addend: the numbers you add

Example: 4 + 1 = 5

     ↑ ↑

  addends

$$\begin{array}{r} 3 \\ + 7 \\ \hline 1\,0 \end{array}$$ ← addends

Glossary can be found on pp. 293–304.

Understand: Write an equation to solve an addition word problem

■ It is important for children to understand that they can use an equation to represent what is occurring in a word problem. They can then solve the equation to help solve the word problem.

■ Consider having children explain the problem in their own words or act out the problem.

■ Have a volunteer explain the problem without using numbers. Without having numbers to focus on, children may think more conceptually about what is occurring in the problem as opposed to just restating numbers. For example, a child might say, "Joanne has some baseball stickers and some football stickers in her album. We want to know how many stickers she has in all."

■ Have children study the addition equation. Ask them to identify what each number and the box stand for. Finally, discuss why this equation will help them solve the problem.

■ An important point for children to understand is that the problem asks how many items are in two groups when they are combined. Often, children have difficulty solving word problems because they do not have a good grasp of which mathematical operation to apply. Continuing to help children solidify what addition does is important in helping them to understand and solve word problems.

Connect: Some word problems have more than one step Use this page to help children understand ways of solving two-step word problems.

■ Ask children to explain or act out the problem. Help them see that to answer the question they must first ask themselves another question. Ask children to suggest what that question would be.

■ Ask children how they solved the first equation. Discuss with them why counting on might be a good strategy for solving this problem. Ask children if there are other strategies that could be used to solve this equation.

■ Discuss what needs to be done in Step 2. If some children say that Kate gave Ted 36 cards, have them reread the problem focusing on the sentence, "Kate gave him more cards." Then ask if the problem says how many cards Kate gave Ted. Discuss with children what they know and what they need to find out.

■ Ask children to explain what the numbers and the box in the equation represent. Discuss why the box, or unknown, is placed where it is.

■ Review the strategy used for solving the problem. Some children might mention that this strategy is like counting on, but counting on by 10s.

■ After children solve the problem, review why this is called a two-step problem. Ask children to describe a two-step problem in their own words.

Connect: Some word problems have more than one step

> Ted had 14 baseball cards and 2 football cards. Kate gave him more cards. Now Ted has 36 cards. How many cards did Kate give him?

Step 1

First find how many cards Ted had at the start.
Write an addition equation.

$14 + 2 = \blacksquare$

Start at 14. Count on 2. $14 \longrightarrow 15, 16$

$14 + 2 = \underline{16}$

Ted had _16_ cards at the start.

Step 2

Next find how many cards Kate gave Ted.
Write an equation. You know Ted had 16 cards to start.
Now he has 36 cards.

$16 + \blacksquare = 36$

Add 10 to 16. $\longrightarrow$ $16 + 10 = 26$
Add 10 more. $\longrightarrow$ $26 + 10 = 36$

$16 + \underline{20} = 36$

▷ Kate gave Ted _20_ cards.

If Kate gave Ted 10 more cards, how many cards would Ted have then? _46_ cards

---

Support English Language Learners

Some children may have difficulty differentiating between the words *sum* and *some*. Write these words on the board, have children pronounce them, and then give an example sentence for each. Have children develop and share a simple definition and motion for the word *sum*. Then, whenever you say the word *sum* aloud during this lesson, children should perform the motion and state the definition that they developed together. Such movement and recitation will help children understand the meaning and use of the word *sum*.

I. **Ty has 17 horses. He has 40 more chickens than horses. How many chickens does he have?**

Step 1

You want to find how many chickens Ty has.

You know he has __17__ horses. One addend is __17__.

He has __40__ more chickens than horses.

The other addend is __40__.

Write an addition equation. __17__ + __40__ = ■

Step 2

Model the problem. Then count on by 10s to add.

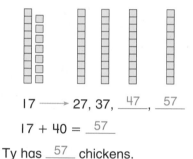

17 ⟶ 27, 37, __47__, __57__

17 + 40 = __57__

Ty has __57__ chickens.

⚘ Think•Pair•Share

MP2 2. There are 12 cows and 5 roosters on the farm.
Write an addition equation to find how many more cows
there are than roosters. Tell how you found your answer.
5 + ■ = 12; There are 7 more cows than roosters. Answers may
vary. Possible answer: I used the related subtraction fact: 12 − 5 = 7

Unit 1 ■ Focus on Operations and Algebraic Thinking **13**

Mathematical Practices

Mathematical Practice Standards underline the teaching and understanding of all concepts and skills presented. The emphasis of specific practices is noted throughout the guided and independent practice of this lesson.

MP2 Reason abstractly and quantitatively.

Item 2: Children need to reason quantitatively to understand the relationship between the numbers of two kinds of animals.

Observational Assessment

Use page 13 to assess children's understanding of how to analyze a word problem, write an equation for the problem, and use a strategy to solve the problem. Take note of those children who do not understand that they are counting on by 10s to add. These children may need to use manipulatives to solve the problem.

⚘ Think•Pair•Share

Peer Collaboration Give children some independent time to think about the problem. Then have them work in pairs to write an equation and decide on a strategy to solve their equation. As they work, ask each pair questions such as:

• *What do you know? What do you need to find out?*

• *What equation did you write?*

• *How did you solve your equation?*

Have pairs share their strategies with the rest of the class. To summarize, point out that in this addition equation there are numbers on both sides of the equal sign.

Return to the Essential Question

Reread the Lesson 1 Essential Question on page 10: *How can you use addition to solve word problems?*

Tell children to think about what they learned in this lesson and answer this question.

(Possible responses: When I read a word problem, I can write an equation to help me solve the problem. I can also use drawings to help me solve the problem. If I need to put groups together, I can add to find out how many there are in all.)

Concept Application

Children may work independently on these pages in the classroom or at home. They may refer to the first four pages of the lesson to revisit the instruction or to see a worked-out example.

Common Errors and **Teaching Tips** may help you support learning either in the classroom or as a follow-up for work done at home.

Teaching Tips

Items 1–4

If children are having difficulty adding when the equation is written horizontally, have them rewrite the equation in a vertical format. Some children may benefit by writing the addends in a place-value chart to help them align the digits properly. Provide manipulatives for children who may need additional help with addition.

Lesson 1   Problem Solving: **Addition**

Independent Practice

Draw a picture to model the problem. Write an addition equation. Then solve the problem.

1. There are 13 ducks in the pond. Then 7 more ducks come into the pond. How many ducks are in the pond now?
   Check children's work.

   $\underline{13} + \underline{7} = \underline{20}$

   There are $\underline{20}$ ducks in the pond now.

2. There are 28 flowers in the vase. Marta puts 3 more flowers into the vase. How many flowers are in the vase now?
   Check children's work.

   $\underline{28} + \underline{3} = \underline{31}$

   There are $\underline{31}$ flowers in the vase now.

3. Connor has 10 more toy cars than Aidan. Aidan has 14 toy cars. How many toy cars does Connor have?
   Check children's work.

   $\underline{14} + \underline{10} = \underline{24}$

   Connor has $\underline{24}$ toy cars.

4. Alana has 12 more baseball cards than Tina. Tina has 17 baseball cards. How many baseball cards does Alana have?
   Check children's work.

   $\underline{17} + \underline{12} = \underline{29}$

   Alana has $\underline{29}$ baseball cards.

Talking About Math

Collaborative Conversations After children have completed the problems individually, arrange them in pairs to share their work. For problem 3, one partner displays his or her drawing and explains how it shows the equation. Then partners exchange rolls and the other partner repeats the process for problem 4.

Circle the correct equation to solve each part of the problem. Then solve the problem.

5. There were 6 blueberry muffins and 11 corn muffins in a box. The baker put 7 more blueberry muffins into the box. How many muffins are there in the box in all?

Find how many muffins at the start.

$6 + 11 = 17$ (circled) $6 + 5 = 11$ $6 + 7 = 13$

Find how many muffins in the box in all.

$11 + 7 = 18$ $17 + 7 = 24$ (circled) $13 + 7 = 20$

There are __24__ muffins in the box in all.

Complete each equation to solve the problem.

6. There were 5 puzzles and 7 games in the toy box. Olga put 4 more puzzles into the box. How many puzzles and games are in the toy box now?

Find how many puzzles and games in the box to start.

__5__ puzzles + __7__ games = __12__ in all

Find how many puzzles and games in the box now.

__12__ + __4__ = __16__

There are __16__ puzzles and games in the toy box now.

Teaching Tips

Item 5

Encourage children to draw a picture for each step of the problem.

Item 6

If a sufficient number of puzzles and games are available in the classroom, have children count out the number of each called for in the problem. (Alternatively, have children represent the puzzles and games by marking the required numbers of letters, "P" and "G," on index cards or sticky notes.) Then have children use these puzzles and games to model the problem.

Digital Connection

Interactive Whiteboard Ask one child to say a word problem about animals on a farm. The child might offer, for example, "There are 5 horses and 8 cows in a barn. How many animals are in the barn?" Ask a second child to draw a picture of the problem by making marks of different colors instead of trying to draw the animals. Ask a third child to write an equation under the drawing that can be used to solve the problem. Finally, ask a fourth child to solve the problem. Repeat this activity as time allows.

Independent Practice

Common Errors

Items 7–9

Some children might see the two numbers in the word problem and add them together without analyzing what they know and what they need to find out. To help correct this, have children retell the problem in their own words. Make sure they say what the problem tells them and what they need to find. Then have them write the equation. Have them point to the numbers or to the box in the equation and explain what each represents.

Teaching Tips

Items 7–9

If children are struggling, consider this approach. In item 7, ask children what the numbers 15 and 24 each represent. Then ask them to read the question at the end of the problem. Ask them how they could find out how many apples are in the basket. If necessary, ask how many oranges would have to be taken out of the basket so that only apples are left. This procedure can also be used with items 8 and 9.

Independent Practice

Write the addition equation you can use to solve the problem. Then solve the problem.

7. There are 15 oranges and some apples in a fruit basket. There are 24 oranges and apples in all in the basket. How many apples are in the basket?

$$\underline{15} + \blacksquare = \underline{24}$$

There are $\underline{9}$ apples in the basket.

8. Brad has 15 shells in a bag. He adds more shells to the bag. Now there are 35 shells in the bag. How many shells did Brad add to the bag?

$$\underline{15} + \blacksquare = \underline{35}$$

Brad added $\underline{20}$ shells to the bag.

9. Judy did some homework for 25 minutes. After dinner she did more homework for 20 minutes. How much time did Judy spend doing homework?

$$\underline{25} + \underline{20} = \blacksquare$$

Judy spent $\underline{45}$ minutes doing homework.

10. Tara has 28 rocks in her collection. Juan has a rock collection too. Together Tara and Juan have 68 rocks. How many rocks does Juan have in his collection?

$$\underline{28} + \blacksquare = \underline{68}$$

Juan has $\underline{40}$ rocks in his collection.

Math-to-Social Studies Connection

President's Age To become President of the United States, a person needs to be at least 35 years old. Have children use a strategy of their choice to solve the following word problem. *A person who is now 33 years old wants to run for President in four years. Will that person be old enough then? Explain.* Group children in pairs to share their strategies, solutions, and explanations.

If times allows, extend this activity by listing the years of the next several presidential elections. Have children use a hundred chart to count on from their ages to the first election year in which they would be old enough to run for President.

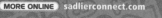

Independent Practice

Solve each problem.

11. There were some pennies in a jar. Irene put 40 more pennies into the jar. Then there were 82 pennies in the jar. How many pennies were in the jar at the start?

$$\underline{42} + \underline{40} = \underline{82}$$

There were __42__ pennies in the jar at the start.

12. Kevin had 34 stamps in his collection. He bought 20 more stamps. Then his uncle gave him 3 more stamps. How many stamps does Kevin have in all?

$$\underline{34} + \underline{20} = \underline{54}$$

$$\underline{54} + \underline{3} = \underline{57}$$

Kevin has __57__ stamps in all.

MP8 13. Mrs. Smith has 56 beads to put into two bags. She put some of the beads in a blue bag. She put 31 beads in a purple bag. How many beads did Mrs. Smith put in the blue bag?

Write an equation to show how many beads there are in the blue bag. Then solve the equation.

$$\underline{31} + \underline{25} = \underline{56}$$

Mrs. Smith put __25__ beads in the blue bag.

Then Mrs. Smith bought more beads. She put all her new beads into the purple bag. She now has 71 beads in the purple bag. How many new beads did Mrs. Smith buy?
40 new beads; Answers may vary. Possible answer: I know that
Tell how you found your answer. Mrs. Smith has 31 beads in her purple bag to start. She now has 71. 31 + ■ = 71. I counted on by 10s and found that Mrs. Smith bought 40 new beads.

Unit 1 ■ Focus on Operations and Algebraic Thinking **17**

Common Errors

Item 12

Some children may not realize that this is a two-step problem. Ask children how they can find out how many stamps Kevin had in his collection before his uncle gave him 3 more stamps. Have them use the first equation outline to write and solve an equation to show this.

Teaching Tips

Item 11

In this problem the number that belongs on the first line in the equation is unknown. Children will solve for this and then write the number in the equation.

Item 13

Because of the amount of information presented here, it may help if children make several drawings or use counters to solve.

Mathematical Practices
MP8 **Look for and express regularity in repeated reasoning.**

Item 13: Children use counting on by 10s to solve the problem.

Common Core Focus:

2.OA.1 Use addition and subtraction within 100 to solve one- and two-step word problems involving situations of adding to, taking from, putting together, taking apart, and comparing, with unknowns in all positions.

OBJECTIVE

Represent subtraction problems and use strategies to solve them.

ESSENTIAL QUESTION

Focus children on the lesson objective by reading the Essential Question aloud. Lead them to understand that subtractions are unknown-addend problems. Children can count on to solve subtractions. Sometimes they will subtract to compare two groups to determine which group has more or fewer.

PREREQUISITE SKILLS

Use Foundational Skills Handbook page 280, *Subtraction Problems*, to review subtracting.

FLUENCY PRACTICE

Fluency practice is available at **sadlierconnect.com**.

Concept Development

Understand: Use drawings and equations to solve subtraction word problems

■ In this lesson, children analyze what is occurring in situational problems. They use information from the problems to form equations. These equations contain a symbol to stand for an unknown quantity. Children then use drawings to help solidify their understanding of the situations.

■ Make sure children understand that the box in the equation 17 − ■ = 7 stands for the number that they need to subtract from 17.

Guided Instruction

Lesson 2 Problem Solving: **Subtraction**

Guided Instruction

Essential Question:
How can you use subtraction to solve word problems?
2.OA.1

Words to Know
subtract
difference

In this lesson you will learn different ways to solve subtraction word problems.

Understand: Use drawings and equations to solve subtraction word problems

> There were 17 birds in a tree. Some flew away. Now there are 7 birds. How many birds flew away?

You want to find how many birds flew away.

Now there are fewer birds than before, so you will subtract to find the answer.

Draw a picture. Start with 17 circles. Cross out one at a time until 7 are left. Count how many you cross out.

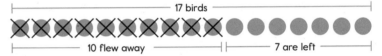

Write a subtraction equation.

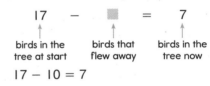

$$17 - 10 = 7$$

The number being subtracted from 17 is 10.

▷ 10 birds flew away.

Words to Know

subtract: take items away from a group

Example: $5 - 3 = 2$

difference: the answer in subtraction

Example: $6 - 1 = 5$
The difference between 6 and 1 is 5.

Glossary can be found on pp. 293–304.

Lesson 2

Guided Instruction

Understand: Use related addition and subtraction equations to solve a subtraction word problem

There were some apples on a tray.
Steve takes 20 apples. Then 18 apples are left.
How many apples were on the tray at the start?

Make a drawing to show the problem.

⬜ apples on the tray at start	
20 apples that Steve takes	18 apples left

First write a subtraction equation. Use the numbers you know.

$$\underset{\substack{\uparrow \\ \text{apples on} \\ \text{tray at start}}}{⬜} - \underset{\substack{\uparrow \\ \text{apples that} \\ \text{Steve takes}}}{20} = \underset{\substack{\uparrow \\ \text{apples left}}}{18}$$

Use 18 and 20 to write a related addition equation. The 18 apples left and the 20 that Steve takes together equal the number of apples at the start.

$18 + 20 = ⬜$

Add: $18 + 20 = 38$

The sum, 38, was the missing number in the subtraction equation.

$38 - 20 = 18$

Remember!
Related addition and subtraction equations use the same numbers.

⇨ There were 38 apples on the tray at the start.

Understand: Use related addition and subtraction equations to solve a subtraction word problem

■ Read the problem with the class, and then have children look at the drawing that shows the problem. This type of drawing is useful in helping children understand situational problems. It is proportionally accurate and shows what is happening in the problem. Discuss with children how each section of the drawing relates to the problem.

■ Discuss with children how the subtraction equation relates to the problem. Make sure they realize that the unknown is the amount they are subtracting from.

■ Help children understand that an addition equation related to the subtraction equation is needed to solve the problem. The drawing may help some children understand what to do. The *20 apples that Steve takes* and the *18 apples left* are joined together and equal *the number of apples on the tray at the start*. This shows that the related addition sentence, 20 + 18, is the number of apples on the tray at the start.

Support English Language Learners

Write the word *difference* on the board. Some children may understand this word to mean objects that are not alike. Explain that the word *difference* in mathematics has a special meaning. It can be used to compare numbers of objects. Give this example. *What is the difference between 9 seashells and 6 seashells?* Ask children to give other examples of comparing numbers of objects. Then, have each child draw a picture and write related numbers to represent what the word *difference* means. Under the picture, each child should write a sentence describing the picture. Tell children to include the word *difference* in their sentences. Display the drawings in the classroom.

Connect: Solve subtraction word problems that have two steps

■ After children read the problem, ask them how they know that this problem has two steps. Have children explain the different actions that happen in the problem and the order in which they happen.

■ Because this problem can be modeled, encourage children to act out the two steps of the problem by using actual blocks or counters. As they model, have children relate each of their actions to one of the equations and its solution.

Connect: **Solve subtraction word problems that have two steps**

> Polly and Jeff are building a tower with blocks. When the tower is 14 blocks tall, Polly takes 5 blocks off. Then Jeff puts 9 blocks on. How many blocks are in the tower now?

Step 1

Find how many blocks are in the tower after Polly takes 5 off.

Write and solve an equation to find the difference.

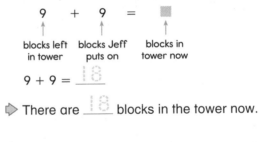

$$14 - 5 = \underline{\quad 9 \quad}$$

There are ___9___ blocks in the tower after Polly takes 5 off.

Step 2

Find how many blocks are in the tower after Jeff puts 9 on.

Write and solve an equation.

9 + 9 = ▦

↑ blocks left in tower   ↑ blocks Jeff puts on   ↑ blocks in tower now

$$9 + 9 = \underline{\quad 18 \quad}$$

▷ There are ___18___ blocks in the tower now.

20   Unit 1 ■ Focus on Operations and Algebraic Thinking

Math-to-Real-World Connection

Apples Write this situational word problem on the board. *There are 10 apples. The children eat 6 apples. Their mother comes home with 5 more apples. How many apples are there now?*

Have children use the structure for a two-step problem to make a drawing and an equation for each step of this problem. They should label each step. You may wish to have children do this work in pairs.

Lesson 2

Guided Practice

1. **A theater has 45 seats. The people who came to see the show are seated. There are 10 empty seats. How many people are seated?**

Step 1

Draw a picture to model the problem. Show 45 seats. Cross off 10 to stand for the empty seats.

Step 2

How many seats are there in all? _45_

How many empty seats are there? _10_

Write a subtraction equation to help you find how many people are seated.

_45_ – _10_ = ▪   45 – 10 = _35_

There are _35_ people seated.

👑 Think·Pair·Share

MP1　2. Brandon has 30 fewer baseball cards than Luke. Luke has 7 more baseball cards than Margaret. Margaret has 89 baseball cards.

How many baseball cards does Brandon have? _66_

Talk about how you found your answer.
See Additional Answers.

Mathematical Practices

Mathematical Practice Standards underline the teaching and understanding of all concepts and skills presented. The emphasis of specific practices is noted throughout the guided and independent practice of this lesson.

| MP1 | **Make sense of problems and persevere in solving them.** |

Item 2: Children determine the meaning of the problem and look for a starting point to its solution. Children then describe how they determined their answer.

Observational Assessment

Use page 21 to assess children's understanding of how to use pictures and equations to solve subtraction word problems. Take note of any children who do not write the correct subtraction equation after modeling the situation.

👑 Think·Pair·Share

Peer Collaboration Ask pairs to share their work to solve this problem. The following questions can help children organize their thinking:

- *How many baseball cards does Margaret have?*

- *How can you find out how many baseball cards Luke has?*

- *How can you find out how many baseball cards Brandon has?*

- *What words in the problem helped you to figure out whether to add or subtract?*

To summarize, point out that there are three children in the problem and that the problem consists of two steps.

Return to the Essential Question

Reread the Lesson 2 Essential Question on page 18: *How can you use subtraction to solve word problems?*

Tell children to think about what they learned in this lesson to answer this question.
(Possible responses: When I read a word problem I can tell whether I can subtract to solve it. I can use drawings, equations, and related addition equations to solve subtraction word problems.)

Additional Answers

Item 2: Possible answer: Since Brandon has 30 fewer cards than Luke, I need to find how many cards Luke has. He has 7 more than Margaret's 89, so I can add. 89 + 7 = 96. Brandon has 30 fewer cards than Luke's 96. So, I can subtract 96 − 30 = 66.

Concept Application

Children may work independently on these pages in the classroom or at home. They may refer to the first four pages of the lesson to revisit the instruction or to see a worked-out example.

Common Errors and **Teaching Tips** may help you support learning either in the classroom or as a follow-up for work done at home.

Common Errors

Item 2

Children may set up this equation incorrectly. They need to understand that the problem asks how many marbles Lara took, not how many marbles are left. Ask children to identify what they know from the start, which is that there were 22 marbles and that 12 marbles were left. Then guide children to find out what number plus 12 equals 22. Have them use counters to act out the problem.

Draw a picture to model the problem.
Write a subtraction equation.
Then solve the problem.

1. There were 19 bananas. Ernie takes 13. How many bananas are left?
   Check children's work.

   $$\underline{19} - \underline{13} = \underline{6}$$
   There are $\underline{6}$ bananas left.

2. There were 22 marbles in a jar. Lara took some marbles. Then 12 marbles were left in the jar. How many marbles did Lara take?
   Check children's work.

   $$\underline{22} - \underline{10} = \underline{12}$$
   Lara took $\underline{10}$ marbles.

3. There are 35 flowers in a vase. 10 are white and the rest are red. How many flowers are red?
   Check children's work.

   $$\underline{35} - \underline{10} = \underline{25}$$
   There are $\underline{25}$ red flowers.

4. Ryan has 30 fewer counters than Sam. Sam has 48 counters. How many counters does Ryan have?
   Check children's work.

   $$\underline{48} - \underline{30} = \underline{18}$$
   Ryan has $\underline{18}$ counters.

Talking About Math

Collaborative Conversations Have children work in pairs. Children should each explain to their partner how they solved problem 2. Tell them to say what is happening in the problem and to be sure to include what they need to find out.

Lesson 2

Independent Practice

Complete each equation to solve the problem.

5. There were 13 children at the playground.
Then 5 children left to go home for lunch,
and 4 children left to go to the lunchroom.
How many children are at the playground now?

Find how many children left the playground.

$\underline{\quad 5 \quad} + \underline{\quad 4 \quad} = \underline{\quad 9 \quad}$

Find how many children did not leave
the playground.

$\underline{\quad 13 \quad} - \underline{\quad 9 \quad} = \underline{\quad 4 \quad}$

How many children are at the playground now?

$\underline{\quad\quad 4 \text{ children} \quad\quad}$

6. One morning Angelo made 45 pizzas in his shop.
He sold 14 pizzas at lunchtime. Then he sold 6 more
after lunch. How many pizzas were left over?

Find how many pizzas Angelo sold in all.

$\underline{\quad 14 \quad} + \underline{\quad 6 \quad} = \underline{\quad 20 \quad}$

Find how many pizzas were left over.

$\underline{\quad 45 \quad} - \underline{\quad 20 \quad} = \underline{\quad 25 \quad}$

How many pizzas were left over?

$\underline{\quad\quad 25 \text{ pizzas} \quad\quad}$

Unit 1 ■ Focus on Operations and Algebraic Thinking   **23**

Teaching Tips

Items 5 and 6

Help children see the similarity between
these two problems.

In problem 5, two groups leave. Children
add to find the total that leaves. Then
they subtract to find how many remain.

In problem 6, two groups of pizzas are
sold. Children add to find the total
sold. Then they subtract to find how
many remain.

Digital Connection

Using Shapes Have children use either digital manipulatives or the
drawing tool on a software program to help them solve problem 5. If
they are using the drawing tool, they can choose a shape to represent
the 13 children on the playground at the start. They can cluster 5 of the
shapes and then 4 of the shapes to represent the addition for a sum of 9.
Then they can delete the 9 shapes altogether to solve the problem.

Independent Practice

Common Errors

Item 8

Children may think they need to use an addition equation because they do not know how many pennies Jacob has. Help them recognize that what they know is that Jacob has fewer pennies than Connor. Ask children what *fewer* means in the problem. Have children use play coins to work out this problem and then record what they do.

Teaching Tips

Item 9

Some children may have difficulty finding the correct numbers to use in the addition equation. Help them understand that the subtraction equation can be rewritten. The total is the greater number in both equations (*39*). Have children find where to write the total in the addition equation. Then, continue by placing the other known number as an addend (*19*). Children should use any strategy that they are familiar with to solve for the unknown, such as counting on by 10s.

Independent Practice

Circle the correct equation to solve the problem.

7. Larry has 24 stickers. Rita has 13 stickers. How many fewer stickers does Rita have than Larry?

   $24 - 13 = 11$ ⭕ $24 + 13 = 37$ $37 - 13 = 24$

8. Jacob has 21 fewer pennies than Connor. Connor has 47 pennies. How many pennies does Jacob have?

   $47 + 21 = 68$ $47 - 21 = 26$ ⭕ $68 - 21 = 47$

Write a related addition equation to help solve the problem.

9. There were 39 cows eating together in a field. Some walked away. Now there are 19 cows eating together. How many cows walked away?

   $39 - \blacksquare = 19$

   related equation:

   $\underline{19} + \underline{20} = \underline{39}$

   $\underline{20}$ cows walked away.

10. There were 53 cars parked in a lot. Now there are 23 cars in the lot. How many cars were moved out of the lot?

    $53 - \blacksquare = 23$

    related equation:

    $\underline{23} + \underline{30} = \underline{53}$

    $\underline{30}$ cars were moved out.

Math-to-Shopping Connection

Set Up a Store Cut pictures from magazines to represent items that children can buy. Assign an amount of money to each child before starting the activity. Have children write a word problem for each pictured item they wish to buy. Tell them to solve the problem before they can buy that item. For example, a child may want to buy a soccer ball for $20. He says that he has $55. Have the child write an equation and tell how much money he will have left after buying the soccer ball. As an extension, have children trade their word problems with a partner and solve each other's problems.

Lesson 2

Independent Practice

MP4 **11.** Amanda had saved some quarters.
She used 30 quarters.
Then she had 12 quarters left.
How many quarters did Amanda have at the start?
Explain how you solved the problem
and make a drawing to model the problem.

_____42 quarters_____

Answers may vary. Possible answer: The 30 quarters Amanda
used and the 12 quarters that she had left need to be put together
to find the number of quarters at the start. 30 + 12 = 42, so
Amanda had 42 quarters at the start.

Possible drawing:

number of quarters at start	
30 quarters Amanda used	12 quarters left

MP2 **12.** Travis rides his bike 20 fewer miles than Jonah.
Travis rides 9 miles in all. Jonah rides 10 miles
and then stops for a snack. After his snack,
Jonah gets back on his bike and rides some more.
How many miles did Jonah ride after his snack?
Explain how you solved the problem.

_____19 miles_____

Answers may vary. Possible answer: I know that Travis rides
20 fewer miles than Jonah and that Travis rides 9 miles. So
I can add 20 miles to the 9 miles Travis rides to find how many
miles Jonah rides. 9 + 20 = 29, so Jonah rides 29 miles in all.
I subtract the 10 miles Jonah rides before his snack to find
the number of miles he rides after his snack. 29 − 10 = 19

Unit 1 ■ Focus on Operations and Algebraic Thinking **25**

Teaching Tips

Item 11

Have children use play coins or counters
to first model the problem. Then refer
them to page 19 for an example of a
drawing used to represent subtraction.
For this problem, since the two bars
of the drawing (the quarters used and
the quarters left) would be together,
the drawing that children make should
model addition.

Common Errors

Item 12

Some children may find the total miles
that Travis rode rather than finding the
number of miles he rode after his snack.
It can be helpful for children to draw
a number line to model this problem
situation.

Mathematical Practices

MP2	**Reason abstractly and quantitatively.**

Item 12: Children make sense of the different quantities given
in the problem.

MP4	**Model with mathematics.**

Item 11: Children model the problem by drawing a picture.

Common Core Focus:

2.OA.2 Fluently add and subtract within 20 using mental strategies. By end of Grade 2, know from memory all sums of two one-digit numbers.

OBJECTIVE

Add and subtract fluently within 20.

ESSENTIAL QUESTION

After reading the Essential Question aloud, make sure children understand that there are different strategies that can be used to add and subtract fluently within 20. Throughout this lesson, encourage children to try different addition and subtraction strategies so they can determine which are most helpful to them.

PREREQUISITE SKILLS

Use Foundational Skills Handbook page 281, *Related Facts,* to assist children with writing related addition and subtraction facts.

FLUENCY PRACTICE

Fluency practice is available at **sadlierconnect.com**.

Concept Development

Understand: Make a ten to help you add

■ This presentation focuses on how children can adapt addition facts in order to add to a 10.

■ Have children read the word problem. Discuss how the equation matches the problem. Suggest that they make drawings to represent the problem.

■ The use of a ten frame can be very helpful to children. For example, if a child places 6 counters in the ten frame, it is easy to see that 4 more counters are needed to make 10.

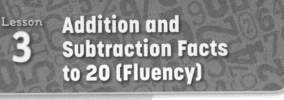

Essential Question:
What strategies can you use to add and subtract?
2.OA.2

Guided Instruction

In this lesson you will learn different ways to add and subtract.

Understand: Make a ten to help you add

> Lisa has 8 blue buttons. Ryan has 7 red buttons. How many buttons do they have in all?

Write an equation for the problem.

$8 + 7 = \blacksquare$

Remember!
When you count on 2 from 8, say, "9, 10."

Use 8 blue counters and 7 red counters to model the problem. Then move 2 of the red ones to make a ten.

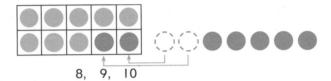

8, 9, 10

Add the red counters that are left to the 10.

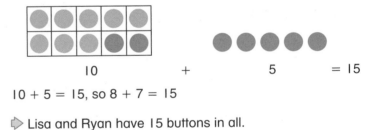

10 + 5 = 15

$10 + 5 = 15$, so $8 + 7 = 15$

▷ Lisa and Ryan have 15 buttons in all.

Support English Language Learners

Children may not be used to hearing the word *related* in terms of mathematics, such as *related addition facts*. They may be familiar with the word *related* meaning people that belong to the same family.

Give each child a sheet of drawing paper. Write the word *related* on the board, and tell children to write this same word in the middle of their paper. Then, have children draw a picture of their family above the word *related*. On the board, write the related facts 4 + 7 = 11, 7 + 4 = 11, 11 − 7 = 4, and 11 − 4 = 7. Have children copy these facts onto their papers below the word *related*. Have volunteers share how their family members are related. Then, have them talk about how the facts they just wrote are related.

MORE ONLINE sadlierconnect.com

Lesson 3

Guided Instruction

Understand: Make a ten to help you subtract

> There were 15 cars parked. 8 cars were moved out. How many cars are left?

Write an equation for the problem. $15 - 8 = \blacksquare$

Step 1

Make a ten to help you subtract.

$8 = \underline{5} + \underline{3}$ so $15 - 8$ is like $15 - \underline{5} - \underline{3}$.

To make a ten, subtract $\underline{5}$ from 15. $15 - 5 = \underline{10}$.

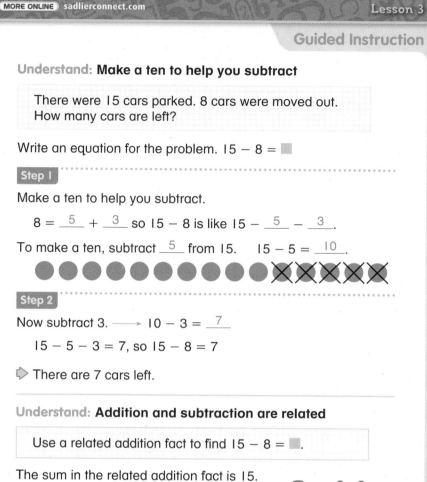

Step 2

Now subtract 3. ⟶ $10 - 3 = \underline{7}$

$15 - 5 - 3 = 7$, so $15 - 8 = 7$

⇨ There are 7 cars left.

Understand: Addition and subtraction are related

> Use a related addition fact to find $15 - 8 = \blacksquare$.

The sum in the related addition fact is 15.
An addend in the related addition fact is 8.

Remember!
Related facts use the same numbers.

$8 + \underline{7} = 15$

$8 + 7 = 15$ and $15 - 8 = 7$ are related facts.

⇨ $15 - 8 = 7$

Unit 1 ■ Focus on Operations and Algebraic Thinking **27**

Understand: Make a ten to help you subtract

■ Have children look at the equation for the problem. Then ask them to tell why 8 was changed to 5 plus 3, not 6 plus 2, which also equals 8.

■ Make sure children understand that subtracting 5 from a number is the same as subtracting 2 and then 3 from it. It may also help children to use counters and show other options for subtracting 5, such as subtracting 1 and then 4.

■ To reinforce the make-a-ten strategy, discuss with children whether it is easier to subtract a number less than 9 from 10 or from a greater number, such as 12. Children may say that they find it easier to subtract from 10 by finding numbers that add to make 10.

Understand: Addition and subtraction are related

■ Ask children to explain why these facts are related. Have them name two additional related facts, for example: $7 + 8 = 15$ and $15 - 7 = 8$.

Math-to-Weather Connection

Snowy Months Explain to children that weather information is gathered using many years of data. One such type of weather information is the amount of yearly snowfall.

Share the following word problem with children and have them work in pairs to find a solution. They should write an equation, use a strategy of their choice to solve the equation, and write a related fact. *In Buffalo, New York, it snowed 13 inches in March and 8 inches in November. How much more snow fell in March than in November?*

Guided Instruction

Connect: Use related facts to help you add and subtract Use this page to help children understand how to use a related fact to add or subtract.

■ Discuss with children what is meant by the sum and addends in an addition sentence. You may wish to write several addition examples on the board to give children practice in naming the sums and addends.

■ Help children understand why they are making a ten. You may wish to have them look back at pages 26 and 27 on which they used a ten to add and subtract.

■ To help children understand Step 2, explain that in an equation, whatever appears on one side of the equal sign has the same value as whatever appears on the other side.

■ Use cubes to model 7 + 5 = 12. Then demonstrate that by taking cubes from one addend and adding them to the other addend, the answer remains the same. For example, take 3 cubes from the group of 5 and add them to the group of 7. This changes 7 + 5 to 10 + 2. Point out that the sum, 12, remains the same.

■ For Step 3, reinforce the idea of related facts by presenting another addition fact, such as 7 + 6 = 13, and asking children to tell what subtraction facts are related to this addition fact.

Guided Instruction

Connect: Use related facts to help you add and subtract

$$14 - 9 = \blacksquare$$

Step 1

Use the two numbers you know to write a related addition fact.

Which number will be the sum? __14__

Which number will be an addend? __9__

__9__ + $\blacksquare$ = __14__

Step 2

What is the missing addend in $9 + \blacksquare = 14$?

Make a ten.   9 and how many more is 10? __1__

$9 + 1 = 10$.   10 and how many more is 14? __4__

You added __1__ to make 10.

Then you added __4__ to make 14.

__1__ + __4__ = 5, so the missing addend is 5.

$9 + 5 = 14$

Step 3

Use the related addition fact to write the subtraction fact.

$9 + 5 = 14$ and $14 - 9 = 5$ are related facts.

▷ $14 - 9 = 5$

28   Unit 1 ■ Focus on Operations and Algebraic Thinking

Math-to-Sports Connection

Keeping Score Explain that a scorekeeper keeps track of how many points teams score in a game. At school sporting events, scorekeeping is usually done with a pencil and paper. Write the following situational addition problem on the board. Have children work in pairs to solve this problem. *In a football game, a team had a score of 9 points. Then they score 7 more points. Use the make-a-ten strategy to find the team's new score.*

Lesson 3

Guided Practice

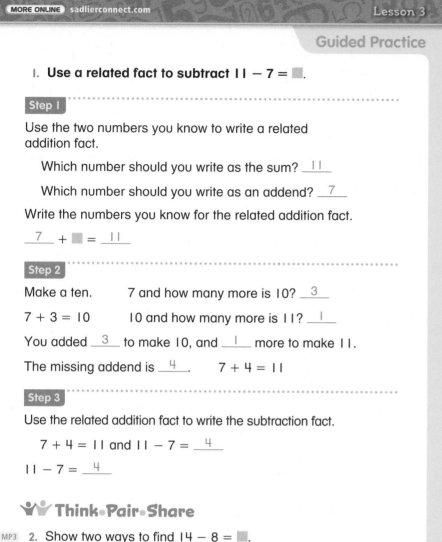

1. Use a related fact to subtract 11 − 7 = ■.

Step 1

Use the two numbers you know to write a related addition fact.

Which number should you write as the sum? __11__

Which number should you write as an addend? __7__

Write the numbers you know for the related addition fact.

__7__ + ■ = __11__

Step 2

Make a ten.   7 and how many more is 10? __3__

7 + 3 = 10   10 and how many more is 11? __1__

You added __3__ to make 10, and __1__ more to make 11.

The missing addend is __4__.   7 + 4 = 11

Step 3

Use the related addition fact to write the subtraction fact.

7 + 4 = 11 and 11 − 7 = __4__

11 − 7 = __4__

☸ Think•Pair•Share

MP3 **2. Show two ways to find 14 − 8 = ■.**

Talk about your work. See Additional Answers.

Observational Assessment

Use page 29 to assess children's understanding of how to add and subtract by making a ten or by using a related fact.

☸ Think•Pair•Share

Peer Collaboration Have children work independently using strategies of their choice to solve the problem. Then, pair children and have them share their strategies and solutions. As they collaborate, ask each pair of children questions such as:

- *How can you use the make-a-ten strategy to find the answer?*

- *How can you use a related addition fact to find the answer?*

To summarize, point out that children can use the make-a-ten strategy or use a related addition fact to subtract.

Return to the Essential Question

Reread the Lesson 3 Essential Question on page 26: *What strategies can you use to add and subtract?*

Tell children to think about what they learned in this lesson and to answer this question.
(Possible responses: I know that I can use the make-a-ten strategy to add and subtract. I also know that I can use related addition facts to subtract.)

Additional Answers

Item 2: Answers will vary. Possible answer: One way is that I can subtract 4 from 14 to make 10 because 14 − 8 is the same as 14 − 4 − 4. So 14 − 4 = 10. I then need to subtract 4 from 10, so 10 − 4 = 6. Another way is that I can write a related addition fact. ■ + 8 = 14, which means 6 + 8 = 14, so 14 − 8 = 6.

Mathematical Practices
Mathematical Practice Standards underline the teaching and understanding of all concepts and skills presented. The emphasis of specific practices is noted throughout the guided and independent practice of this lesson.

MP3	**Construct viable arguments and critique the reasoning of others.**

Item 2: Children will use different strategies to solve a problem and share their reasoning with others. Children will also analyze the work of their peers.

Concept Application

Children may work independently on these pages in the classroom or at home. They may refer to the first four pages of the lesson to revisit the instruction or to see a worked-out example.

Common Errors and **Teaching Tips** may help you support learning either in the classroom or as a follow-up for work done at home.

Common Errors

Items 2, 3, 6, and 8

Children may read these problems incorrectly as additions. Make sure they pay attention to the operation signs to understand that these are subtractions.

Teaching Tips

Items 2, 3, 6, and 8

Suggest to children that they try to use related addition facts to solve these problems and then use the pictures to check their work.

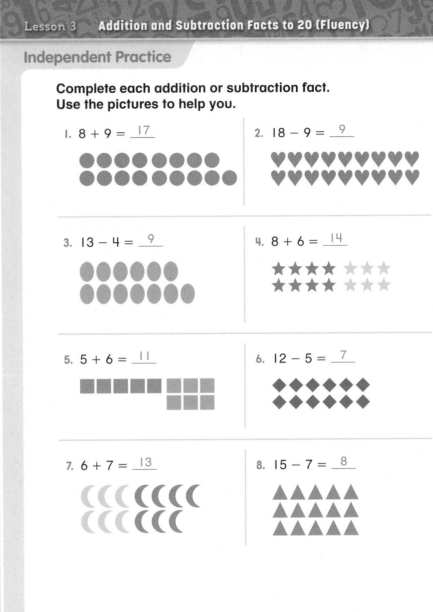

Complete each addition or subtraction fact. Use the pictures to help you.

1. $8 + 9 =$ __17__

2. $18 - 9 =$ __9__

3. $13 - 4 =$ __9__

4. $8 + 6 =$ __14__

5. $5 + 6 =$ __11__

6. $12 - 5 =$ __7__

7. $6 + 7 =$ __13__

8. $15 - 7 =$ __8__

Talking About Math

Collaborative Conversations Have children work in pairs. Have one partner discuss why the pictures in each addition have different color objects representing the addition. Then have the other partner explain why the pictures in each subtraction have all the same color objects representing the subtraction.

MORE ONLINE sadlierconnect.com

Lesson 3

Write a related subtraction fact.

9. $9 + 9 = 18$

$\underline{18} - \underline{9} = \underline{9}$

10. $4 + 7 = 11$

$\underline{11} - \underline{7} = \underline{4}$

11. $7 + 6 = 13$

$\underline{13} - \underline{6} = \underline{7}$

12. $8 + 7 = 15$

$\underline{15} - \underline{7} = \underline{8}$

13. $6 + 6 = 12 \longrightarrow \underline{12} - \underline{6} = \underline{6}$

Write a related addition fact.

14. $17 - 8 = 9$

$\underline{9} + \underline{8} = \underline{17}$

15. $15 - 6 = 9$

$\underline{9} + \underline{6} = \underline{15}$

16. $12 - 8 = 4$

$\underline{4} + \underline{8} = \underline{12}$

17. $11 - 9 = 2$

$\underline{2} + \underline{9} = \underline{11}$

18. $14 - 7 = 7 \longrightarrow \underline{7} + \underline{7} = \underline{14}$

Unit 1 ■ Focus on Operations and Algebraic Thinking **31**

Teaching Tips

Items 10-12
These items only list one possible related subtraction fact as an answer. You might consider having children write an additional related subtraction fact for each.

Items 14-17
These items only list one possible related addition fact as an answer. You might consider having children write an additional related addition fact for each.

Digital Connection

Interactive Whiteboard Have children use the digital whiteboard to explore the concept of related addition facts. Start by having a volunteer make a drawing to illustrate a fact with objects, such as 4 + 7. Call on someone else to write the addition fact under the objects (4 + 7 = ▇). Have the children move the objects together counting them aloud to show that there are eleven. Write this fact on the board as the equation 4 + 7 = 11. Now have a child write a related subtraction fact such as 11 − 7 = ▇. Ask the child to demonstrate the subtraction by moving the objects. Continue until all 4 related facts have been shown.

Independent Practice

Common Errors

Item 21

The unknown in this problem is the first number in a subtraction. Some children may see the numbers 8 and 9 and attempt to use the related facts for 1, 8, and 9.

Assist children by discussing the meaning of subtraction. ■ − 8 = 9 means that you take away 8 and are left with 9. Ask children if they can take 8 objects away from a group of 1.

Teaching Tips

Items 19–34

These items present children with the opportunity to use all the strategies they have learned in this lesson. It may be helpful to take a few minutes to review the strategies before children start to solve. Remind children to pay close attention to the signs as they work through the problems.

Independent Practice

Add or subtract.

19. $14 - 7 = \underline{7}$

20. $9 + \underline{3} = 12$

21. $\underline{17} - 8 = 9$

22. $\underline{5} + 6 = 11$

23. $9 + 3 = \underline{12}$

24. $18 - \underline{9} = 9$

25. $7 + \underline{6} = 13$

26. $\underline{11} - 2 = 9$

27. $16 - \underline{8} = 8$

28. $8 + 9 = \underline{17}$

29. $16 - \underline{7} = 9$

30. $\underline{9} + 7 = 16$

31. $5 + 8 = \underline{13}$

32. $15 - \underline{6} = 9$

33. $11 - \underline{3} = 8$

34. $8 + \underline{6} = 14$

32 Unit I ■ Focus on Operations and Algebraic Thinking

Math-to-Botany Connection

Fast Growing Seaweed Share with children that kelp is a type of seaweed that usually grows as fast as 10–12 inches per day. Have children work in pairs to solve the following word problem, using any strategy that works best for them. *A scientist measures pieces of giant kelp that she finds in the ocean. One piece grew 9 inches one day and 7 inches the next day. How many inches did that piece of giant kelp grow in those two days?*

Lesson 3

Independent Practice

MP3 **35.** You want to find the missing number in $12 - 8 = \blacksquare$.
Show two ways to do this. Explain your thinking.

> **One way**
>
> Answers may vary. Possible answer: I made a 10 by subtracting 2 from 12; $12 - 2 - 6$. My new equation is $10 - 6$, which equals 4. So the missing number is 4. $12 - 8 = 4$.

> **Another way**
>
> Answers may vary. Possible answer: I thought of the related addition fact, $\blacksquare + 8 = 12$. I know that $4 + 8 = 12$, so the missing number is 4. $12 - 8 = 4$

MP3 **36.** Robert says that the facts below are **all** related facts for $13 - 9 = 4$.

$$13 + 9 = 22 \qquad 9 + 4 = 13 \qquad 13 + 4 = 17$$
$$13 - 4 = 9 \qquad 4 + 9 = 13$$

Is he correct? ___No___

Why or why not? Explain.

Answers may vary. Possible answer: Robert is not correct because $13 + 9 = 22$ and $13 + 4 = 17$ are not related facts for $13 - 9 = 4$. Related facts have the same numbers. So the related facts for $13 - 9 = 4$ all have to have 13, 9, and 4.

Common Errors

Item 35

Many children may be able to use a related fact, but will not remember the make-a-ten strategy. To help children remember the make-a-ten strategy, ask them to tell which problem is easier to solve, $12 - 8 = \blacksquare$ or $10 - 6 = \blacksquare$.

Teaching Tips

Item 36

It may help to have children find all the related facts themselves before they try to determine if Robert is correct.

Mathematical Practices	
MP3	**Construct viable arguments and critique the reasoning of others.**

Item 35: Children make conjectures and build logical progressions in two different ways to determine the unknown quantity.

Item 36: Children critique the reasoning of a peer and supply an argument for their critique.

Common Core Focus:

2.OA.3 Determine whether a group of objects (up to 20) has an odd or even number of members.

OBJECTIVE

Determine if a number is odd or even.

ESSENTIAL QUESTION

Read the Essential Question aloud. Ask children if they have heard the terms even or odd. Elicit a discussion with the class about when they have used the terms even and odd. At this point, the conversation does not have to focus only on the mathematical definition.

FLUENCY PRACTICE

Fluency practice is available at **sadlierconnect.com**.

Concept Development

Understand: Even numbers of objects make pairs

■ Make sure children understand that a pair contains two of the same thing.

■ Discuss with children what the numbers under each circled pair of toy cars represent.

■ Have children describe an even number in their own words. Ask them how they could tell if a two-digit number is even by looking at the digit in the ones place.

Lesson

4 Odd and Even Numbers

Essential Question:
How can you tell if a number is odd or even?
2.OA.3

Words to Know
even number
odd number

Guided Instruction

In this lesson you will learn about odd numbers and even numbers.

Understand: Even numbers of objects make pairs

> Rich has 8 toy cars. Does he have an odd number or an even number of toy cars?

Start with 8 toy cars.

Make pairs. Are there any left over?

    2   4   6   8

There are four pairs of toy cars.
No toy cars are left over.
8 is an **even number**.

Remember!
A pair is a group of 2 objects.

An even number has the digit 0, 2, 4, 6, or 8 in the ones place.

▷ Rich has an even number of toy cars.

Words to Know

even number: even numbers make pairs

Example: An even number has 0, 2, 4, 6, or 8 in the ones place.

odd number: odd numbers of objects make pairs with 1 left over

Example: An odd number has 1, 3, 5, 7, or 9 in the ones place.

Glossary can be found on pp. 293–304.

MORE ONLINE sadlierconnect.com

Guided Instruction

Understand: Odd numbers of objects make pairs with 1 left over

Tania has 7 apples. Does she have an odd number or an even number of apples?

Start with 7 apples. Make pairs. Are there any left over?

```
    2          4          6        7
```

There are 3 pairs with 1 left over.

7 is an odd number.

An odd number has the digit 1, 3, 5, 7, or 9 in the ones place.

▷ Tania has an odd number of apples.

Understand: Skip-count by 2s to tell if a number is even or odd

How many flowers? Is that number odd or even?

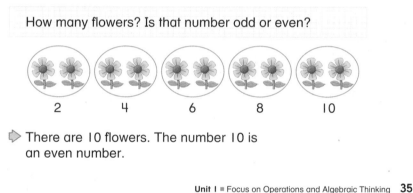

```
   2         4         6         8        10
```

▷ There are 10 flowers. The number 10 is an even number.

Unit 1 ■ Focus on Operations and Algebraic Thinking **35**

Understand: Odd numbers of objects make pairs with 1 left over

■ Discuss with children the number of pairs of apples that are circled and the number under each pair.

■ Discuss why one apple is not in a pair. Make sure that children understand that if 1 object is not paired with another, then the number is odd.

■ If time is available, you might wish to have children model the numbers 3, 5, and 9 to discover that these are odd numbers. Provide children with small objects and lengths of yarn, and have them use the yarn to encircle pairs of objects.

Understand: Skip-count by 2s to tell if a number is even or odd

■ Have children use the pictures of flowers to model skip-counting by 2s. Discuss with them why this shows that 10 is an even number.

■ Have children look back at the seven apples at the top of the page. Ask them what they think will happen if they count by 2s to reach 7. Discuss how skip-counting can show that a number is odd.

Support English Language Learners

Children may not be used to hearing numbers called odd and even. If they are familiar with the word *odd,* they may know it to mean different or unusual. Children may be more familiar with the word *even* meaning fair or the same.

Help children understand that the words *odd* and *even* have special math meanings. Even numbers make pairs (groups of two). Odd numbers make pairs with 1 left over. Write the following sentence frames on the board, and draw pictures to match. Have children come up and circle pairs and then fill in the blanks of the sentence frames. *Jeff has 13 baseball cards. 13 is an _____ number. Logan has 18 baseball cards. 18 is an _____ number.* Repeat this activity as children become more comfortable with saying odd and even.

Guided Instruction

Connect: You can write an equation to show that even numbers make two equal groups

Use this page to help children model how to make two equal groups from an even number.

■ Ask children how they know that the number of basketballs is even.

■ Discuss how the equation shows that the even number 4 is made up of two equal groups.

■ Have children look at the large group of fish. Ask whether there is an odd or an even number of fish in each of the two smaller groups. Make sure children understand that even numbers can be divided into two smaller, equal groups, but that each of the smaller groups might stand for odd numbers.

Guided Instruction

Connect: You can write an equation to show that even numbers make two equal groups

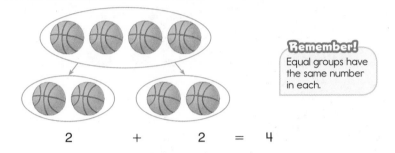

How can you put 4 basketballs into two equal groups?

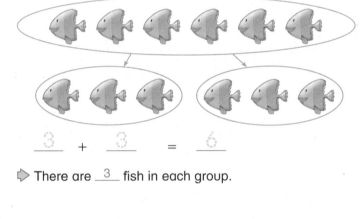

Remember!
Equal groups have the same number in each.

2   +   2   =   4

▷ A group of 4 can make two groups of 2.

How can you put 6 fish into two equal groups?

_3_   +   _3_   =   _6_

▷ There are __3__ fish in each group.

Math-to-Cooking Connection

How Many Pancakes? Bring a box of pancake mix to class. Ask a child to examine the box and find how many pancakes the recipe can make. Discuss if this is an odd or even number and how children can tell.

Extend the activity to ask if the recipe was used two times to make pancakes, how many pancakes could be made and whether that number would be even or odd. This activity can be done with any recipe that makes individual or countable items.

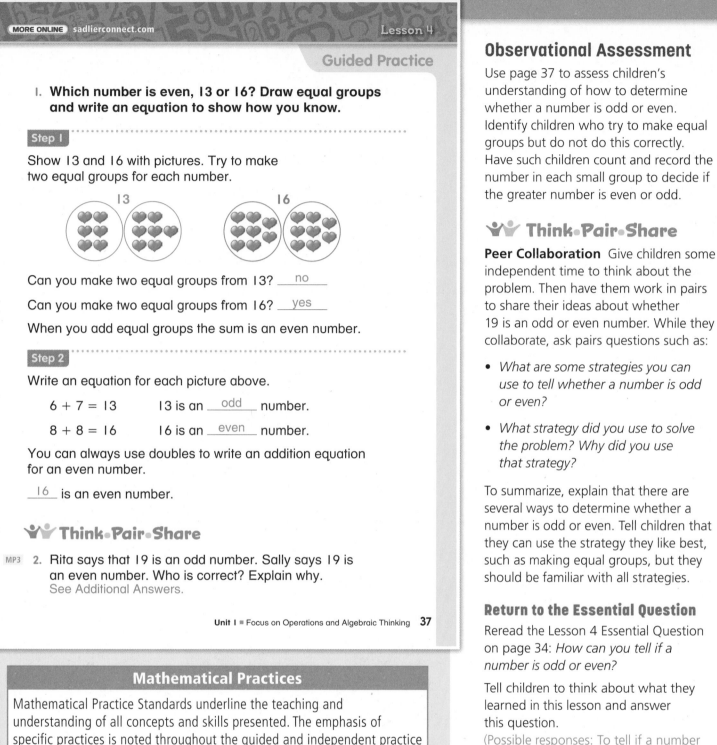

I. **Which number is even, 13 or 16? Draw equal groups and write an equation to show how you know.**

Step 1

Show 13 and 16 with pictures. Try to make two equal groups for each number.

13   16

Can you make two equal groups from 13? ___no___

Can you make two equal groups from 16? ___yes___

When you add equal groups the sum is an even number.

Step 2

Write an equation for each picture above.

6 + 7 = 13   13 is an ___odd___ number.

8 + 8 = 16   16 is an ___even___ number.

You can always use doubles to write an addition equation for an even number.

___16___ is an even number.

Think•Pair•Share

MP3   2. Rita says that 19 is an odd number. Sally says 19 is an even number. Who is correct? Explain why.
See Additional Answers.

Unit 1 ■ Focus on Operations and Algebraic Thinking **37**

Mathematical Practices

Mathematical Practice Standards underline the teaching and understanding of all concepts and skills presented. The emphasis of specific practices is noted throughout the guided and independent practice of this lesson.

| MP3 | **Construct viable arguments and critique the reasoning of others.** |

Item 2: Children analyze a problem in order to explain which solution is correct.

Observational Assessment

Use page 37 to assess children's understanding of how to determine whether a number is odd or even. Identify children who try to make equal groups but do not do this correctly. Have such children count and record the number in each small group to decide if the greater number is even or odd.

Think•Pair•Share

Peer Collaboration Give children some independent time to think about the problem. Then have them work in pairs to share their ideas about whether 19 is an odd or even number. While they collaborate, ask pairs questions such as:

- *What are some strategies you can use to tell whether a number is odd or even?*

- *What strategy did you use to solve the problem? Why did you use that strategy?*

To summarize, explain that there are several ways to determine whether a number is odd or even. Tell children that they can use the strategy they like best, such as making equal groups, but they should be familiar with all strategies.

Return to the Essential Question

Reread the Lesson 4 Essential Question on page 34: *How can you tell if a number is odd or even?*

Tell children to think about what they learned in this lesson and answer this question.
(Possible responses: To tell if a number is odd or even, I can look at the ones digit, try to put the number into pairs, or try to make two equal groups for the number.)

Additional Answers

Item 2: Answers will vary. Possible answer: Rita is correct. 19 is an odd number because it cannot be divided into two equal groups. I cannot use doubles to write an addition equation for 19.

Concept Application

Children may work independently on these pages in the classroom or at home. They may refer to the first four pages of the lesson to revisit the instruction or to see a worked-out example.

Common Errors and **Teaching Tips** may help you support learning either in the classroom or as a follow-up for work done at home.

Common Errors

Item 2

Children may need to be reminded that, if there is a zero in the ones place of a two-digit number, the number is even. Ask children for ideas to explain why zero is an even number.

Teaching Tips

Items 2, 5, and 6

The pictures of the objects are close together in these problems. Suggest to children that they look at the whole picture before they start circling groups of two. They should think of a logical way to work, for example starting at the top and group from left to right, so they do not forget to include an object.

Independent Practice

Circle pairs of objects. Then tell if the number is even or odd.

1.

7 is an ___odd___ number.

2.

10 is an ___even___ number.

3.

4 is an ___even___ number.

4.

5 is an ___odd___ number.

5.

14 is an ___even___ number.

6.

11 is an ___odd___ number.

Talking About Math

Collaborative Conversations Have children work in pairs. One partner should name a group of objects in the classroom, such as the tables or desks. The other partner should count the objects and tell whether this number is odd or even. Children should switch roles and repeat these procedures with another group of objects in the classroom. Suggest that children try different strategies to determine whether the number of objects is odd or even.

MORE ONLINE sadlierconnect.com

Independent Practice

Circle the correct answer.

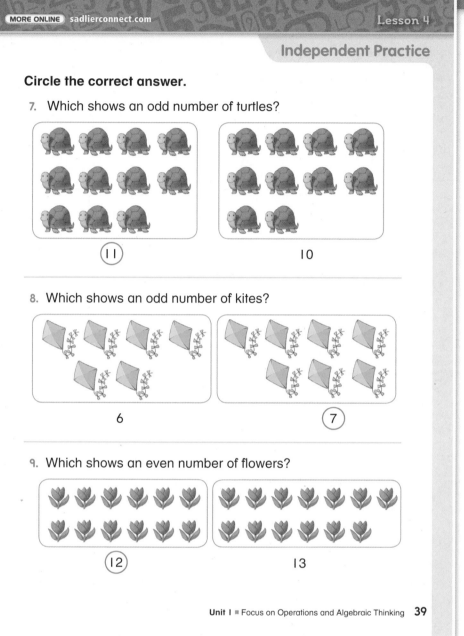

7. Which shows an odd number of turtles?

(11)   10

8. Which shows an odd number of kites?

6   (7)

9. Which shows an even number of flowers?

(12)   13

Teaching Tips

Items 7–9

You may wish to discuss with children how the arrangement of the objects makes it either easier or harder to use different strategies. In items 7 and 9, the objects are lined up, so circling pairs may be a good strategy to use. Item 8 is set up so that children might choose to circle two equal groups.

Digital Connection

Digital Manipulatives Use an Internet search engine to find a Web site that provides digital manipulatives and counters. Using a set of digital manipulatives, have one child place a random number of objects on the virtual workmat. Then have another child use any strategy to decide whether there is an odd or even number of objects. Have children switch roles to repeat the activity. Encourage other children to identify different numbers of objects as odd or even as time allows.

Independent Practice

Common Errors

Items 10-13

Some children may circle just one number and then stop. Make sure children realize that they need to find all the even numbers or all the odd numbers for each item.

Teaching Tips

Items 10-20

To be sure that children understand the three different question formats on this page, it may be helpful to review the instructions for each.

Independent Practice

Circle the correct answers.

10. Circle all the odd numbers.

    14   16   (17)   18   (19)

11. Circle all the even numbers.

    (2)   (4)   7   9   (10)

12. Circle all the even numbers.

    11   15   (16)   (18)   (20)

13. Circle all the odd numbers.

    8   (9)   (11)   12   14

Write true or false.

14. 12 is an odd number. ___false___

15. 16 is an even number. ___true___

16. 15 and 19 are both odd numbers. ___true___

Complete the sentences. Write _even_ or _odd_.

17. 22 is an ___even___ number.

18. 35 is an ___odd___ number.

19. 13 is an ___odd___ number.

20. 28 is an ___even___ number.

Math-to-Science Connection

Animal Legs Animals are classified based on similar characteristics. One very noticeable characteristic is number of legs. Write the following chart on the board. Call up volunteers to determine whether each number of legs is odd or even and to write _odd_ or _even_ in the row for that animal.

Animal	Number of Legs	Odd or Even?
Dog	4	
Woodpecker	2	
Spider	8	
Grasshopper	6	

After completing the chart, children will notice that every animal has an even number of legs.

21. Fill in the missing numbers to show that 14 is an even number.

$$\underline{7} + \underline{7} = 14$$

22. Fill in the missing numbers to show that 17 is an odd number.

$$\underline{8} + \underline{8} + \underline{1} = 17$$

MP1 23. Henry writes 15 on the board. He says that 15 is an odd number. Draw a picture to show if he is correct. Talk about your answer.

Check children's work.
Answers may vary. Possible answer: I used pairs and had 1 left over. So Henry is correct because 15 is an odd number.

MP2 24. Look at the numbers below. Find the even number. Use equal groups to prove you are correct. Then write an addition equation to check your work.

22   21   19

Check children's work.
Answers may vary. Possible answer: 22 is an even number. I made 2 groups of 11. 11 + 11 = 22.

Common Errors

Item 24

Some children may confuse making equal groups with seeing if the number can be split up into many groups of two. While making groups of two will also help determine whether a number is even or odd, children are asked to see if two equal groups can be made. These two groups are then used to write an equation.

Teaching Tips

Items 21 and 22

Discuss with children that one way to determine if a number is even is to see if it can be divided into two equal groups. Remind children that they cannot make two equal groups from an odd number. They can use this information to help complete the equations. If children need additional help, have them act out the equations with manipulatives or make drawings.

Mathematical Practices

MP1	**Make sense of problems and persevere in solving them.**

Item 23: Children make sense of the problem to determine if the answer is correct and then justify their thinking.

MP2	**Reason abstractly and quantitatively.**

Item 24: Children identify the even number from among the quantities listed and then make equal groups to check their response.

Common Core Focus:

2.OA.4 Use addition to find the total number of objects arranged in rectangular arrays with up to 5 rows and up to 5 columns; write an equation to express the total as a sum of equal addends.

OBJECTIVE

Use repeated addition to find the total number of objects in an array.

ESSENTIAL QUESTION

Read the Essential Question aloud. Ask children if there are any words that they do not know. Some children might not know the word *array*. Arrays show groups of objects in rows and columns. Explain that these orderly arrangements make it easier to find the total number of objects.

FLUENCY PRACTICE

Fluency practice is available at **sadlierconnect.com**.

Concept Development

Understand: Use repeated addition to find how many in all

■ In grade 2, children continue to develop strategies for adding whole numbers. Repeated addition is a strategy for finding how many in all in an array.

■ Be sure children know the basic addition facts fluently.

■ Knowing how to add the same number repeatedly is the underlying skill needed for multiplication. By definition, multiplication is repeated addition, so with a solid understanding of repeated addition, children will be prepared to learn how to multiply, a major focus of grade 3.

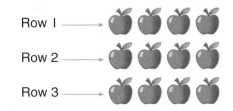

Lesson

5   Arrays

Guided Instruction

In this lesson you will learn how to write equations to show how many in an array.

Understand: Use repeated addition to find how many in all

> Rosie put some red apples into a box.
> There are 3 rows of apples in the box.
> There are 4 apples in each row.
> How many apples in all are in the box?

Row 1 ⟶ 🍎 🍎 🍎 🍎

Row 2 ⟶ 🍎 🍎 🍎 🍎

Row 3 ⟶ 🍎 🍎 🍎 🍎

There are 4 apples in Row 1.
There are 4 apples in Row 2.
There are 4 apples in Row 3.

Write an equation to find how many apples in all. You can add to find how many in all.

$4 + 4 + 4 = 12$

⇨ There are 12 apples in all.

Words to Know

array: objects arranged in equal rows and columns

Example:

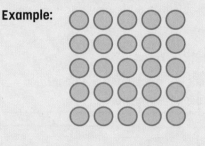

Glossary can be found on pp. 293–304.

Lesson 5

Guided Instruction

Understand: You arrange things in equal rows and equal columns to make an array

Look at the rows. Write an equation for the array.

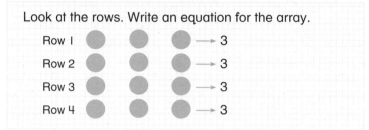

The array has 4 rows with 3 counters in each row.

▷ 3 + 3 + 3 + 3 = 12

Now look at the columns. Write an equation for the array.

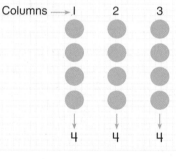

The array has 3 columns with 4 counters in each column.

▷ 4 + 4 + 4 = 12

Unit 1 ■ Focus on Operations and Algebraic Thinking **43**

Understand: You arrange things in equal rows and equal columns to make an array

■ It is important that children recognize the structure of an array. They need to see both the rows and the columns that form the array. Continue to emphasize that all the rows have the same number of objects in them. In the same way, point out that all the columns have the same number of objects in them.

■ Explain that some arrays, but not all, have the same number of objects in both the rows and the columns.

■ In Lesson 4, children worked on fluency with addition facts within 20. Remind children to use other strategies, such as counting on, to find the total number of objects in an array. This will be helpful when children work with arrays of more than 20 objects.

■ Ask children to compare the images of the two arrays on this page by telling how they are alike. Children should recognize that the arrays are the same. Then, ask them to compare the equations that are used to find the total number of counters in the array. Children should recognize that the sum for both equations is the same. Some children may observe that the addend in one problem is the same as the number of times the other addend is repeated.

■ If children are struggling, encourage them to circle the counters by row in the first array or by column in the second array.

Support English Language Learners

As children work with arrays, they will need to become familiar with the terms *row* and *column*. Explain that an array is made up of rows and columns.

Have children use connecting cubes to make arrays. First, instruct them to make 3 rows with 4 cubes in each row. Have children say the word *row* aloud as they motion their arm across or horizontally, as if drawing a row. Then repeat the process asking children to make 4 columns with 2 cubes in each column. Ask children to move their arms up and down, or vertically, as they say the word *column* aloud.

Throughout the lesson, reinforce the vocabulary by having children trace the rows or columns in an array while saying the correct term.

Connect: Different arrays can show the same number Use this page to help children strengthen their understanding of using repeated addition to find the total number of objects in an array.

- Ask children to compare the arrays on this page. Children may say that the second array is the same as the first except turned. They may recognize that the number of rows in the first array is the same as the number of columns in the second array, and *vice versa*.

- Mathematically, these arrays are basic to children's understanding of the Commutative Property of Multiplication. In grade 3, children will learn that, for example, $4 \times 2 = 2 \times 4$ because both expressions equal 8.

- If time permits, ask children to use counters to try to make a different array that shows 8. Possible arrays include one row of eight counters or eight rows of one counter.

- Mathematically proficient children are able to make sense of the relationships between the equations that represent these arrays. Encourage children to explain why the same addition equation, $2 + 2 + 2 + 2 = 8$, can represent each array even though the arrays are different. Continue to connect the numbers in the equations to the pictured images of the arrays. As children can better visualize what an equation means, they will have a better understanding of how to use addition to solve problems.

Connect: Different arrays can show the same number

Sandy and Ralph have the same number of counters. They each used all their counters to make an array. Do both arrays show the same number?

Look at Sandy's rows and columns.
There are 2 rows. There are 4 in each row.
Write an equation to find how many in all.

Sandy's array

$4 + 4 = \underline{8}$

There are 4 columns. There are 2 in each column. Write an equation to find how many in all.

$2 + 2 + 2 + 2 = \underline{8}$

Look at Ralph's rows and columns.

Ralph's array

How many rows? $\underline{4}$

How many in each row? $\underline{2}$

Write an equation to find how many in all.

$\underline{2} + \underline{2} + \underline{2} + \underline{2} = \underline{8}$

How many columns? $\underline{2}$

How many in each column? $\underline{4}$

Write an equation to find how many in all.

$\underline{4} + \underline{4} = \underline{8}$

Compare the equations.

▷ Both arrays show the same number, 8.

44   Unit I ■ Focus on Operations and Algebraic Thinking

Math-to-Cooking Connection

Muffin Pans Show children a muffin pan. Have the children identify whether the muffin pan shows an array. Ask the children to tell how many muffins can be placed in each row and in each column. Have the children use repeated addition to determine the total number of muffins the pan can hold.

If possible, provide a variety of muffin pans that can hold various amounts of muffins.

Lesson 5

Guided Practice

1. **Write two equations for this array.**

Step 1

Look at the rows.

There are __2__ rows. There are __6__ in each row.

Write one equation.

__6__ + __6__ = __12__

Step 2

Look at the columns.

There are __6__ columns. There are __2__ in each column.

Write another equation.

__2__ + __2__ + __2__ + __2__ + __2__ + __2__ = __12__

The two equations for the array are

__6__ + __6__ = __12__ and __6__ + __6__ + __6__ + __6__ + __6__ + __6__ = __12__

♕ Think•Pair•Share

MP8 **2.** Draw a different array for 12. Write two equations for your array. Then compare the array above to your array. Talk about how the arrays are alike and how they are different.

Check that children's drawings show a 3 × 4 array. Equations should be 3 + 3 + 3 + 3 = 12 and 4 + 4 + 4 = 12. Sample explanation: My array has 3 rows and 4 columns. Each row has 4 counters. Each column has 3 counters. Both arrays show 12.

Unit 1 ■ Focus on Operations and Algebraic Thinking **45**

Mathematical Practices

Mathematical Practice Standards underline the teaching and understanding of all concepts and skills presented. The emphasis of specific practices is noted throughout the guided and independent practice of this lesson.

| MP8 | **Look for and express regularity in repeated reasoning.** |

Item 2: Children make use of the structure of the rows and columns in an array to find a new array that shows the same number. They look closely to discern patterns in the arrays.

Observational Assessment

Use page 45 to assess children's understanding of how to use repeated addition to find the total number of objects in an array. Be sure children are counting the objects correctly. Children may need to underline the word *rows* or *columns* to reinforce what they are counting. Emphasize that the total number is the same regardless of which equation is used.

♕ Think•Pair•Share

Peer Collaboration Ask pairs to share the arrays they drew. In addition to 3 rows of 4 objects and 4 rows of 3 objects, children could also draw 1 row of 12 objects and 12 rows of 1 object. Ask each pair of children questions such as:

• *How did you know that your array shows 12?*

• *Did you try any arrays that did not work? Why did those arrays not work?*

To summarize, explain that there are several arrays that can show 12. While the number of rows and columns may be different, or switched, the total number of objects will be the same.

Return to the Essential Question

Reread the Lesson 5 Essential Question on page 42: *How can you find how many objects are in an array?*

Tell children to think about what they learned in this lesson to answer this question.
(Possible responses: An array is made up of objects arranged in rows and columns. The whole array has the shape of a rectangle. You can count the number of rows and how many are in each row. Then use repeated addition. You can also count the number of columns and how many are in each column before using repeated addition.)

Independent Practice

Concept Application

Children may work independently on these pages in the classroom or at home. They may refer to the first four pages of the lesson to revisit the instruction or to see a worked-out example.

Common Errors and **Teaching Tips** may help you support learning either in the classroom or as a follow-up for work done at home.

Common Errors

Items 1–6

Children may reverse the number of rows and the number of columns. Remind children that rows go across and columns go up and down.

Lesson 5   **Arrays**

Independent Practice

Look at the arrays. Write how many rows and columns.

1. ___4___ rows ___2___ columns

2. ___2___ rows ___3___ columns

3. ___4___ rows ___4___ columns

4. ___3___ rows ___4___ columns

5. ___3___ rows ___5___ columns

6. ___3___ rows ___3___ columns

46 Unit I ■ Focus on Operations and Algebraic Thinking

Copyright © by William H. Sadlier, Inc. All rights reserved.

Math-to-Art Connection

Painting Displays Tell children that art teachers often need to determine how to display art that the class has made. Give examples of ways in which art can be arranged, such as in 4 rows of 5 paintings or 5 columns of 4 paintings. Model how to draw an array that represents how the paintings are displayed. Have children use the model to write a repeated addition equation and to find the total number of paintings on display.

46 Unit 1 ■ Focus on Operations and Algebraic Thinking

Lesson 5

Independent Practice

Circle the two arrays that show the same number.

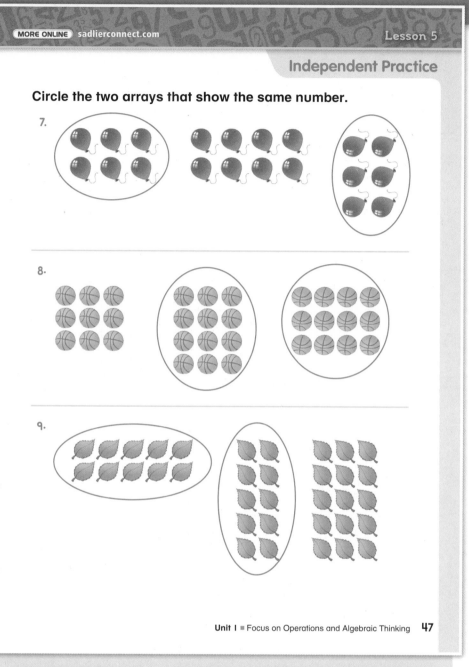

7.

8.

9.

Teaching Tips

Items 7–9

Encourage children to look for a pattern in the pairs of arrays that show the same number. Children should recognize that the number of rows and the number of columns are reversed.

Talking About Math

Using Arrays to Explain Have children select one problem from items 7–9. Ask them to tell what objects could be arranged like this array. They should explain why the objects might be put into an array.

Independent Practice

Common Errors

Items 10-13

Children may write the number of rows as the addends in the first equation instead of the number in each row. If so, remind children that the first equation will repeat the number of objects in each row.

Teaching Tips

Item 14

If children are struggling, remind them that the sum in the equation must equal the total number of objects in the array.

Independent Practice

Write two equations for each array.

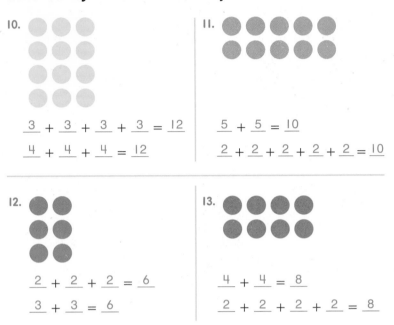

10. $\underline{3} + \underline{3} + \underline{3} + \underline{3} = \underline{12}$

$\underline{4} + \underline{4} + \underline{4} = \underline{12}$

11. $\underline{5} + \underline{5} = \underline{10}$

$\underline{2} + \underline{2} + \underline{2} + \underline{2} + \underline{2} = \underline{10}$

12. $\underline{2} + \underline{2} + \underline{2} = \underline{6}$

$\underline{3} + \underline{3} = \underline{6}$

13. $\underline{4} + \underline{4} = \underline{8}$

$\underline{2} + \underline{2} + \underline{2} + \underline{2} = \underline{8}$

14. Circle the equations for this array.

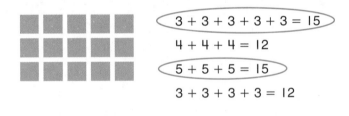

$3 + 3 + 3 + 3 + 3 = 15$ ⟵ circled

$4 + 4 + 4 = 12$

$5 + 5 + 5 = 15$ ⟵ circled

$3 + 3 + 3 + 3 = 12$

Digital Connection

Interactive Whiteboard Using an interactive whiteboard, have each child randomly select a number between 2 and 25. Then, ask each child to move objects to try to make an array of that number. Encourage children to look for multiple arrays that make the same number.

Lesson 5

Independent Practice

MP3 **15.** Mrs. Bennett drew these arrays. Tommy thinks they show the same number. Connor does not. Who is correct? Explain your answer using equations.

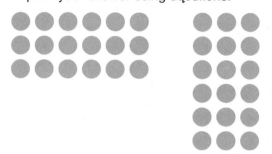

Answers may vary. Possible answer: Tommy is correct. Both arrays show 18. One has 3 rows and 6 columns, 6 + 6 + 6 = 18. The other has 6 rows and 3 columns, 3 + 3 + 3 + 3 + 3 + 3 = 18. Both equations show the same number, 18.

MP4 **16.** Draw an array with 4 rows and 5 counters in each row. Write two equations for the array.

Check that children's drawings show a 4 × 5 array. Equations should include 4 + 4 + 4 + 4 + 4 = 20 and 5 + 5 + 5 + 5 = 20.

Draw a different array to show 20. Use 2 rows. Write two equations for the array.

Check that children's drawings show a 2 × 10 array. Equations should include 2 + 2 + 2 + 2 + 2 + 2 + 2 + 2 + 2 + 2 = 20 and 10 + 10 = 20.

Unit 1 ■ Focus on Operations and Algebraic Thinking **49**

Teaching Tips

Item 15

Encourage children to write equations to represent each array. Remind them that the sum in the equation is the number that the array represents.

Return to the

Remind children to return to the Progress Check self-assessment, page 7, to check off additional items they have mastered during the unit.

Mathematical Practices	
MP3	**Construct viable arguments and critique the reasoning of others.**
Item 15: Children analyze a problem situation and give reasons to justify the correct answer.	
MP4	**Model with mathematics.**
Item 16: Children model the number 20 in two ways using arrays.	

The Common Core Review covers all the standards presented in the unit. Use it to assess your children's mastery of the unit's concepts and skills.

Depth of Knowledge

The depth of knowledge is a ranking of the content complexity of assessment items based on Webb's Depth of Knowledge (DOK) levels. The levels increase in complexity as shown below.

Level 1: Recall and Reproduction
Level 2: Basic Skills and Concepts
Level 3: Strategic Reasoning and Thinking
Level 4: Extended Thinking

Item	Standard	DOK
1	2.OA.2	2
2	2.OA.2	2
3	2.OA.3	2
4	2.OA.3	2
5	2.OA.2	1
6	2.OA.2	1
7	2.OA.2	1
8	2.OA.2	1
9	2.OA.2	1
10	2.OA.2	1
11	2.OA.2	1
12	2.OA.2	1
13	2.OA.1	2
14	2.OA.1	3
15	2.OA.1	2
16	2.OA.1	2
17	2.OA.3	4
18	2.OA.4	1
19	2.OA.4	2
20	2.OA.4	4

Write a related subtraction fact.

1. $8 + 6 = 14$

   $\underline{14} - \underline{6} = \underline{8}$

   $14 - 8 = 6$

2. $4 + 9 = 13$

   $\underline{13} - \underline{9} = \underline{4}$

   $13 - 4 = 9$

Circle the correct answers.

3. Circle all the even numbers.

   (12)   13   15   17   (18)

4. Circle all the odd numbers.

   4   6   (7)   8   (9)

Add or subtract.

5. $16 - 9 = \underline{7}$

6. $8 + \underline{3} = 11$

7. $\underline{13} - 5 = 8$

8. $\underline{8} + 9 = 17$

9. $15 - 6 = \underline{9}$

10. $14 - \underline{7} = 7$

11. $\underline{7} + 8 = 15$

12. $9 + 9 = \underline{18}$

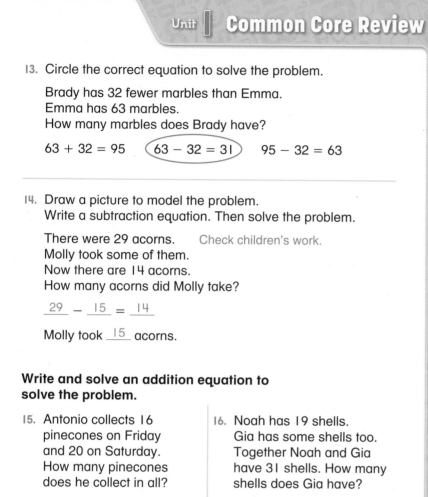

13. Circle the correct equation to solve the problem.

Brady has 32 fewer marbles than Emma.
Emma has 63 marbles.
How many marbles does Brady have?

63 + 32 = 95   (63 − 32 = 31)   95 − 32 = 63

14. Draw a picture to model the problem.
Write a subtraction equation. Then solve the problem.

There were 29 acorns.   Check children's work.
Molly took some of them.
Now there are 14 acorns.
How many acorns did Molly take?

<u>29</u> − <u>15</u> = <u>14</u>

Molly took <u>15</u> acorns.

Write and solve an addition equation to solve the problem.

15. Antonio collects 16 pinecones on Friday and 20 on Saturday. How many pinecones does he collect in all?

<u>16</u> + <u>20</u> = ■

Antonio collects <u>36</u> pinecones in all.

16. Noah has 19 shells. Gia has some shells too. Together Noah and Gia have 31 shells. How many shells does Gia have?

<u>19</u> + ■ = <u>31</u>

Gia has <u>12</u> shells.

This chart correlates the Common Core Review items with the lessons in which the concepts and skills are presented.

Item	Lesson
1	3
2	3
3	4
4	4
5	3
6	3
7	3
8	3
9	3
10	3
11	3
12	3
13	2
14	2
15	1
16	1
17	4
18	5
19	5
20	5

Unit 1 ■ Focus on Operations and Algebraic Thinking **51**

Talking About Math

Direct children to respond to the Unit 1 Essential Question. (This can also be found on page 9.)

Essential Question:
How can you solve addition and subtraction problems?

Possible responses:
- You can use the inverse relationship of addition and subtraction to solve problems and to check answers.
- You can use drawings and equations to solve word problems.
- You can use strategies like count on and make a ten.

Unit Assessment

- Unit 1 Common Core Review, *pp. 50–52*
- Unit 1 Performance Task ONLINE

Additional Assessment Options

Optional Purchase:
- iProgress Monitor ONLINE
- Progress Monitor Student Benchmark Assessment Booklet

Additional Answers

Item 20: Check children's drawings. Equations should include $2 + 2 + 2 = 6$ and $3 + 3 = 6$. Possible explanation: There are 2 rows of 3, so one equation is $3 + 3 = 6$. There are 3 columns of 2, so another equation is $2 + 2 + 2 = 6$.

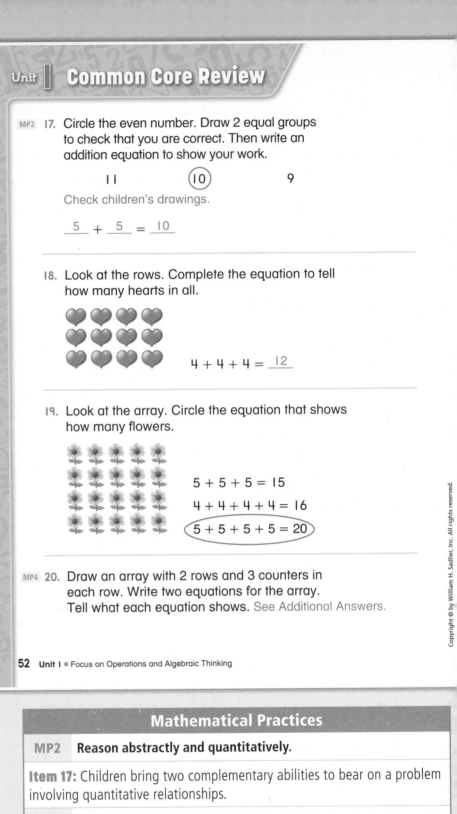

Unit 1 Common Core Review

MP2 17. Circle the even number. Draw 2 equal groups to check that you are correct. Then write an addition equation to show your work.

11   (10)   9

Check children's drawings.

$$\underline{5} + \underline{5} = \underline{10}$$

18. Look at the rows. Complete the equation to tell how many hearts in all.

$$4 + 4 + 4 = \underline{12}$$

19. Look at the array. Circle the equation that shows how many flowers.

$$5 + 5 + 5 = 15$$
$$4 + 4 + 4 + 4 = 16$$
$$\boxed{5 + 5 + 5 + 5 = 20}$$

MP4 20. Draw an array with 2 rows and 3 counters in each row. Write two equations for the array. Tell what each equation shows. See Additional Answers.

52 Unit 1 ■ Focus on Operations and Algebraic Thinking

Mathematical Practices

MP2	**Reason abstractly and quantitatively.**

Item 17: Children bring two complementary abilities to bear on a problem involving quantitative relationships.

MP4	**Model with mathematics.**

Item 20: Children draw an array to represent a mathematical situation and write equations that describe it.

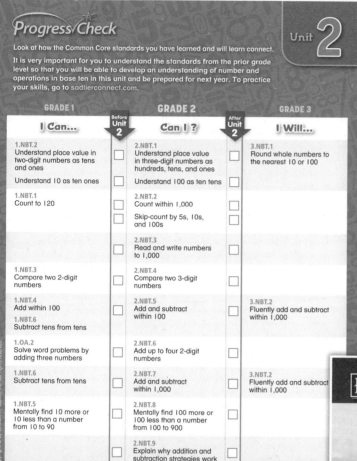

Progress Check — Unit 2

Look at how the Common Core standards you have learned and will learn connect.

It is very important for you to understand the standards from the prior grade level so that you will be able to develop an understanding of number and operations in base ten in this unit and be prepared for next year. To practice your skills, go to sadlierconnect.com.

GRADE 1 I Can...	Before Unit 2	GRADE 2 Can I ?	After Unit 2	GRADE 3 I Will...
1.NBT.2 Understand place value in two-digit numbers as tens and ones	☐	2.NBT.1 Understand place value in three-digit numbers as hundreds, tens, and ones	☐	3.NBT.1 Round whole numbers to the nearest 10 or 100
Understand 10 as ten ones		Understand 100 as ten tens	☐	
1.NBT.1 Count to 120	☐	2.NBT.2 Count within 1,000	☐	
		Skip-count by 5s, 10s, and 100s	☐	
		2.NBT.3 Read and write numbers to 1,000	☐	
1.NBT.3 Compare two 2-digit numbers	☐	2.NBT.4 Compare two 3-digit numbers	☐	
1.NBT.4 Add within 100	☐	2.NBT.5 Add and subtract within 100	☐	3.NBT.2 Fluently add and subtract within 1,000
1.NBT.6 Subtract tens from tens				
1.OA.2 Solve word problems by adding three numbers	☐	2.NBT.6 Add up to four 2-digit numbers	☐	
1.NBT.6 Subtract tens from tens	☐	2.NBT.7 Add and subtract within 1,000	☐	3.NBT.2 Fluently add and subtract within 1,000
1.NBT.5 Mentally find 10 more or 10 less than a number from 10 to 90	☐	2.NBT.8 Mentally find 100 more or 100 less than a number from 100 to 900	☐	
		2.NBT.9 Explain why addition and subtraction strategies work	☐	

Unit 2 ■ Focus on Number and Operations in Base Ten

Student Page 53

Progress Check

Progress Check is a self-assessment tool that children can use to gauge their own progress. Research shows that motivation increases as children gradually become accountable for their own learning.

Before children begin work on Unit 2, have them check the boxes in front of any standards they think they can know well. Tell them it is okay if they cannot check any boxes. They will have a chance to learn and practice all the standards as they work through this unit.

Let children know that, after they complete Lesson 15, they will review the boxes they checked today. Before having them begin the Common Core Review, you will be prompted to have them revisit this page. Remind them to keep this page in a safe place where they can find it later.

HOME ◆ CONNECT...

The Home Connect feature keeps parents or other adult family members apprised of what their children are learning. The key learning objectives are listed, and some ideas for related activities and discussions are included.

Tell children that there is an activity connected to their classroom learning that they can do at home with their families.

Encourage children and their families to share their experiences using the ideas on the Home Connect page. Afterward, you may wish to invite children to share the work they did at home with the class.

HOME ◆ CONNECT...

Your child will learn about the value of digits in a number, called place value. Your child will learn that 10 ones is equal to 1 ten and that 10 tens is equal to 100 ones, or 1 hundred. Your child will write numbers in a place-value chart to show how many hundreds, tens, and ones are in a three-digit number.

hundreds	tens	ones
1	5	7

The 1 in 157 is in the hundreds place. It has a value of 1 hundred, or 100.
The 5 in 157 is in the tens place. It has a value of 5 tens, or 50.
The 7 in 157 is in the ones place. It has a value of 7 ones, or 7.
157 has 1 hundred, 5 tens, and 7 ones.

Your child will learn to skip-count by 5s, 10s, and 100s.

Activity: Write a number from 0 to 9 on index cards—one number on a card. Give your child three cards and ask your child to arrange the cards to make a three-digit number. Have your child tell the number of hundreds, tens, and ones in the number he or she made.

You might ask your child to arrange the cards in the order that creates the greatest number. Then ask your child to arrange them in the order that creates the least number. As a bonus, ask your child to find the difference between the greatest number and the least number!

In this unit, your child will:

- Understand hundreds, tens, and ones in place value.
- Skip-count by 5s, 10s, and 100s.
- Read and write numbers to 1,000.
- Compare numbers.
- Add and subtract two-digit numbers and three-digit numbers within 1,000.
- Add more than two numbers.
- Mentally add or subtract 10 or 100.

NOTE: All of these learning goals for your child are based on the Grade 2 Common Core State Standards for Mathematics.

Ways to Help Your Child

If your child needs help or excels at math you might talk to your child's math teacher. He or she will be able to suggest opportunities to work with your child to keep your child engaged.

ONLINE
For more Home Connect activities, continue online at sadlierconnect.com

54 Unit 2 ■ Focus on Number and Operations in Base Ten

Student Page 54

UNIT PLANNER

	Lesson	Standard(s)	Objective
6	Place Value: Hundreds, Tens, and Ones	**2.NBT.1**	Use place value to find the value of each digit in a three-digit number.
7	Skip-Count by 5s, 10s, and 100s	**2.NBT.2**	Skip-count by 5s, 10s, and 100s within 1,000.
8	Read and Write Numbers to 1,000	**2.NBT.3**	Read and write numbers with numerals, in words, and in expanded form.
9	Compare Numbers	**2.NBT.4**	Use place value to compare two 3-digit numbers.
10	Add Two-Digit Numbers	**2.NBT.5, 2.NBT.9**	Add two 2-digit numbers within 100 using place value.
11	Subtract Two-Digit Numbers	**2.NBT.5, 2.NBT.9**	Subtract 2-digit numbers using place value and regrouping.
12	Add More than Two Numbers	**2.NBT.6**	Add up to four 2-digit numbers using place value and regrouping of ones.
13	Add Three-Digit Numbers within 1,000	**2.NBT.7**	Add three-digit numbers within 1,000.
14	Subtract Three-Digit Numbers within 1,000	**2.NBT.7**	Subtract three-digit numbers.
15	Mentally Add and Subtract 10 or 100	**2.NBT.8**	Use mental math to add or subtract 10 or 100.

Essential Question	Words to Know
How do you find the value of each digit in a 3-digit number?	place-value chart, digit
How can you count by 5s, 10s, and 100s?	skip-count
What are some ways to read and write numbers?	expanded form
How can you compare two numbers using the symbols >, <, = ?	greater than (>), less than (<), equal to (=)
How can you add two 2-digit numbers?	regroup
How can you subtract a 2-digit number from a 2-digit number?	
How can you add three or four 2-digit numbers?	
How can you add two 3-digit numbers?	
How can you subtract three-digit numbers?	
How can you use mental math to add or subtract 10 or 100?	

Unit Assessment

- Unit 2 Common Core Review, *pp. 136–138*
- Unit 2 Performance Task (ONLINE)

Additional Assessment Options

- Performance Task 1, *pp. 139–142*
  (ALSO ONLINE)

Optional Purchase:
- iProgress Monitor (ONLINE)
- Progress Monitor Student Benchmark Assessment Booklet

(ONLINE) Digital Resources

- Home Connect Activities
- Unit Performance Tasks
- Additional Practice
- Fluency Practice
- Teacher Resources
- iProgress Monitor (optional purchase)

Go to SadlierConnect.com to access your Digital Resources.

For more detailed instructions see page T3.

LEARNING PROGRESSIONS

This page provides more in-depth detail on the development of the standards across the grade levels. See also the unit Progress Check page in the Student Edition for a roadmap of the Learning Progressions.

Grade 1

- Students solve word problems by adding three whole numbers that total 20 or less. (1.OA.2)
- Students count to 120 from any number less than 120, and read and write numerals from 0 to 120. They represent a number of objects with a written numeral. (1.NBT.1)
- Students understand that the places in two-digit numbers represent amounts of tens and ones. (1.NBT.2a, 1.NBT.2b, 1.NBT.2c)
- Students apply place value meaning to compare two two-digit numbers using >, =, and < symbols. (1.NBT.3)
- Students add within 100 using models, drawings, and strategies based on place value, properties of operations, and/or the relationship between addition and subtraction. Understand that when adding two-digit numbers it may be necessary to compose a ten. (1.NBT.4)
- Students mentally find 10 more or 10 less than a given two-digit number. (1.NBT.5)
- Students subtract multiples of 10 from multiples of 90 in the range 10 to 90. (1.NBT.6)

Grade 2

- Students extend their understanding of place value to hundreds, viewing a hundred as a new unit composed of 10 tens. (2.NBT.1a, 2.NBT.1b)
- Students count within 1,000 and skip count by 5s, 10s, and 100s. (2.NBT.2)
- Students read and write numbers to 1,000. (2.NBT.3)
- Students compare two 3-digit numbers using >, =, and < symbols. (2.NBT.4)
- Students fluently add and subtract within 100. They explain why addition and subtraction strategies work. (2.NBT.5, 2.NBT.9)
- Students add up to four two-digit numbers and add and subtract within 1,000, using strategies based on place value, properties of operations, and the relationship between addition and subtraction. (2.NBT.6, 2.NBT.7)
- Students mentally add 10 or 100 to numbers from 100 to 900 and mentally subtract 10 or 100 from numbers from 100 to 900. (2.NBT.8)

Grade 3

- Students round whole numbers to the nearest 10 or 100. (3.NBT.1)
- Students apply strategies and algorithms based on place value and properties of operations to fluently add and subtract within 1,000. (3.NBT.2)

Focus on Number and Operations in Base Ten

Essential Question:
How does place value help you add and subtract?

Unit 2 ■ Focus on Number and Operations in Base Ten **55**

Essential Question:
How does place value help you add and subtract?

As children become involved with the Essential Question they will use place-value models to build a deeper understanding of adding and subtracting greater numbers and expanding and comparing numbers according to place value.

Conversation Starters

Have children discuss the photograph. Ask questions such as: *What do you see in the picture? How would you count to find the number of marbles in a box full of marbles? What are some reasons that a full box of marbles might be difficult to count?*

Ask children to suggest ways of counting the marbles shown in the picture. *Is the number of marbles shown a 1-digit, 2-digit, or 3-digit number? How can you tell?* (2-digit number; I can see that there are more than 9 marbles. I tried to count, so I know that there are fewer than 100 marbles.) *If you could lay out the marbles so that none are on top of others, how could you use place value to count them?* (I could make groups of 10, count the groups by 10s, and then count the number left.) *How could you use place value to add two groups of marbles like the ones in the picture?* (I could count the numbers of tens and ones in each group, add the ones and make another ten if needed, and then add the tens.)

Let children work in pairs to circle two groups of marbles in the photo and then write an addition sentence to represent the total number of marbles in their groups.

Activity

Materials: drawing paper

Explain that there are over 70 marbles in the photograph. Children may want to count the marbles, but their totals are likely to vary because some marbles are stacked or covered, and because there is the likelihood of skipping over some marbles or counting some more than once.

Have each child draw one, two, or three rows of 10 marbles each. Then, have them draw another row with fewer than 10 marbles. Children may draw simple circles to represent their marbles. Then have them work in pairs to write addition sentences to find the total number of marbles they drew. If time allows, suggest that children color the marbles they drew.

Common Core Focus:

2.NBT.1 Understand that the three digits of a three-digit number represent amounts of hundreds, tens, and ones. Understand the following as special cases: **a.** 100 can be thought of as a bundle of ten tens—called a "hundred." **b.** The numbers 100, 200, 300, 400, 500, 600, 700, 800, 900 refer to one, two, three, four, five, six, seven, eight, or nine hundreds (and 0 tens and 0 ones).

OBJECTIVE

Use place value to find the value of each digit in a three-digit number.

ESSENTIAL QUESTION

After reading the Essential Question aloud, write the numbers 13 and 31 on the board. Ask children to think about why these numbers do not have the same value even though they contain the same digits. Explain that in this lesson, children will expand their knowledge about tens and ones to include hundreds.

FLUENCY PRACTICE

Fluency practice is available at **sadlierconnect.com**.

Concept Development

Understand: Models can show that 10 tens is the same as 1 hundred

■ Children will establish that 10 ones make 1 ten, and 10 tens make 1 hundred. By using models, children can visualize these relationships and form a foundational understanding of the base-ten system.

Understand: A place-value chart shows the value of each digit in a number

■ Knowing the difference between a *digit* and a *number* will help children understand the value of numbers.

Essential Question:
How do you find the value of each digit in a 3-digit number?

2.NBT.1

Words to Know
place-value chart
digits

In this lesson you will learn about place value in 3-digit numbers using hundreds, tens, and ones.

Understand: Models can show that 10 tens is the same as 1 hundred

This is 1 ten. ⟶ ▭▭▭▭▭
It is made up of 10 ones.
How can you group tens to make 1 hundred?

Put 10 tens together. The new model has 100 ones.

▷ The models show that 10 tens is the same as 1 hundred.

Understand: A place-value chart shows the value of each digit in a number

What does this place-value chart show?

hundreds	tens	ones
1	2	0

Digits are used to show numbers.
The digits are 0, 1, 2, 3, 4, 5, 6, 7, 8, 9.

▷ The place-value chart shows that the number 120 has 1 hundred, 2 tens, and 0 ones.

Words to Know

place-value chart: a chart that shows the value of each digit

Example:

tens	ones
6	4

64 has 6 tens and 4 ones.

digits: 0, 1, 2, 3, 4, 5, 6, 7, 8, 9 are used to write numbers

Example:
digits

Glossary can be found on pp. 293–304.

Lesson 6

Connect: Use what you know to find the value of each digit in a number

Ella uses place-value blocks to show the number 243. What is the value of each digit in 243?

Step 1

Write how many hundreds, tens, and ones.

How many hundreds? There are __2__ hundreds.

How many tens? There are __4__ tens.

How many ones? There are __3__ ones.

Step 2

Use the place-value chart to show the value of each digit in 243.

hundreds	tens	ones
2	4	3

The 2 in 243 stands for __2__ hundreds.

The 4 in 243 stands for __4__ tens.

The 3 in 243 stands for __3__ ones.

Unit 2 ▪ Focus on Number and Operations in Base Ten **57**

Support English Language Learners

As English language learners work with place value, they may need help understanding the difference between *one* and *ones*, *ten* and *tens*, and *hundred* and *hundreds*. Write these word pairs on the board.

Point to the first word in each pair, and invite a child to write the digit that the word represents under it. Model the value of each of these numbers by using counters to make sets of 1, 10, and 100.

Ask children to circle the letter that makes the second word in each pair different from the first word. Explain that the *–s* at the end of the word does not refer to a number but to the place value of a digit in the number.

Connect: Use what you know to find the value of each digit in a number Use this page to help children strengthen their understanding of place value and the role it plays in the value of each number.

■ Ask children to compare the place-value models and the place-value chart below. Encourage them to explain how each is a different representation of the same number.

■ The structure of the place-value system is critical to understanding the value of numbers. Children should know that the rightmost digit in a number represents ones. The digit to the left of the ones represents tens, and the digit to the left of the tens represents hundreds. This means that the digit farthest to the left represents the greatest value in a number.

■ Children should know that a ones block always stands for 1, a tens block for 10, and a hundreds block for 100. Reinforcing the constancy of this structure will help children better understand the base-ten system.

■ Ask children to use their own words to explain how they know the value of each digit in a number. They should refer to the position of the digit in the number, the column in the place-value chart, or the type of place-value model used.

■ Mathematically proficient children will understand that the digit in each place represents a multiple of 1, 10, or 100. It tells how many of each of the place-value models to use to represent the number.

■ Write another 3-digit number on the board. Encourage children to tell how they would use the place-value models to represent the number.

Guided Practice

Observational Assessment

Use pages 58–59 to assess children's understanding of place value. Be sure children are counting the hundreds, tens, and ones correctly. Children may not understand how to represent a number that has no tens or ones. Emphasize that the place-value models and the place-value charts are different ways to represent the values of the digits in the number.

Guided Practice

I. What number do the place-value models show? What is the value of each digit in that number?

Step 1

Find the numbers of hundreds, tens, and ones.

How many hundreds? __4__ hundreds

How many tens? __3__ tens

How many ones? __8__ ones

The number is __438__.

Step 2

Use the place-value chart to show the value of each digit.

hundreds	tens	ones
4	3	8

The __4__ stands for __4__ hundreds.

The __3__ stands for __3__ tens.

The __8__ stands for __8__ ones.

Math-to-Reading Connection

Letters, Syllables, and Words Remind children that to learn how to read they first had to recognize letters and identify the sounds of the letters. Then they learned to combine letters to make different sounds, and eventually syllables, which they combined to form words. Explain that there are rules about how to put letters together in order for words to have meaning.

Explain that there are also rules about how to form numbers. Children have to recognize the digits and understand their values before they can form greater numbers. Then, they will learn to put the digits together to represent other numbers. Stress that the value of each number depends on how its digits are arranged.

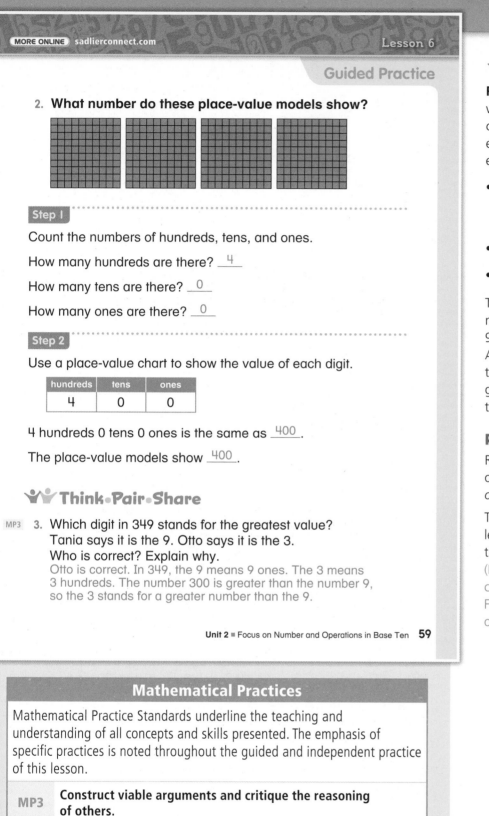

2. **What number do these place-value models show?**

Step 1

Count the numbers of hundreds, tens, and ones.

How many hundreds are there? __4__

How many tens are there? __0__

How many ones are there? __0__

Step 2

Use a place-value chart to show the value of each digit.

hundreds	tens	ones
4	0	0

4 hundreds 0 tens 0 ones is the same as __400__.

The place-value models show __400__.

☺☺☺ Think·Pair·Share

MP3 **3.** **Which digit in 349 stands for the greatest value?**
Tania says it is the 9. Otto says it is the 3.
Who is correct? Explain why.
Otto is correct. In 349, the 9 means 9 ones. The 3 means
3 hundreds. The number 300 is greater than the number 9,
so the 3 stands for a greater number than the 9.

Unit 2 ■ Focus on Number and Operations in Base Ten **59**

☺☺☺ Think·Pair·Share

Peer Collaboration Ask pairs to share whether they think Tania or Otto is correct. Ask children to explain what each digit in the number 349 means. Ask each pair of children questions such as:

- *How could you represent the number using place-value models or a place-value chart?*

- *Which place has the greatest value?*

- *Which digit is in the hundreds place?*

To summarize, point out that in this number, the greatest digit is 9, but the 9 does not have the greatest value. Also explain that place value determines the value of the digit. The digit in the greatest place-value position always has the greatest value.

Return to the Essential Question

Reread the Lesson 6 Essential Question on page 56: *How do you find the value of each digit in a 3-digit number?*

Tell children to think about what they learned in this lesson to answer this question.

(Possible responses: Use a place-value chart to find the value of each digit. From right to left, the digits represent ones, tens, and hundreds.)

Mathematical Practices

Mathematical Practice Standards underline the teaching and understanding of all concepts and skills presented. The emphasis of specific practices is noted throughout the guided and independent practice of this lesson.

MP3	**Construct viable arguments and critique the reasoning of others.**

Item 3: Children compare the place-value positions of two digits in a number. They explain how position determines the value of each digit.

Concept Application

Children may work independently on these pages in the classroom or at home. They may refer to the first four pages of the lesson to revisit the instruction or to see a worked-out example.

Common Errors and **Teaching Tips** may help you support learning either in the classroom or as a follow-up for work done at home.

Common Errors

Items 3–4

Children may write 26 for their solution to item 3 because there are no ones. Remind children who do this that when a number has hundreds and tens but no ones, they should write a 0 in the ones place. Similarly, some children may write 48 for their solution to item 4 because there are no tens. Remind children who do this that when a number has hundreds and ones but no tens, they should write a 0 in the tens place.

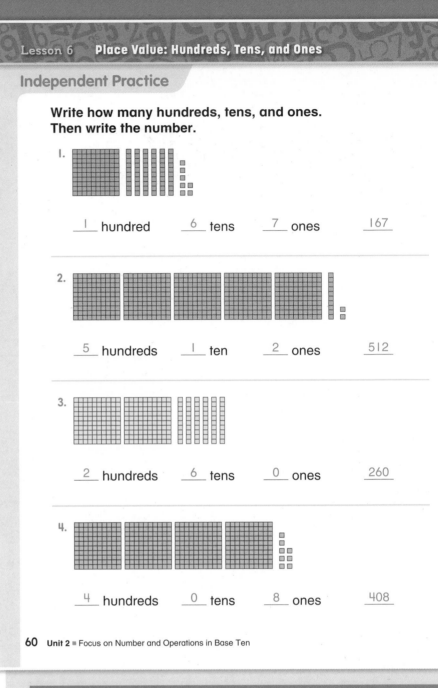

Lesson 6   **Place Value: Hundreds, Tens, and Ones**

Independent Practice

Write how many hundreds, tens, and ones. Then write the number.

1.
___1___ hundred   ___6___ tens   ___7___ ones   167

2.
___5___ hundreds   ___1___ ten   ___2___ ones   512

3.
___2___ hundreds   ___6___ tens   ___0___ ones   260

4.
___4___ hundreds   ___0___ tens   ___8___ ones   408

Talking About Math

Modeling Numbers Give children several ones, tens, and hundreds place-value models. Each child should write a number from 100 to 999 and show that number with the place-value models. Then, have children work in pairs telling their number to their partners, stating each digit's value, and explaining how they modeled the number.

Lesson 6

Independent Practice

Circle the number that the place-value models show.

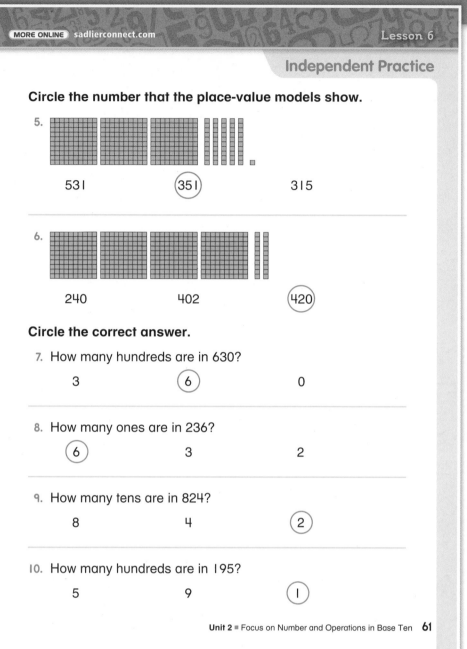

5.

531   (351)   315

6.

240   402   (420)

Circle the correct answer.

7. How many hundreds are in 630?

3   (6)   0

8. How many ones are in 236?

(6)   3   2

9. How many tens are in 824?

8   4   (2)

10. How many hundreds are in 195?

5   9   (1)

Teaching Tips

Items 7-10

Encourage children to draw a place-value chart to help them find the location of the digits in each number.

Digital Connection

Interactive Whiteboard Using an interactive whiteboard, write a number and have children model it using virtual place-value models. Then, have children write the number in a place-value chart. Repeat the process as time allows.

Common Errors

Items 16 and 20

Some children may neglect to write the 0 in the ones or tens place. Encourage children to first write the number in a place-value chart. This will help them envision the 4 hundreds, 5 tens, and 0 ones, or 450, for item 16 and the 8 hundreds, 0 tens, and 4 ones, or 804, for item 20.

Teaching Tips

Items 11-15

Encourage children to circle the specified digit in the number before writing its place value. This will reinforce children's perception of the digit's position in the number.

Lesson 6   Place Value: Hundreds, Tens, and Ones

Independent Practice

11. What is the value of the 9 in 893? _____9 tens_____

12. What is the value of the 3 in 403? _____3 ones_____

13. What is the value of the 0 in 508? _____0 tens_____

14. What is the value of the 7 in 745? _____7 hundreds_____

15. What is the value of the 0 in 310? _____0 ones_____

16. What number has 4 hundreds 5 tens 0 ones? _____450_____

17. What number has 5 hundreds 3 tens 1 one? _____531_____

18. What number has 2 hundreds 2 tens 6 ones? _____226_____

19. What number has 3 hundreds 7 tens 2 ones? _____372_____

20. What number has 8 hundreds 0 tens 4 ones? _____804_____

Math-to-Measurement Connection

Roller Coasters The tallest steel roller coaster in the United States has a highest point of 456 feet. The tallest wooden roller coaster reaches a height of 181 feet. Share this data with the class and write the numbers on the board for them to see. Have children give the value for each digit in each number.

Lesson 6

Independent Practice

Teaching Tips

Item 21

Encourage children to write the number that the model represents before they try to determine if Marta is correct.

MP4 **21.** Mr. Jones wrote 742 on the board. He asked the class to show the number with place-value models. Marta used the models below. Do Marta's models show the correct number? What might she have done wrong? Talk about it with a partner.

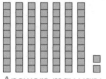

Answers may vary. Possible answer: Marta's models do not show the correct number. Her models show 472, not 742. Marta showed 4 hundreds instead of 7 hundreds and 7 tens instead of 4 tens. She may have confused the hundreds place and the tens place.

MP3 **22.** Use the digits 4, 5, and 2 to write three different 3-digit numbers. Tell what each digit in each number stands for. Answers may vary. Possible answer: 452, 524, 245; all the numbers I wrote have the digits 4, 5, and 2, but the digits are in different places. The 5 means 5 tens in 452, 5 hundreds in 524, and 5 ones in 245. The 4 means 4 hundreds in 452, 4 ones in 524, and 4 tens in 245. The 2 means 2 ones in 452, 2 tens in 524, and 2 hundreds in 245.

Unit 2 ■ Focus on Number and Operations in Base Ten **63**

Mathematical Practices	
MP3	**Construct viable arguments and critique the reasoning of others.**
Item 22: Children use the same digits to write different numbers.	
MP4	**Model with mathematics.**
Item 21: Children determine how to model the number 742 with place-value models.	

Common Core Focus:

2.NBT.2 Count within 1,000; skip-count by 5s, 10s, and 100s.

OBJECTIVE
Skip-count by 5s, 10s, and 100s within 1,000.

ESSENTIAL QUESTION
Focus children on the lesson objective by reading the Essential Question. Have children count by 1s to 20. Tell them that they could reach 20 more quickly if they counted by other amounts, such as by 5s or 10s. Also point out that they could reach greater amounts more quickly if they count by 100s instead of by 1s.

FLUENCY PRACTICE
Fluency practice is available at **sadlierconnect.com**.

Concept Development

Understand: Skip-counting by 5s.

■ On this page, children learn to count in multiples of 5.

■ Direct children to use the number chart to look for patterns as they skip-count by 5s. They should recognize that the numbers they say when they skip-count by 5s all end in 5 or 0. Use this time to review place value. Remind children that all the numbers they say when skip-counting by 5s have either 5 ones or 0 ones.

■ Explain that when you skip-count by 5s, you say every fifth number. Tell children they can think of skip-counting as adding 5 to the number that came just before it, or as counting "bundles" of 5.

Essential Question: How can you count by 5s, 10s, and 100s? 2.NBT.2

Words to Know
skip-count

Guided Instruction

In this lesson you will learn to skip-count by 5s, 10s, and 100s.

Understand: Skip-counting by 5s

> Justine has 6 groups of 5 pennies.
> When she skip-counts the pennies by 5s, what numbers does she say?
> How many pennies does she have in all?

Skip-counting is counting by a number other than 1.
These counters are in 6 groups of 5.
Justine skip-counts them by 5s.

•••	•••	•••	•••	•••	•••
••	••	••	••	••	••
5	10	15	20	25	30

The last number Justine counts tells how many in all.
The blue boxes in this number chart show skip-counting by 5s.

1	2	3	4	5	6	7	8	9	10
11	12	13	14	15	16	17	18	19	20
21	22	23	24	25	26	27	28	29	30

▷ When Justine counts her pennies, she says the numbers 5, 10, 15, 20, 25, 30. She has 30 pennies in all.

Words to Know

skip-count: when you count by a number other than 1

Example:

skip-counting by 5s

•••	•••	•••	•••	•••
••	••	••	••	••
5	10	15	20	25

Glossary can be found on pp. 293–304.

Understand: Skip-counting by 10s

What numbers do you say when you skip-count by 10s to 100?

A number chart can help you skip-count.

1	2	3	4	5	6	7	8	9	10
11	12	13	14	15	16	17	18	19	20
21	22	23	24	25	26	27	28	29	30
31	32	33	34	35	36	37	38	39	40
41	42	43	44	45	46	47	48	49	50
51	52	53	54	55	56	57	58	59	60
61	62	63	64	65	66	67	68	69	70
71	72	73	74	75	76	77	78	79	80
81	82	83	84	85	86	87	88	89	90
91	92	93	94	95	96	97	98	99	100

Remember!
Patterns can help you count.

Look for a pattern in the number chart. The numbers in the blue boxes show skip-counting by 10s. Each number is 10 more than the number just above it.

Skip-count the models by 10s.

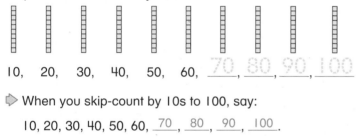

10, 20, 30, 40, 50, 60, 70, 80, 90, 100

▷ When you skip-count by 10s to 100, say:

10, 20, 30, 40, 50, 60, _70_, _80_, _90_, _100_.

Unit 2 ■ Focus on Number and Operations in Base Ten **65**

Understand: Skip-counting by 10s.

■ Have children extend what they know about skip-counting by 5s by explaining how to skip-count by 10s. Children should be able to conclude that skip-counting by 10s is counting every tenth number.

■ Direct children to use the 1-to-100 number chart to determine which numbers they will say when they skip-count by 10s. Help them describe the pattern that the blue boxes form in the chart.

■ Encourage children to relate what they know about place value to the numbers that form the pattern. Have them describe how the place values of these numbers are alike and how they are different. Children should recognize that the ones digit is always 0 while the digit in the tens place increases by 1 with each count. Children should also relate that an increase of 1 in the tens place is an increase of 10 in the value of the number.

■ Point out that the place-value models stand for groups, or bundles, of ten. Finding the next number when skip-counting by 10 is the same as adding 10 to the number that came just before it.

Support English Language Learners

Write the word *skip-count* on the board. Circle the word *skip*. Call on volunteers to demonstrate the act of skipping. Then say that *skip* has more than one meaning.

Explain that to skip also means to pass over something. Line up a row of pencils. Touch all but one of them in sequence, and explain that you skipped that one—that you passed over it when you were touching all the other pencils.

Point out that in the same way, when you skip-count you pass over some numbers. Unlike the pencil example, though, there is a pattern to how many you pass over when you skip-count.

Connect: What you know about skip-counting to skip-count by 100s Use this page to help children strengthen their understanding of skip-counting.

■ Review skip-counting by 5s and 10s. Ask children to identify similarities or patterns. Guide a discussion about the place values of the numbers children say when skip-counting by 10s.

■ Have children explain how many tens and ones the numbers will have when they skip-count by 100s. Ask them to identify the place value of the digit that changes. Help children to conclude that skip-counting by 100s is like adding 100 with each count.

■ Discuss strategies for using a pattern to find the missing number in the 100-to-700 sequence. Relate the pattern to the number of place-value hundreds models there are. Lead children to conclude that the missing number is 500 because that number is represented by 5 hundreds models.

■ Confirm that when children skip-count by 100s, the digit in the hundreds place increases by 1 with each count. Read the last number pattern aloud, emphasizing the hundreds digits.

Lesson 7   **Skip-Count by 5s, 10s, and 100s**

Guided Instruction

Connect: What you know about skip-counting to skip-count by 100s

When Pat skip-counted by 100s to 700, she said 100, 200, 300, 400, ■, 600, 700.
What number did Pat miss saying?

Use hundreds models to show 700.
Start at 100. Skip-count by 100s to 700.
Look for a pattern to help find the missing number.

| 100 | 200 | 300 | 400 | 500 | 600 | 700 |

Skip-count: 100, 200, 300, 400, 500, 600, 700

When you count by 100s, the digit in the hundreds place changes. The digits in the tens and ones places stay the same.

▷ Pat missed saying 500.

You can start at any number and still find a pattern.
Start at 140. Skip-count by 100s to 940.
What pattern do you see?

140, 240, 340, 440, 540, 640, 740, 840, 940

Do the digits in the hundreds place stay the same? no

Do the digits in the tens and ones places stay the same? yes

66   Unit 2 ■ Focus on Number and Operations in Base Ten

Sports Connection

Football Tell children that a football field, marked in yards, can be used for skip-counting by 10s. The field itself is labeled from 0 to 50 by 10s from each end. However, there is actually a line every five yards, so children could count the lines, or skip-count by 5s, to determine the distance across the whole field.

Explain that when a running back sprints down the field with the ball, the announcer will often skip-count to describe how far he has run. Imagine the announcer saying, "There he goes: 10 yards, 20 yards, 30 yards, 40 yards, and he's down!"

Lesson 7

Guided Practice

I. **What are the missing numbers?**

5, 10, 15, 20, ■, 30, ■, ■

Step 1

Look for a pattern to find the first missing number.

The pattern shows skip-counting by what number? __5__

When you skip-count by 5, the ones digit is __0__ or __5__.

What number comes before the first missing number? __20__

The ones digit in the first missing number is __5__.

What is the first missing number? __25__

Step 2

Use the pattern to find the other missing numbers.

What is the ones digit in the missing number

that comes next after 30? __5__

What is that missing number? __35__

What is the last missing number? __40__

The missing numbers are __25__, __35__, and __40__.

Think•Pair•Share

MP3 2. Lucy is number 114 in a line for a museum. Bill is 10 people behind Lucy in the line. Erica is 10 people behind Bill. What number is Erica? Talk about how you know.

Erica is number __134__ in the line. See Additional Answers.

Mathematical Practices

Mathematical Practice Standards underline the teaching and understanding of all concepts and skills presented. The emphasis of specific practices is noted throughout the guided and independent practice of this lesson.

MP3	**Construct viable arguments and critique the reasoning of others.**

Item 2: Children describe how they know their answer is correct.

Observational Assessment

Use page 67 to assess children's understanding of skip-counting. Be sure that children are able to describe the pattern in the digits of the numbers. Discuss how they can use this pattern to find the missing numbers.

Think•Pair•Share

Peer Collaboration Ask pairs to share what Erica's number is. Ask children to explain how they found her number. To help them relate the process to skip-counting, ask these questions:

- *If you are behind someone in line, will your number be greater than or less than that person's number?*

- *By which number will you skip-count to solve this problem?*

- *Which digits will stay the same?*

To summarize, point out that skip-counting can help children find missing numbers. They can skip-count by 5s, 10s, or 100s. When they skip-count by 10s, the ones digit stays the same. When they skip-count by 100s, the ones and tens digits stay the same.

Return to the Essential Question

Reread the Lesson 7 Essential Question on page 64: *How can you count by 5s, 10s, and 100s?*

Tell children to think about what they learned in this lesson to answer this question.

(Possible responses: I learned to use a number chart to find skip-counting patterns. When skip-counting by 10s or 100s, the digit in the 10s or 100s place increases by 1 with each count.)

Additional Answers

Item 2: Possible answer: If I skip-count by 10s from 114, the digit in the ones place stays the same and the digit in the tens place changes. So 10 more than 114 is 124 and 10 more than 124 is 134.

Concept Application

Children may work independently on these pages in the classroom or at home. They may refer to the first four pages of the lesson to revisit the instruction or to see a worked-out example.

Common Errors and **Teaching Tips** may help you support learning either in the classroom or as a follow-up for work done at home.

Teaching Tips

Items 1–4

Remind children to skip-count instead of counting each of the objects. Tell them that, as they skip-count, they should write the total number of objects they have counted so far and not just the number of objects above each line.

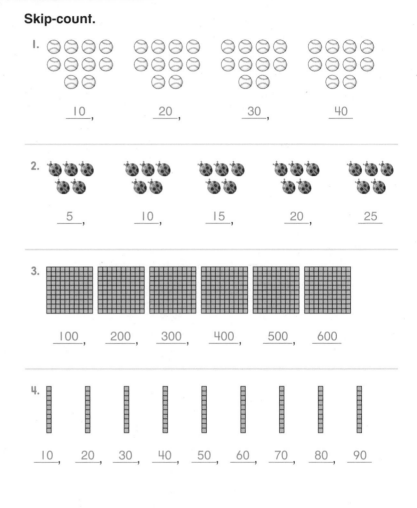

Talking About Math

Using Skip-Counting in a Narrative Ask children to tell a story that uses skip-counting. Guide them to see that, as they tell their stories, they will need to add equal groups of an object. Remind them that their story needs to have a beginning, a middle, and an end. Invite children to share their stories with the class.

Independent Practice

Write the missing numbers.

5. Skip-count by 5s.   5, 10, 15, _20_, 25, _30_, 35

6. Skip-count by 100s.   100, 200, _300_, _400_, 500, 600

7. Skip-count by 10s.   10, _20_, 30, _40_, _50_, 60, 70

Circle the correct answer.

8. Linda skip-counted like this:
   100, 110, 120, 130, 140, 150, 160
   How did she skip-count?

   by 5s   (by 10s)   by 100s

9. Theo started at 300. He skip-counted by 100s. Which shows how Theo counted?

   (300, 400, 500, 600, 700)

   100, 200, 300, 400, 500

   300, 310, 320, 330, 340

10. See how Mia skip-counted.

    5, 10, 15, 20, 25, 30, ▨

    What was the last number she said?

    40

    (35)

    45

Unit 2 ■ Focus on Number and Operations in Base Ten **69**

Common Errors

Item 8

Children may say that Linda counted by 100s because each number is a 3-digit number. Remind children to look at which digit is changing when skip-counting. This will help them determine the number by which Linda skip-counted.

Teaching Tips

Items 5–7

Some children may benefit by using concrete models to show the skip-counting. Provide connecting cubes and place-value models (tens and hundreds) for children's use.

Digital Connection

Internet Resources Use the Internet to find videos that involve skip-counting. Ask children to count along with any video. Encourage children to count in a rhythmic pattern to reinforce the patterns. Pause the videos and ask children to find the missing, or next, number. Follow up with having children write their own examples of skip-counting.

Common Errors

Items 14–15

Children may not recognize the pattern in each of these number sequences since the pattern does not end in 0, or 00. Remind children that skip-counting can be started from any number.

Teaching Tips

Items 11–17

Encourage children to check their work by making sure the number they write is greater than the number just to its left and less than the number just to its right.

Independent Practice

11. Skip-count by 100s.

    250, 350, 450, <u>550</u>, 650, <u>750</u>, 850, <u>950</u>

12. Skip-count by 10s.

    140, 150, 160, <u>170</u>, 180, <u>190</u>, <u>200</u>, 210, <u>220</u>, <u>230</u>

13. Skip-count by 5s.

    100, <u>105</u>, 110, 115, <u>120</u>, 125, 130, <u>135</u>, <u>140</u>, 145, <u>150</u>

14. Skip-count by 100s.

    176, 276, <u>376</u>, 476, <u>576</u>, <u>676</u>, 776, <u>876</u>, <u>976</u>

15. Skip-count by 10s.

    335, <u>345</u>, <u>355</u>, 365, <u>375</u>, <u>385</u>, 395, <u>405</u>

16. Skip-count by 5s.

    580, <u>585</u>, <u>590</u>, 595, <u>600</u>, <u>605</u>, 610, 615, <u>620</u>

17. Skip-count by 5s.

    470, <u>475</u>, <u>480</u>, 485, <u>490</u>, 495, <u>500</u>, <u>505</u>, 510

Math-to-Science Connection

Skip-Counting in Measurements Some measuring devices used in science have scales that allow for skip-counting. Collect an assortment of measuring tools, such as a metric ruler, measuring tape, beaker, or graduated cylinder. Encourage children to examine the labeling scales on the measuring tools. Have children write down examples of how they might skip-count along the scales. Ask for volunteers to share the examples that they found.

Lesson 7

Independent Practice

18. Skip-count by 10s.

380, <u>390</u>, <u>400</u>, 410, <u>420</u>, <u>430</u>, 440, 450, <u>460</u>

Count by 1s to find the missing numbers.

19.

788	789	790	791	792	793	794
795	796	797	798	799	800	801
802	803	804	805	806	807	808

20.

612	613	614	615	616	617	618
619	620	621	622	623	624	625
626	627	628	629	630	631	632

21. Suppose you are counting by 1s. What are the next five numbers that come just after 347?

347, <u>348</u>, <u>349</u>, <u>350</u>, <u>351</u>, <u>352</u>

MP3 22. Rita skip-counted: 215, 225, 235, 245, 255, 265, 275.
She says she started at 215 and skip-counted by 5s.
Thomas says she skip-counted by 10s.
Who is right? Explain.
See Additional Answers.

Unit 2 ■ Focus on Number and Operations in Base Ten **71**

Common Errors

Items 19-21

Children may try to skip just one number when told to count by 1s in a skip-counting lesson. Remind them that counting by 1s is the same as what they have thought of as counting.

Additional Answers

Item 22: Thomas is right; Possible answer: When you skip-count by 5s, the ones digit changes. When you skip-count by 10s, the tens digit changes. In Rita's skip-counting, the ones digit stayed the same and the tens digit changed; so Rita was skip-counting by 10s.

Mathematical Practices	
MP3	**Construct viable arguments and critique the reasoning of others.**

Item 22: Children analyze a problem situation involving skip-counting to determine which of two answers is correct.

Common Core Focus:

2.NBT.3 Read and write numbers to 1,000 using base-ten numerals, number names, and expanded form.

OBJECTIVE

Read and write numbers with numerals, in words, and in expanded form.

ESSENTIAL QUESTION

Read the Essential Question aloud to children. Ask them how they have seen numbers written. Explain that they will learn that a number can be written three different ways.

FLUENCY PRACTICE

Fluency practice is available at **sadlierconnect.com**.

Concept Development

Understand: Place-value models can help you read and write numbers

■ Children learn to write a number with words and in expanded form, which uses the value of each digit to write the number as a sum.

■ Explain that the instructions "write the number" mean to use digits to write the number represented by the model. Remind children of the value of each type of place-value model. Guide them to use their understanding of place value to write the number.

■ Ask a child to read aloud the number modeled. Be sure that they do not say the word *and* immediately after they say *hundred*. Then ask them to write the words for the number exactly as they said them.

■ Discuss the value of each digit. Write the value as a number. Explain that when the digits are used as one number, it is the same as adding their values. Extend this understanding to include expanded form. Model how to use a place-value chart to find the sums.

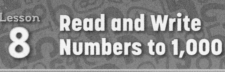

Essential Question:
What are some ways to read and write numbers?
2.NBT.3

Words to Know
expanded form

Guided Instruction

In this lesson you will learn ways to read and write numbers to 1,000.

Understand: Place-value models can help you read and write numbers

Uma shows a number using place-value models. What number do the models show? Write the number, the number name, and the expanded form of the number.

The models show 3 hundreds, 6 tens, 5 ones.

Write the number: ③ ⑥ ⑤
Write and read the number name: three hundred sixty-five.

Write the number 365 in expanded form. Use the value of each digit as an addend. Start with the hundreds.
    The 3 stands for 3 hundreds, or 300.
    The 6 stands for 6 tens, or 60.
    The 5 stands for 5 ones, or 5.

The addition 300 + 60 + 5 shows 365 in expanded form.

▷ The number is 365.
    The number name is three hundred sixty-five.
    The expanded form is 300 + 60 + 5.

Words to Know

expanded form: A number expressed in a way that shows the value of each digit.

Example: 284 in expanded form is 200 + 80 + 4

Glossary can be found on pp. 293–304.

Connect: A place-value chart can help you read and write numbers

What number does the place-value chart show?

hundreds	tens	ones
5	4	6

Write the number, the number name, and the expanded form.

The place-value chart shows that there are

___5___ hundreds, ___4___ tens, and ___6___ ones.

Use digits to write the number.

5 hundreds, 4 tens, 6 ones is the same as ___546___.

Write the number name.

___five hundred forty-six___

Write the number in expanded form.

The value of the digit in the hundreds place is ___500___.

The value of the digit in the tens place is ___40___.

The value of the digit in the ones place is ___6___.

The expanded form of 546 is ___500___ + ___40___ + ___6___.

▷ The number is 546.

The number name is five hundred forty-six.

The expanded form is ___500___ + ___40___ + ___6___.

Connect: A place-value chart can help you read and write numbers. Use this page to help children strengthen their understanding of different ways to write a number.

■ Have children name the number on the place-value chart. Explain how just by looking at the order of the digits in the chart, children can see how to write the number.

■ Remind children that the place-value chart will not show exactly how to read the number or how to write it in words. While it can give you the first two words—the number word and the word *hundred*—it cannot tell you the entire number.

■ Children will need to use their understanding of place value to translate 4 tens as forty and 6 ones as six. Point out that the words *tens* and *ones* are not used in the number name.

■ Encourage children to use the digits and their place values to write the number in expanded form. Children should first identify the digit in each place and then use the chart to determine its value. This fundamental understanding of place value is reinforced by expanded form.

Support English Language Learners

Have children create fans by making accordion folds on sheets of paper. Model how to do this, and help children who struggle. Then, ask children to hold the fan so that the folds are compressed between the outer edges. Tell them to open their fans. Explain that they *expanded* their fan when they made it bigger.

Point out that, in the same way, expanded form is a "bigger" way to write a number. This way is not used very often because it is takes up too much space. Explain that when the number is written with digits, is easier to read, so the digit form is used most of the time.

Guided Practice

Observational Assessment

Use pages 74–75 to assess children's understanding of reading and writing numbers. Be sure that children are able to use a place-value model and a place-value chart to identify the value of each digit in a 3-digit number and then apply that knowledge to writing the number using base-ten numerals, number names, and expanded form.

Guided Practice

I. **What number do the models show?**

Write the number, the number name, and the expanded form.

The models show __6__ hundreds __9__ tens __3__ ones.

Write the 3-digit number that the models show. __693__

The number name for the number that the models show is __six hundred ninety-three__.

Write the number in expanded form.

What is the value of the digit in the hundreds place? __600__

What is the value of the digit in the tens place? __90__

What is the value of the digit in the ones place? __3__

The number in expanded form is __600 + 90 + 3__.

Math-to-Writing Connection

Reports Explain that, in later grades, children may have to write research papers that include numbers. Say that knowing when to write numbers with digits or with words is an important skill to learn. Point out that, as a general rule, numbers less than one hundred are written using words. Three-digit numbers are usually written with digits.

Guided Practice

2. **Write the number, the number name, and the expanded form to show 7 hundreds 0 tens 9 ones.**

Step 1

Write the number in a place-value chart.

hundreds	tens	ones
7	0	9

Write the 3-digit number. __709__

Write the number name. ___seven hundred nine___

Step 2

Write the number in expanded form.

What does the 7 in 709 stand for? __7 hundreds__ or __700__

What does the 0 in 709 stand for? __0 tens__ or __0__

What does the 9 in 709 stand for? __9 ones__ or __9__

You do not write an addend for 0 in expanded form.

The number in expanded form is __700__ + __9__.

♔ Think•Pair•Share

MP3 3. Frank wrote the number name and the expanded form for 350 this way.

> Number name: three hundred fifty
> Expanded form: 300 + 5

Is Frank's work correct? Why or why not?

Answers may vary. Possible answer: When Frank wrote the expanded form, he mixed up the numbers of tens and ones. He should have written the expanded form for 350 as 300 + 50.

Unit 2 ■ Focus on Number and Operations in Base Ten **75**

♔ Think•Pair•Share

Peer Collaboration Ask pairs to share their ideas about whether Frank is correct. Encourage them to consider place value in determining their answers by asking:

- *What is the value of each digit in 350?*
- *What is the sum of 300 plus 5?*
- *Is that sum the same as 350?*

To summarize, point out that a number can be written with digits, in words, or as a sum in expanded form. To read a 3-digit number, you say the place value *hundred* after you name the first digit, but you do not say *tens* or *ones* after you name the tens and ones digits. A number in expanded form is written as the sum of the place values.

Return to the Essential Question

Reread the Lesson 8 Essential Question on page 72: *What are some ways to read and write numbers?*

Tell children to think about what they learned in this lesson to answer this question.

(Possible responses: You can write a number in words or with digits. The number word is exactly what you would say when you read the number. The expanded form of a number uses the place value of each digit to write the number as a sum.)

Mathematical Practices

Mathematical Practice Standards underline the teaching and understanding of all concepts and skills presented. The emphasis of specific practices is noted throughout the guided and independent practice of this lesson.

MP3	**Construct viable arguments and critique the reasoning of others.**

Item 3: Children construct an argument to decide whether an answer is correct.

Concept Application

Children may work independently on these pages in the classroom or at home. They may refer to the first four pages of the lesson to revisit the instruction or to see a worked-out example.

Common Errors and **Teaching Tips** may help you support learning either in the classroom or as a follow-up for work done at home.

Common Errors

Items 1-4

Be sure children understand that each place-value hundreds model stands for 100, each tens model stands for 10, and each ones model stands for 1.

Items 3-4

Watch for children who do not recognize that there are no tens in Item 3 and no ones in item 4.

Teaching Tips

Items 3-4

Remind children that they must write one digit, from 0 to 9, in each place.

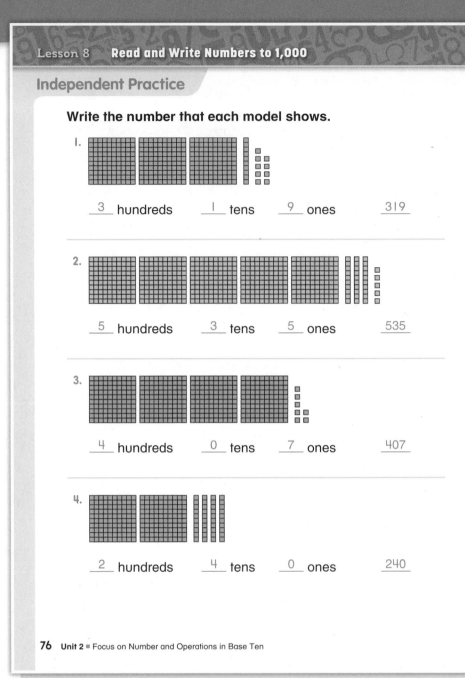

Lesson 8   **Read and Write Numbers to 1,000**

Independent Practice

Write the number that each model shows.

1. ___3___ hundreds   ___1___ tens   ___9___ ones   319

2. ___5___ hundreds   ___3___ tens   ___5___ ones   535

3. ___4___ hundreds   ___0___ tens   ___7___ ones   407

4. ___2___ hundreds   ___4___ tens   ___0___ ones   240

76 Unit 2 ■ Focus on Number and Operations in Base Ten

Talking About Math

Collaborative Conversations Arrange children in small groups. Give each group one 3-digit number written in numerals, one 3-digit number written in words, and one 3-digit number written in expanded form. Have each child identify the number of hundreds, tens, and ones in each number. While doing so, children should explain their thought process within their small group. Encourage the group to listen carefully to what everyone says and to ask the speakers to explain anything they do not understand.

MORE ONLINE sadlierconnect.com   Lesson 8

Independent Practice

Match the number with its number name.

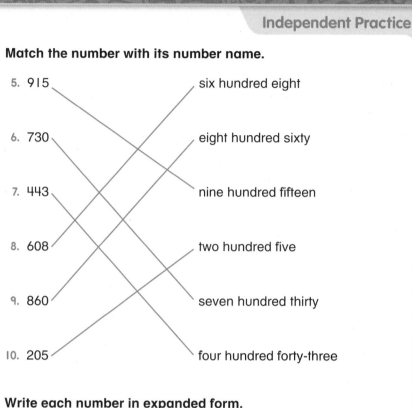

5. 915   six hundred eight

6. 730   eight hundred sixty

7. 443   nine hundred fifteen

8. 608   two hundred five

9. 860   seven hundred thirty

10. 205   four hundred forty-three

Write each number in expanded form.

11. 274 ___200 + 70 + 4___   12. 337 ___300 + 30 + 7___

13. 999 ___900 + 90 + 9___   14. 840 ___800 + 40___

15. 206 ___200 + 6___   16. 707 ___700 + 7___

Unit 2 ■ Focus on Number and Operations in Base Ten **77**

Teaching Tips

Items 5–10

Reinforce that, when we read a number name, we say the word *hundred,* not *hundreds. Hundreds* refers to place value. *Hundred* refers to a number.

Items 11–16

Some children may benefit by writing each number in a place-value chart before writing it in expanded form. This will help children see the value of each digit based on its placement in the chart.

Digital Connection

Interactive Whiteboard Write a mixed-up list of several 3-digit numbers on the board. Show each in three ways—with numerals, in words, and in expanded form. Ask children to drag the matching values together on the screen. Have children describe their work.

Independent Practice

Common Errors

Item 23

Watch for children who write 600 + 37 as the expanded form of 637. Remind them that each addend they write must show the value of that digit in the number.

Teaching Tips

Items 17–20

Encourage children to write the numbers in a place-value chart before determining the answer. Ask questions such as: *Where would you place a 7 to represent 700?* This will help guide children in translating expanded form to standard form.

Independent Practice

Circle the correct answer.

17. Which is the same as 700 + 40 + 3?   (743)   7,043   703

18. Which is the same as 400 + 50?   405   (450)   415

19. Which is the same as 200 + 40 + 5?   205   (245)   254

20. Which is the same as 800 + 8?   880   800   (808)

Write the number and the expanded form for each number name.

21. five hundred two   502   500 + 2

22. nine hundred ten   910   900 + 10

23. six hundred thirty-seven   637   600 + 30 + 7

24. one hundred eighty   180   100 + 80

Math-to-School Connection

Using Expanded Form Discuss with children the number of days in their school year. (Most schools are in session for 180 days.) Have children write the number name and the expanded form for the number. Explain that most years have 365 days. Ask children to write this number with its number name and in expanded form. Calculate the number of days each year that children are not in school. Do not involve children in this calculation, but announce the number and ask them to write it with its number name and in expanded form.

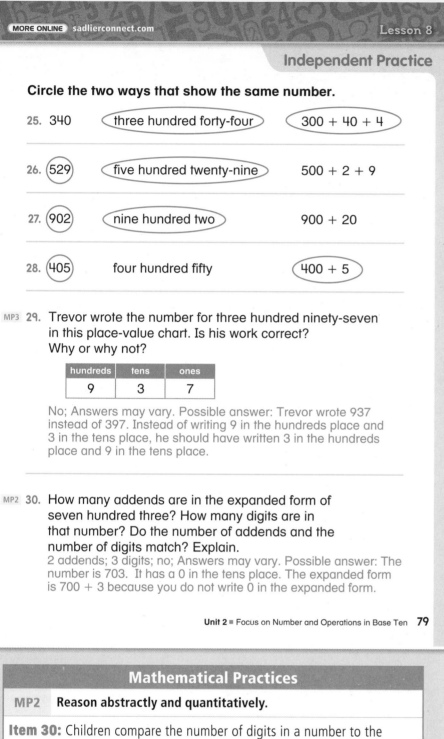

Circle the two ways that show the same number.

25. 340   (three hundred forty-four)   (300 + 40 + 4)

26. (529)   (five hundred twenty-nine)   500 + 2 + 9

27. (902)   (nine hundred two)   900 + 20

28. (405)   four hundred fifty   (400 + 5)

MP3 **29.** Trevor wrote the number for three hundred ninety-seven in this place-value chart. Is his work correct? Why or why not?

hundreds	tens	ones
9	3	7

No; Answers may vary. Possible answer: Trevor wrote 937 instead of 397. Instead of writing 9 in the hundreds place and 3 in the tens place, he should have written 3 in the hundreds place and 9 in the tens place.

MP2 **30.** How many addends are in the expanded form of seven hundred three? How many digits are in that number? Do the number of addends and the number of digits match? Explain.

2 addends; 3 digits; no; Answers may vary. Possible answer: The number is 703. It has a 0 in the tens place. The expanded form is 700 + 3 because you do not write 0 in the expanded form.

Unit 2 ■ Focus on Number and Operations in Base Ten   **79**

Common Errors
Item 27
In reading the number 902, children may insert the word *and* between the words *hundred* and *two*. Remind children not to use the word *and* when they read or write a 3-digit number that includes hundreds.

Mathematical Practices	
MP2	**Reason abstractly and quantitatively.**

Item 30: Children compare the number of digits in a number to the number of addends in its expanded form.

MP3	**Construct viable arguments and critique the reasoning of others.**

Item 29: Children reason about whether the number is represented correctly in the place-value chart.

Copyright © by William H. Sadlier, Inc. All rights reserved.

Common Core Focus:

2.NBT.4 Compare two three-digit numbers based on meanings of the hundreds, tens, and ones digits, using >, =, and < symbols to record the results of comparisons.

OBJECTIVE

Use place value to compare two 3-digit numbers.

ESSENTIAL QUESTION

Focus children on the lesson objective by reading the Essential Question aloud. Explain that they will now use place value to compare even greater numbers than they did before. They will use the symbols >, <, and = to represent these comparisons.

PREREQUISITE SKILLS

Use Foundational Skills Handbook page 282, *Compare Numbers,* to review comparing two 2-digit numbers using the symbols >, <, or =.

FLUENCY PRACTICE

Fluency practice is available at **sadlierconnect.com**.

Concept Development

Understand: Using place-value models to compare two numbers

■ Before children begin the problem, have them identify what the place-value models represent—hundreds, tens, and ones.

■ Be sure children understand the difference between the symbols > and <. Remind them that the "open" end of the symbol should always face the greater number.

■ It may be helpful to have children first circle the two digits that differ between the two numbers. This process will reinforce children's understanding that the digits in this place are the ones to compare.

Lesson 9 — Compare Numbers

Essential Question:
How can you compare two numbers using the symbols >, <, = ?
2.NBT.4

Words to Know
greater than (>)
less than (<)
equal to (=)

Guided Instruction

In this lesson you will learn to compare two 3-digit numbers using place value.

Understand: Using place-value models to compare two numbers

Which number is greater, 152 or 125?

Place-value models can help you compare the numbers.

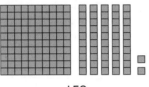   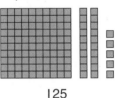

152   125

Start with the greatest place: hundreds

Compare the hundreds.
Both 152 and 125 have 1 hundred.

Move on to the next greatest place: tens

Compare the tens.
The number 152 has 5 tens.
The number 125 has 2 tens.

So 152 is greater than 125, because 5 tens is greater than 2 tens.

Remember!
> means greater than.

▷ The number 152 is greater than the number 125.
Write this as 152 > 125.

Words to Know

greater than (>): a number has a greater value than another number

Example:

13 is greater than 12

13 > 12

Glossary can be found on pp. 293–304.

Guided Instruction

Understand: **Using place-value charts to compare two numbers**

Lucy has 382 stickers. Brady has 387 stickers.
Who has fewer stickers?

Write both numbers in place-value charts.

hundreds	tens	ones
3	8	2

hundreds	tens	ones
3	8	7

Start with the greatest place: hundreds. Compare.
382 and 387 both have 3 hundreds.

Move on to the next greatest place: tens. Compare.
382 and 387 both have 8 tens.

Move on to the last place: ones. Compare.
382 has 2 ones. 387 has 7 ones.

Remember!
< means less than.

So 382 is less than 387 because 2 is less than 7.
382 < 387

▷ Lucy has fewer stickers than Brady.

Understand: **Comparing numbers with the same digits in the same places**

Which number is greater, 187 or 187?

Remember!
= means
equal to.

Compare hundreds, tens, and ones.
The hundreds, tens, and ones are the same.

▷ So 187 is equal to 187. Write 187 = 187.

Unit 2 ■ Focus on Number and Operations in Base Ten **81**

Understand: **Using place-value charts to compare two numbers**

■ It is important for children to see the relationship between place-value models and a place-value chart. Have them compare the way numbers are modeled with hundreds, tens, and ones blocks on page 80 with the way numbers are shown in the place-value charts on this page. Clarify that both strategies are ways to show the same thing, the place values of the digits of a number.

■ Have children identify what the question is asking and what they are looking for. Ask children if *fewer* means "greater than" or "less than."

■ Check that children are reading the numbers carefully. Have them compare each number in the problem with the way it appears in the place-value chart digit by digit.

■ It may be helpful to have children write both numbers in the same place-value chart, one above the other.

Understand: **Comparing numbers with the same digits in the same places**

■ If necessary, have children write these numbers in a place-value chart so that they can see that the same digits are in the same place.

■ Remind children that when neither number is greater than or less than the other, then the two numbers are equal, and an equal symbol should be written between them to show this.

Words to Know

less than (<): a number that has a lesser value than another number

Example:

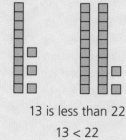

13 is less than 22
13 < 22

equal to (=): two quantities that have the same value
Glossary can be found on pp. 293–304.

Guided Instruction

Connect: Use place value and symbols to compare two 3-digit numbers Use this page to help children strengthen their understanding of the different strategies to use when comparing two 3-digit numbers.

■ Remind children to use a place-value chart if necessary. This may help them organize the digits of the number and make the value of each digit more apparent.

■ After Step 2, ask children why they are not asked to compare the digits in the ones place. Children should understand that they are able to determine which number is greater by comparing the digits in the tens place so it is not necessary to compare the ones.

■ Be sure children check the symbol used to compare the two numbers. The "open" end of the symbol should be facing the greater number.

■ In the *true or false* section, it may be helpful to have children underline or circle the place in which the digits differ as a way to justify their answer.

Guided Instruction

Connect: Use place value and symbols to compare two 3-digit numbers

Compare 684 and 677. Use >, <, or = in your answer.

Step 1

Use place value to compare 684 and 677.

684 = _6_ hundreds _8_ tens _4_ ones

677 = _6_ hundreds _7_ tens _7_ ones

Start with the greatest place-value position.

Which place will you look at first? __hundreds__

Compare. 684 and 677 both have _6_ hundreds.

Step 2

Compare the digits in the next greatest place.

684 has _8_ tens. 677 has _7_ tens.

8 tens is greater than 7 tens.

684 is greater than 677.

Step 3

Write the symbol <, >, or = to compare. 684 ⟩ 677

▷ 684 > 677

Write *true* or *false*.

406 > 416 __false__   509 < 499 __false__   746 = 746 __true__

Support English Language Learners

Help English language learners understand when to use *greater than* and *less than*. Children may think that *bigger than* or *smaller than* can be used to compare numbers. They may say, for example, "The number 15 is bigger than the number 12."

Clarify for children that *bigger* and *smaller* tell about the size of objects but not the size of numbers. To compare numbers, we think about their *values*. To show value, we use *greater than* and *less than*. So 15 is not *bigger than* 12, but it is *greater than* 12. And 12 is not *smaller than* 15, but it is *less than* 15.

Guided Practice

I. **Write >, <, or = to compare: 989 ⬤ 998**

Step 1

989 = __9__ hundreds __8__ tens __9__ ones

998 = __9__ hundreds __9__ tens __8__ ones

First compare the __hundreds__ .

989 and 998 both have __9__ hundreds.

Step 2

Next compare the __tens__ .

989 has __8__ tens. 998 has __9__ tens.

8 is __less__ than 9. So 989 is __less__ than 998.

Step 3

Write >, <, or =.

989 (<) 998

👑 Think·Pair·Share

MP2   2. Compare. Write > or <.

998 (>) 989   989 (<) 998

Tell how your comparisons are alike and how
they are different. 998 > 989; 989 < 998; Answers may vary.
Possible answer: Both comparisons use the same numbers, but they
use different symbols. When the "less than" number came first, I used
the symbol <. When the "greater than" number came first, I used the
symbol >.

Unit 2 ■ Focus on Number and Operations in Base Ten   **83**

Mathematical Practices

Mathematical Practice Standards underline the teaching and
understanding of all concepts and skills presented. The emphasis of
specific practices is noted throughout the guided and independent practice
of this lesson.

MP2   **Reason abstractly and quantitatively.**

Item 2: Children display quantitative reasoning by explaining that
although they are comparing the same two numbers, different symbols are
used to represent these comparisons.

Observational Assessment

Use page 83 to assess children's
understanding of how to compare two
3-digit numbers. Take note of those
children who are unable to correctly
identify the place value of each digit or
who are comparing the numbers from
least place to greatest instead of from
greatest to least.

👑 Think·Pair·Share

Peer Collaboration Ask pairs to share
their work when comparing each set
of numbers. Ask each pair of children
questions such as:

- *Which place did you start with? How
  did you decide?*

- *Which place did you compare when
  determining your answer? How did
  you decide?*

- *The numbers you are comparing in
  each pair are the same. Why didn't
  you use the same symbol for each
  comparison?*

To summarize, point out that different
symbols were used because the digits
were in different order.

Return to the Essential Question

Reread the Lesson 9 Essential Question
on page 80: *How can you compare two
numbers using the symbols >, <, or =?*

Tell children to think about what they
learned in this lesson to answer
this question.
(Possible responses: I can use the place
value of the digits of a number to
compare two numbers. Starting at the
greatest place value, I compare each
place until the digits are different. The
number with the greater different digit
is the greater number. I use the greater-
than symbol, >, or the less-than symbol,
<, to compare the numbers. If the same
digits are in the same place for both
numbers, the numbers are equal and
I use the equal symbol, =.)

Concept Application

Children may work independently on these pages in the classroom or at home. They may refer to the first four pages of the lesson to revisit the instruction or to see a worked-out example.

Common Errors and **Teaching Tips** may help you support learning either in the classroom or as a follow-up for work done at home.

Teaching Tips

Items 1–4

If children do not read the directions carefully, they may circle the incorrect number. Be sure children first identify whether they are looking for the greater or lesser number before circling.

Lesson 9 **Compare Numbers**

Independent Practice

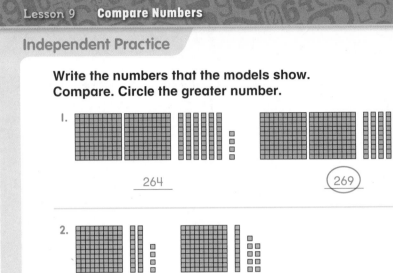

**Write the numbers that the models show.
Compare. Circle the greater number.**

1.   264   (269)

2.   (124)   119

**Write numbers that the models show.
Compare. Circle the lesser number.**

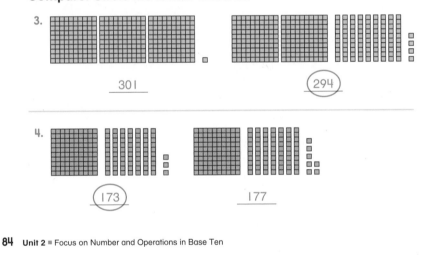

3.   301   (294)

4.   (173)   177

84   Unit 2 ■ Focus on Number and Operations in Base Ten

Talking About Math

Comparing Two Solutions Have children work in pairs to describe how they determined their answers to items 2 and 3. Be sure that children tell which place they used to determine their answer and whether they identified the greater or lesser number. Ask members of the pairs to share their solutions with the class.

Teaching Tips

Items 5-8

Encourage children to cross out greater place values in which there are the same digits and circle place values in which there are different digits.

Compare. Write *greater than, less than,* **or** *equal to.*

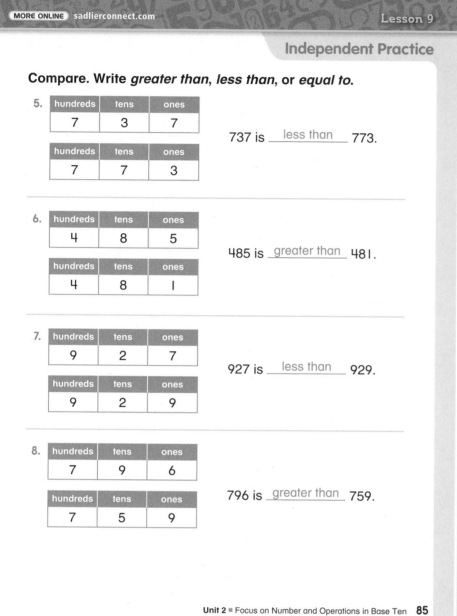

5.

hundreds	tens	ones
7	3	7

hundreds	tens	ones
7	7	3

737 is __less than__ 773.

6.

hundreds	tens	ones
4	8	5

hundreds	tens	ones
4	8	1

485 is __greater than__ 481.

7.

hundreds	tens	ones
9	2	7

hundreds	tens	ones
9	2	9

927 is __less than__ 929.

8.

hundreds	tens	ones
7	9	6

hundreds	tens	ones
7	5	9

796 is __greater than__ 759.

Unit 2 ■ Focus on Number and Operations in Base Ten **85**

Math-to-Math Connection

Representations Using Symbols Remind children that the symbols we use when comparing >, <, and = represent words. Have children discuss other symbols we use in mathematics and what words these symbols represent. For example, children could select the symbols + and – and discuss how they are used and what they mean.

Independent Practice

Common Errors

Item 11

Some children may indicate that 205 is equal to 215 if they looked only at the first and last digits. Remind children to compare each digit.

Teaching Tips

Items 12–25

Encourage children to use one of the strategies presented in the lesson. They may want to draw place-value charts, align the numbers vertically, or circle the digits they are comparing.

Independent Practice

Compare. Write >, <, or =.

9. 842 is ____ 842.   greater than   less than   (equal to)

10. 399 is ____ 404.   greater than   (less than)   equal to

11. 205 is ____ 215.   greater than   (less than)   equal to

12. 457 (<) 475

13. 730 (>) 729

14. 837 (>) 799

15. 381 (=) 381

16. 199 (<) 201

17. 535 (<) 539

18. 288 (<) 298

19. 639 (>) 637

20. 949 (=) 949

21. 102 (<) 121

22. 715 (>) 713

23. 559 (<) 619

24. 348 (>) 347

25. 190 (>) 189

Digital Connection

Random Number Generator Use the Internet to find a random number generator. Set the generator to select numbers between 100 and 999. Randomly generate pairs of numbers and have children compare them.

MORE ONLINE sadlierconnect.com

MP3 **26.** When you are comparing two 3-digit numbers, why do you think it is important to look first at the digits that have the greatest values?

Answers may vary. Possible answer: I would need to find out whether the digits in the hundreds place are the same or different. If they are different, I would not need to look at the tens or ones. If they are the same, I'd compare the digits in the tens place. Also, if the ones or tens digits were different and I compared them first, my answer could be wrong. If I compared 380 and 290 and first compared the tens, I might think that 290 is greater because it has 9 tens and 380 has only 8 tens.

MP3 **27.** Amy collects 388 bottles for recycling. Brian collects 391 bottles for recycling. Who collects more bottles? Explain how you know. Use place value.

Answers may vary. Possible answer: Brian collects more bottles than Amy. 388 and 391 have the same number of hundreds, but 391 has more tens than 388, so 391 is the greater number.

MP6 **28.** Frannie has 156 buttons in a jar. Louise has a jar with fewer buttons than Frannie has. Which could be Louise's jar of buttons? Explain your answer.

158 buttons

154 buttons

161 buttons

Answers may vary. Possible answer: Jar B could be Louise's jar. 154 is less than 156. Both numbers have 1 hundred and 5 tens. 156 has 6 ones and 154 has 4 ones. So 154 is less than 156. 158 and 161 are both greater than 156.

Teaching Tips

Item 26
It may help to give children two numbers to compare, such as 481 and 297. Ask them to compare the numbers starting with the digits in the ones place to see if they get the correct answer. This may help them see why it is important to start by comparing the digits in the hundreds place.

Items 27-28
Before children begin to answer each question, have them identify whether they need to find the greater or lesser number. Have them justify their responses.

Mathematical Practices

MP3	**Construct viable arguments and critique the reasoning of others.**

Item 26: Children justify their reasoning for using the greatest place first to compare two numbers.

Item 27: Children determine the solution to the problem and then construct an argument to justify their answer.

MP6	**Attend to precision.**

Item 28: Children carefully compare three given numbers and then explain why they chose the least number.

Common Core Focus:

2.NBT.5 Fluently add and subtract within 100 using strategies based on place value, properties of operations, and/or the relationship between addition and subtraction;

2.NBT.9 Explain why addition and subtraction strategies work, using place value and the properties of operations.

OBJECTIVE

Add two 2-digit numbers within 100 using place value.

ESSENTIAL QUESTION

Focus children on the lesson objective by reading the Essential Question aloud. Children have already learned to add a 1-digit to a 2-digit number. They have also learned to add a 2-digit number to a multiple of ten. Explain that children will now learn to add two 2-digit numbers.

FLUENCY PRACTICE

Fluency practice is available at **sadlierconnect.com**.

Concept Development

Understand: Using place value to add two 2-digit numbers

■ Have children carefully read the word problem and underline the numbers. Be sure they understand that they need to add these numbers to find how many toy cars there are altogether.

■ Children should describe how the place-value models represent each number. Have them identify which models represent the ones and which represent the tens.

■ Explain that children should add the ones to the ones, and the tens to the tens before adding the total number of tens to the total number of ones.

Lesson
10 Add Two-Digit Numbers

Guided Instruction

Essential Question:
How can you add two 2-digit numbers?
2.NBT.5, 2.NBT.9

Words to Know
regroup

In this lesson you will learn different ways to add within 100 using place value.

Understand: Using place value to add two 2-digit numbers

> Mike has 16 toy cars.
> Oscar has 23 toy cars.
> How many toy cars do they have in all?

Write an addition equation.

$16 + 23 = \blacksquare$

Use models for the tens and ones.

16 = 1 ten 6 ones   23 = 2 tens 3 ones

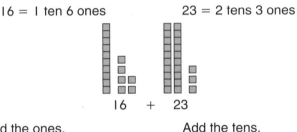

16   +   23

Add the ones.   Add the tens.

6 ones + 3 ones = 9 ones   1 ten + 2 tens = 3 tens

3 tens 9 ones = 39

So 16 + 23 = 39.

▷ Mike and Oscar have 39 toy cars in all.

Words to Know

regroup: use 10 ones to make 1 ten or use 1 ten to make 10 ones

Example: 14 ones = 1 ten 4 ones

2 tens 3 ones = 23 ones

Glossary can be found on pp. 293–304.

Lesson 10

Guided Instruction

Understand: Using properties to add two 2-digit numbers

There are 59 coins in a jar.
Riley adds 33 more.
How many coins are in the jar now?

Write an addition equation.

$59 + 33 = $ ▨

Break up each addend into tens and ones.

$50 + 9 + 30 + 3 = $ ▨

Change the order of the 9 and the 30 to put the tens together and the ones together.

> **Remember!**
> Changing the order of the addends does not change the sum.

$50 + 30 + 9 + 3$

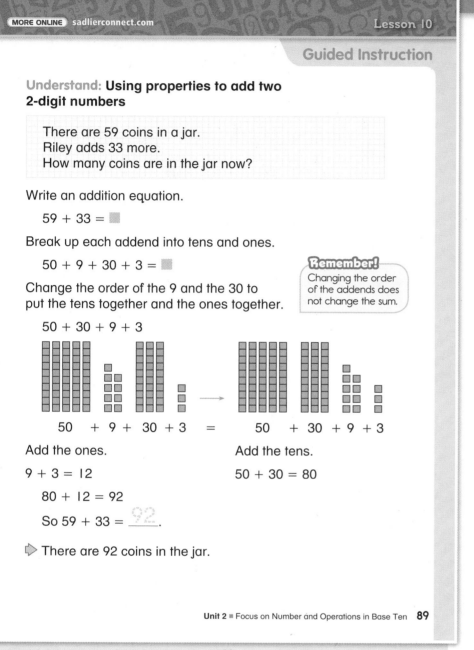

$50 + 9 + 30 + 3 = 50 + 30 + 9 + 3$

Add the ones.

$9 + 3 = 12$

$80 + 12 = 92$

So $59 + 33 = \underline{92}$.

Add the tens.

$50 + 30 = 80$

➡ There are 92 coins in the jar.

Understand: Using properties to add two 2-digit numbers

■ Begin by having children read carefully through the word problem and underline the numbers. Be sure they understand the need to add these numbers to find how many coins there are in the jar in all.

■ Once the addends are rewritten as tens and ones, have children identify which tens and ones go together to reform the original addends (50 and 9; 30 and 3). Do this either before or after changing the order of the addends.

■ Some children may benefit from seeing that 80 + 12 can be rewritten as 80 + 10 + 2. Show that adding the tens results in 90, and then adding the 2 ones, results in 92.

Support English Language Learners

Help English language learners understand that a *prefix* is a group of letters placed before a root word that changes the meaning of the word. Explain that the prefix *re-* means "again." Have children identify words that begin with the prefix "re-". Some examples are: *replay, recharge,* and *reuse.* (Do not accept words such as *read* and *real* as examples.) Children should define the root word, and then define the word once the prefix has been added on.

Finally, focus on the math term *regroup.* The word *group* means, "to bring a set of objects together." So, regroup means, "to bring a set of objects together again, or in a different way."

Connect: Add two 2-digit numbers regrouping ones Use this page to help children strengthen their understanding of how to add two 2-digit numbers by regrouping the ones.

■ Have children identify how each addend is represented in the place-value chart. Then lead a discussion about how the place-value chart relates to the place-value model used in Step 2.

■ Be sure that children see that after the 14 ones are regrouped and the 4 ones are written in the sum, the 1 new ten is recorded in the tens column *above* the other tens. Explain that it is now to be added with the other tens. Have children explain where that new ten came from.

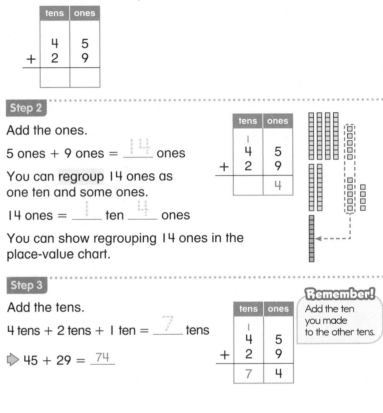

Connect: Add two 2-digit numbers regrouping ones

Add: 45 + 29 = ▇

Step 1

Write the addition in a place-value chart.

	tens	ones
	4	5
+	2	9

Step 2

Add the ones.

5 ones + 9 ones = _____ ones

You can regroup 14 ones as one ten and some ones.

14 ones = _____ ten _____ ones

You can show regrouping 14 ones in the place-value chart.

	tens	ones
	1	
	4	5
+	2	9
		4

Step 3

Add the tens.

4 tens + 2 tens + 1 ten = _7_ tens

▷ 45 + 29 = _74_

	tens	ones
	1	
	4	5
+	2	9
	7	4

Remember! Add the ten you made to the other tens.

Math-to-Physical Education Connection

Making Teams Explain that teachers often have to group children in one way for one activity and then regroup them in a different way for another activity. Provide situational problems such as: *The physical education teacher is putting the second graders into teams for a soccer tournament. One second-grade class has 23 children. The other second-grade class has 19 children. How many second graders are there in all?* Have children use a place-value chart or place-value models to help them solve this problem. Then call on one volunteer to describe how to regroup the ones and another volunteer to describe how to add.

MORE ONLINE sadlierconnect.com

Guided Practice

I. **Add: 24 + 58 =** ▦

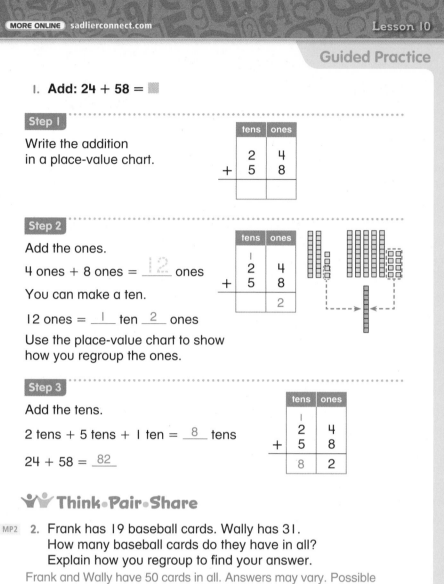

Step 1

Write the addition
in a place-value chart.

tens	ones
2	4
+ 5	8

Step 2

Add the ones.

4 ones + 8 ones = __12__ ones

You can make a ten.

12 ones = __1__ ten __2__ ones

Use the place-value chart to show
how you regroup the ones.

Step 3

Add the tens.

2 tens + 5 tens + 1 ten = __8__ tens

24 + 58 = __82__

☝ Think•Pair•Share

MP2   2. Frank has 19 baseball cards. Wally has 31.
How many baseball cards do they have in all?
Explain how you regroup to find your answer.

Frank and Wally have 50 cards in all. Answers may vary. Possible
answer: 9 ones plus 1 one make 10. I regrouped the 10 ones as
1 ten 0 ones. So 1 ten plus 3 tens plus 1 ten equals 5 tens. That's 50!

Mathematical Practices

Mathematical Practice Standards underline the teaching and
understanding of all concepts and skills presented. The emphasis of
specific practices is noted throughout the guided and independent practice
of this lesson.

| MP2 | **Reason abstractly and quantitatively.** |

Item 2: Children explain the thinking they used to regroup ones in order
to solve an addition problem.

Observational Assessment

Use page 91 to assess children's
understanding of how to add two
2-digit numbers by regrouping ones.
Take note of those children who are not
regrouping the ones correctly. These
children may need additional practice
to strengthen their understanding
of regrouping.

☝ Think•Pair•Share

Peer Collaboration Ask pairs to
share their work after determining
their answer. Ask each pair of children
questions such as:

- *In which place did you add first? How
did you decide?*

- *Did you need to regroup the ones in
this problem? How did you show this
in your work?*

- *How did regrouping the ones
affect your answer? Would you get
a different answer if you did not
regroup the ones?*

To summarize, point out that regrouping
the 10 ones as 1 ten gives one more
ten. Not regrouping would result in an
incorrect answer.

Return to the Essential Question

Reread the Lesson 10 Essential Question
on page 88: *How can you add two
2-digit numbers?*

Tell children to think about what they
learned in this lesson to answer
this question.
(Possible response: I can write the two
numbers in a place-value chart. First,
I add the ones. If the sum of ones is
10 or greater, then I regroup 10 ones
to make 1 ten. Then I add the tens,
including the 1 new ten I made.)

Invite as many volunteers as possible to
express their ideas about adding two
2-digit numbers in their own words.

Independent Practice

Concept Application

Children may work independently on these pages in the classroom or at home. They may refer to the first four pages of the lesson to revisit the instruction or to see a worked-out example.

Common Errors and **Teaching Tips** may help you support learning either in the classroom or as a follow-up for work done at home.

Common Errors

Items 1-2

Watch for children who attempt to add the tens first. Help children understand that when adding two-digit numbers, they must start with the ones, and then add the tens.

Remind children to read the steps shown to the left as they are completing their work.

Independent Practice

1. Add. 13 + 34 = ▨

   Add the ones.

   3 ones + 4 ones = __7__ ones

   Can you make a ten? __no__

   Add the tens.

   1 ten + 3 tens = __4__ tens

   13 + 34 = __47__

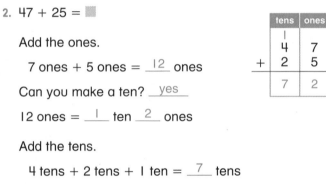

tens	ones
1	3
+ 3	4
4	7

2. 47 + 25 = ▨

   Add the ones.

   7 ones + 5 ones = __12__ ones

   Can you make a ten? __yes__

   12 ones = __1__ ten __2__ ones

   Add the tens.

   4 tens + 2 tens + 1 ten = __7__ tens

   47 + 25 = __72__

tens	ones
1	
4	7
+ 2	5
7	2

Talking About Math

Describing Addition with Regrouping   Provide pairs of children with two addition problems that involve regrouping. One child should pretend to know nothing about addition with regrouping. The other child should act as the teacher to introduce, explain, and teach the concept for one problem. Children should then switch roles as teacher and student and repeat the process for the other problem.

MORE ONLINE sadlierconnect.com

Independent Practice

Add.

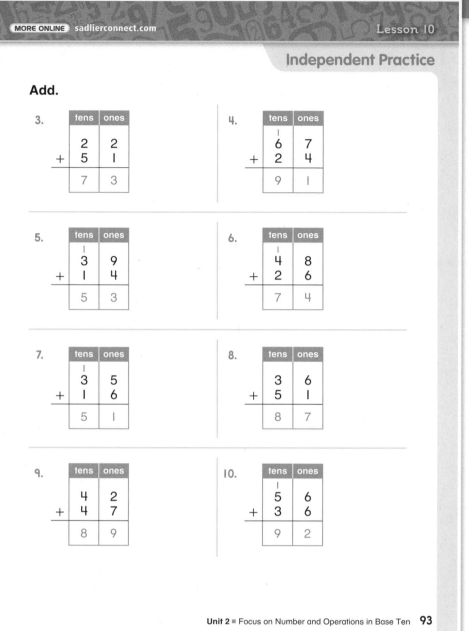

3.
tens	ones
2	2
+ 5	1
7	3

4.
tens	ones
1 6	7
+ 2	4
9	1

5.
tens	ones
1 3	9
+ 1	4
5	3

6.
tens	ones
1 4	8
+ 2	6
7	4

7.
tens	ones
1 3	5
+ 1	6
5	1

8.
tens	ones
3	6
+ 5	1
8	7

9.
tens	ones
4	2
+ 4	7
8	9

10.
tens	ones
1 5	6
+ 3	6
9	2

Common Errors
Items 3-10
Since children have just learned how to regroup, they may expect to regroup for every item. Remind them that they need to regroup only when the number of ones is greater than or equal to 10.

Digital Connection

How-To Video Search the Internet for a video about adding 2-digit numbers with regrouping. Have children watch it and solve along with the video. If the video shows a strategy that children have not learned, compare this new strategy to the strategies that they have already used in the classroom.

Independent Practice

Teaching Tips

Items 11–13

Children should rewrite each item vertically and align the ones and tens in a place-value chart before solving.

Items 14–22

Encourage children to write "H" and "T" above the digits in each item. This way of keeping track of place value will help them to regroup into the tens column.

Independent Practice

Circle the correct answer.

11. $32 + 18 = $ ▓   40   ⓔ50   410

12. $24 + 22 = $ ▓   ⓔ46   56   66

13. $59 + 19 = $ ▓   68   ⓔ78   69

Add.

14.
$$\begin{array}{r} 17 \\ +48 \\ \hline 65 \end{array}$$

15.
$$\begin{array}{r} 54 \\ +29 \\ \hline 83 \end{array}$$

16.
$$\begin{array}{r} 66 \\ +23 \\ \hline 89 \end{array}$$

17.
$$\begin{array}{r} 29 \\ +29 \\ \hline 58 \end{array}$$

18.
$$\begin{array}{r} 14 \\ +38 \\ \hline 52 \end{array}$$

19.
$$\begin{array}{r} 13 \\ +47 \\ \hline 60 \end{array}$$

20.
$$\begin{array}{r} 34 \\ +25 \\ \hline 59 \end{array}$$

21.
$$\begin{array}{r} 16 \\ +58 \\ \hline 74 \end{array}$$

22.
$$\begin{array}{r} 16 \\ +34 \\ \hline 50 \end{array}$$

Math-to-Science Connection

Changing Temperatures Explain that, in different parts of the world, temperatures can change greatly throughout the year. In the United States, winter is usually the coldest season and summer is usually the hottest. Scientists study the weather and how it changes from day to day, month to month, and year to year. Provide situational problems such as: *In Phoenix, Arizona, the average high temperature in December is 66° F. By May, the average high temperature has increased by 29° F. What is the average high temperature in May?*

Have children identify the addends in the word problem and then add the two numbers using regrouping. Once an answer is determined, have children explain strategies they used to solve.

MORE ONLINE sadlierconnect.com

Independent Practice

MP2 **23.** Emily has 69 beads. Sarah has 27. How many beads do they have in all? Write an equation for the problem. Solve the problem in two ways. Talk about each way.

One way: Break addends into tens and ones.

Answers may vary. Possible answer: I write the addition equation 69 + 27 = ▪. I break the addend 69 into 60 + 9, and I break the addend 27 into 20 + 7. I change the order to put tens with tens and ones with ones. 60 + 20 = 80 and 9 + 7 = 16. Then I put the tens and ones together. 80 + 16 = 96. So 69 + 27 = 96. They have 96 beads in all.

Another way: Use regrouping.

Answers may vary. Possible answer: I write the equation 69 + 27 = ▪. I write one number below the other so the two ones are lined up and the two tens are lined up. First I add the ones. 9 ones + 7 ones = 16 ones. I regroup 16 ones as 1 ten 6 ones. Then I add the tens. 6 tens + 2 tens + 1 ten = 9 tens. 9 tens 6 ones is the same as 90 + 6 = 96. So 69 + 27 = 96. They have 96 beads in all.

Unit 2 ■ Focus on Number and Operations in Base Ten **95**

Teaching Tips

Item 23

By now, children should understand the two different strategies for adding two 2-digit numbers. If children are unsure of how to use the strategies, review pages 89 and 90. Remind children to solve this word problem using an equation and then explain their solutions.

Mathematical Practices
MP2 **Reason abstractly and quantitatively.**
Item 23: Children reason quantitatively by determining the solution in two ways and justifying their methods of solving.

Common Core Focus:

2.NBT.5 Fluently add and subtract within 100 using strategies based on place value, properties of operations, and/or the relationship between addition and subtraction. **2.NBT.9** Explain why addition and subtraction strategies work, using place value and the properties of operations.

OBJECTIVE

Subtract 2-digit numbers using place value and regrouping.

ESSENTIAL QUESTION

Focus children on the lesson objective by reading the Essential Question aloud. Children have already learned to subtract multiples of ten. Explain that they will now subtract two 2-digit numbers and will learn how to use regrouping to subtract.

PREREQUISITE SKILLS

Use Foundational Skills Handbook page 284, *Subtract Tens,* to review subtracting multiples of ten.

FLUENCY PRACTICE

Fluency practice is available at **sadlierconnect.com**.

Concept Development

Understand: Subtracting 2-digit numbers using place-value models

■ Have children carefully read the word problem and underline the numbers they will use to subtract.

■ Children should describe how the place-value models together represent the problem.

■ Explain that the second model shows the subtraction, or the taking away. The amount being subtracted is represented by the crossed-out tens and ones.

Subtract Two-Digit Numbers

Essential Question:
How can you subtract a 2-digit number from a 2-digit number?
2.NBT.5, 2.NBT.9

Guided Instruction

In this lesson you will learn how to subtract 2-digit numbers.

Understand: Subtracting 2-digit numbers using place-value models

> There are 57 stickers on a sheet.
> Marcus uses 34 of the stickers.
> How many stickers are left?

Write a subtraction equation.
$57 - 34 = $ ■

Use models.
Cross out as you subtract.

57 = 5 tens 7 ones

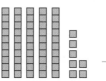

34 = 3 tens 4 ones

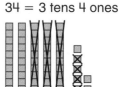

First subtract the ones.
7 ones − 4 ones = 3 ones

Then subtract the tens.
5 tens − 3 tens = 2 tens

5 tens 7 ones − 3 tens 4 ones = 2 tens 3 ones
$57 - 34 = 23$

▷ There are 23 stickers left.

Support English Language Learners

The word *left* can be confusing to English language learners. Many children know the word *left* as a directional term, as in "go to the left." Explain that in subtraction, *left* can mean *remaining.*

Prepare several sentences that use the word *left* in both contexts. Then, sitting with your back to children, say one of your sentences. If the context refers to a direction, simultaneously raise your left hand and point to the left. If the context refers to an amount remaining, then stand up. When children become comfortable distinguishing between the two contexts, allow them to take turns saying a sentence using the word *left* while the rest of the class reacts by raising their left hands or standing.

Lesson 11

Guided Instruction

Understand: Subtracting 2-digit numbers using place-value charts

Lori has 38 marbles.
She gives 23 marbles to a friend.
How many marbles does Lori have now?

Write a subtraction equation.

$38 - 23 = $ ▨

Step 1

Write the subtraction in a place-value chart.

Step 2

Subtract the ones.

8 ones − 3 ones = 5 ones

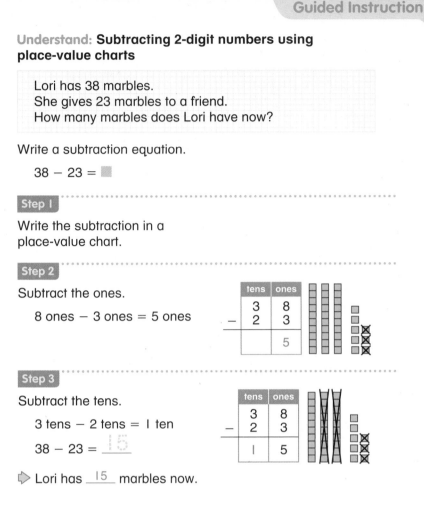

tens	ones
3	8
− 2	3
	5

Step 3

Subtract the tens.

3 tens − 2 tens = 1 ten

$38 - 23 = \underline{15}$

tens	ones
3	8
− 2	3
1	5

▷ Lori has __15__ marbles now.

Understand: Subtracting 2-digit numbers using place-value charts

■ Begin by having children read the problem and then underline the numbers. Explain that the words *have now* in the question mean the same as *left*.

■ Ask children to explain how they know which number from the problem to write first in the subtraction equation. Children should recognize that the first number in the problem, 38, represents the total amount, so they should write it first in the equation. The second number represents the part to be subtracted.

■ Encourage children to explain how the place-value charts relate to the place-value models as shown in Steps 2 and 3.

■ Be sure that children understand that the place-value model shows the total number. The parts of the model that are crossed out represent the number taken away. The part of the model that remains represents the part that is left, or the answer to the problem.

Math-to-Money Connection

Making Change Ask children to tell about a time they paid for something and then received change in return. Explain that it is important to count the change to make sure the amount is correct.

Give pairs of children play money dimes and pennies. Offer scenarios involving amounts less than $1 as you write the corresponding subtraction problems and solutions on the board. Make sure that the problems do not require regrouping. For example: *Tom buys a toy that costs 53 cents. He pays with 7 dimes and 16 pennies. How much change does Tom receive?* Discuss the problem-solving process by talking about the number of ones (pennies) subtracted and the number of tens (dimes) subtracted.

Guided Instruction

Connect: Subtracting 2-digit numbers with regrouping 1 ten as 10 ones Use this page to help children develop their understanding of subtracting 2-digit numbers using regrouping.

■ Discuss how the subtraction equation is represented in Step 2 by both the place-value chart and the place-value models.

■ Have children count by tens and ones to confirm that the 6 tens and the 4 yellow ones in the model represent the total, or 64. Point out that the blue models show the 1 ten regrouped as 10 ones.

■ Supply children with place-value models to explore why 1 ten must be regrouped as 10 ones. Be sure that children understand that they need more than 4 ones in order to take away 9 ones. After children model the regrouping, have them recount the tens and ones to verify that the total has not changed even though the arrangement of the models has changed.

Guided Instruction

Connect: Subtracting 2-digit numbers with regrouping 1 ten as 10 ones

Subtract: $64 - 39 = \blacksquare$

Step 1

Write the subtraction in a place-value chart.

Step 2

To subtract 9 ones from 6 tens 4 ones, first regroup 1 ten as 10 ones. 5 tens are left.

Add the 10 ones to the 4 ones. 4 ones + 10 ones = 14 ones.

tens	ones
5	14
6̶	4̶
− 3	9

Step 3

Subtract ones.

14 ones − 9 ones = _5_ ones

tens	ones
5	14
6̶	4̶
− 3	9
	5

Step 4

Subtract tens.

5 tens − 3 tens = _2_ tens

➭ $64 - 39 = 25$

tens	ones
5	14
6̶	4̶
− 3	9
2	5

Math-to-Travel Connection

Travel Times Explain that when we travel to a place, we often want to get there as soon as possible. Discuss that, if you live far from the place you are traveling to, it will take you longer to get there than if you lived closer. Provide scenarios such as: *James and his friend Cesar both ride the bus to school. James spends 35 minutes riding the school bus. Cesar spends 28 minutes on the bus. How many more minutes does James spend on the bus than Cesar?*

Model how to use a place-value chart and place-value models to subtract, regrouping 1 ten as 10 ones. Have children explain why they must regroup to solve this problem.

Lesson 11

Guided Practice

1. Subtract: 82 − 47 = ▨

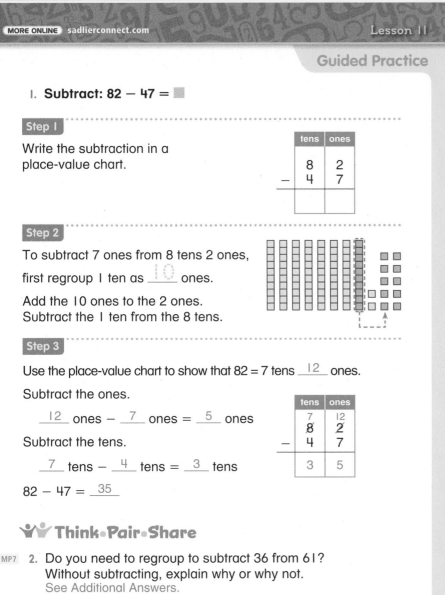

Step 1

Write the subtraction in a place-value chart.

tens	ones
8	2
− 4	7

Step 2

To subtract 7 ones from 8 tens 2 ones, first regroup 1 ten as _10_ ones.

Add the 10 ones to the 2 ones.
Subtract the 1 ten from the 8 tens.

Step 3

Use the place-value chart to show that 82 = 7 tens _12_ ones.

Subtract the ones.

_12_ ones − _7_ ones = _5_ ones

Subtract the tens.

tens	ones
7	12
8̸	2̸
− 4	7
3	5

_7_ tens − _4_ tens = _3_ tens

82 − 47 = _35_

Think·Pair·Share

MP7 **2.** Do you need to regroup to subtract 36 from 61? Without subtracting, explain why or why not.
See Additional Answers.

Unit 2 ■ Focus on Number and Operations in Base Ten **99**

Mathematical Practices

Mathematical Practice Standards underline the teaching and understanding of all concepts and skills presented. The emphasis of specific practices is noted throughout the guided and independent practice of this lesson.

MP7 Look for and make use of structure.

Item 2: Children evaluate the structure of a problem to explain why they need to regroup in order to solve.

Observational Assessment

Use page 99 to assess children's understanding of how to subtract 2-digit numbers. Take note of those children who are not regrouping correctly. Such children may need additional practice to strengthen their understanding of place value and/or regrouping.

⚊ Think·Pair·Share

Peer Collaboration Ask pairs to share their work after determining their answer. Ask children to consider questions such as:

• *Which number represents the total?*

• *Which number would you subtract?*

• *In which place would you subtract first?*

• *How do you decide whether you would need to regroup the ones in this problem?*

To summarize, point out that if the total number of ones is less than the number of ones being subtracted, you need regroup one of the tens as 10 ones.

Return to the Essential Question

Reread the Lesson 11 Essential Question on page 96: *How can you subtract a 2-digit number from a 2-digit number?*

Tell children to think about what they learned in this lesson to answer this question.
(Possible response: I can break the number that represents the total into tens and ones. First I subtract the ones, regrouping 1 ten as 10 ones, if needed. Then I subtract the tens.)

Additional Answers

Item 2: Yes; Answers may vary. Possible answer: There are not enough ones to subtract because 6 ones are more than 1 one. So you need to regroup 6 tens 1 one as 5 tens 11 ones.

Concept Application

Children may work independently on these pages in the classroom or at home. They may refer to the first four pages of the lesson to revisit the instruction or to see a worked-out example.

Common Errors and **Teaching Tips** may help you support learning either in the classroom or as a follow-up for work done at home.

Teaching Tips

Item 2

Encourage children to draw or use place-value models to represent the regrouping of the tens and ones to subtract.

Independent Practice

Subtract.

1. $67 - 46 =$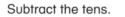

   Subtract the ones.

   __7__ ones − __6__ ones = __I__ one

   Subtract the tens.

   __6__ tens − __4__ tens = __2__ tens

   $67 - 46 =$ __21__

tens	ones
6	7
− 4	6
2	I

2. $83 - 39 =$ ▪

   Can you subtract 9 ones from 3 ones?

   __no__

   Regroup I ten as I0 ones.

   Add I0 ones to the 3 ones.

   Subtract I ten from the 8 tens.

   8 tens 3 ones = __7__ tens __13__ ones

   Subtract the ones.

   __13__ ones − __9__ ones = __4__ ones

   Subtract the tens.

   __7__ tens − __3__ tens = __4__ tens

   $83 - 39 =$ __44__

tens	ones
7	13
8̶	3̶
− 3	9
4	4

Talking About Math

Asking Questions about Subtraction Present children with a 2-digit subtraction problem that involves regrouping. Have them work in pairs to create at least three questions they must ask themselves before being able to solve the problem. Children may create questions such as these: *Do I have enough ones in the greater number to subtract the lesser number? Will I need to regroup? How many ones will I have after regrouping? How many tens will I have after regrouping?* Ask children to explain how these questions can help them solve problems.

Independent Practice

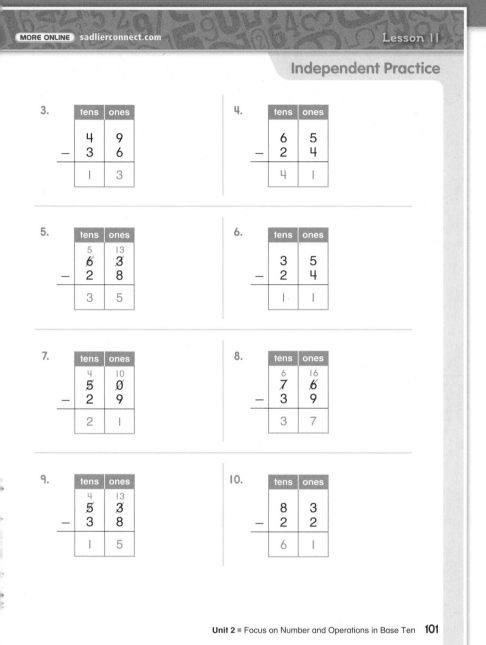

3.

tens	ones
4	9
− 3	6
1	3

4.

tens	ones
6	5
− 2	4
4	1

5.

tens	ones
5	13
6̶	3̶
− 2	8
3	5

6.

tens	ones
3	5
− 2	4
1	1

7.

tens	ones
4	10
5̶	0̶
− 2	9
2	1

8.

tens	ones
6	16
7̶	6̶
− 3	9
3	7

9.

tens	ones
4	13
5̶	3̶
− 3	8
1	5

10.

tens	ones
8	3
− 2	2
6	1

Common Errors

Items 3, 4, 6, and 10

Children may regroup 1 ten even though regrouping is not necessary. Mathematically, children may still arrive at the correct solution, but the likelihood is that they will forget to regroup the extra 10 ones as 1 ten. Remind children to always compare the digits in the ones column in order to decide if they need to regroup. Point out that if the first ones digit is greater than the second ones digit, then regrouping is not necessary.

Items 5, 7–9

Children may forget to subtract 1 ten from the tens place after regrouping it as 10 ones. Provide children with place-value blocks to help them visualize and work out the solutions.

Digital Connection

Place-Value Models Use a computer search engine to find a program with interactive place-value models that can be used on the whiteboard. Have volunteers use the models to discuss and demonstrate how to solve subtraction problems that require regrouping 1 ten as 10 ones. Have the class tell whether they agree with each solution and why.

Teaching Tips

Items 11–13

Children may find it easier to choose the correct solution if they first rewrite each problem vertically aligning the digits in the tens and ones places.

Items 14–22

Remind children to cross out and rename the digits in the tens and ones places if they need to regroup before subtracting.

Independent Practice

Circle the correct answer.

11. $79 - 34 =$ ▨   35   (45)   113

12. $51 - 16 =$ ▨   67   (35)   45

13. $64 - 56 =$ ▨   18   120   (8)

Subtract.

14.
$$\begin{array}{r} 59 \\ -18 \\ \hline 41 \end{array}$$

15.
$$\begin{array}{r} 67 \\ -29 \\ \hline 38 \end{array}$$

16.
$$\begin{array}{r} 97 \\ -45 \\ \hline 52 \end{array}$$

17.
$$\begin{array}{r} 41 \\ -23 \\ \hline 18 \end{array}$$

18.
$$\begin{array}{r} 86 \\ -32 \\ \hline 54 \end{array}$$

19.
$$\begin{array}{r} 65 \\ -38 \\ \hline 27 \end{array}$$

20.
$$\begin{array}{r} 94 \\ -35 \\ \hline 59 \end{array}$$

21.
$$\begin{array}{r} 73 \\ -45 \\ \hline 28 \end{array}$$

22.
$$\begin{array}{r} 82 \\ -48 \\ \hline 34 \end{array}$$

Math-to-Community Connection

Community Cutbacks Explain that sometimes communities must cut amounts they spend to save money. Provide scenarios involving the subtraction of 2-digit numbers. For example: *Last year, the parks department workers in one town planted 65 trees. This year, in order to save money, workers will plant only 48 trees. How many fewer trees will they plant this year than last year?*

Have children identify the numbers they will use to subtract and write an equation to represent each problem. They may wish to write the problem in a place-value chart to help organize the ones and tens. Watch for children who incorrectly regroup the tens and provide additional instruction if needed. Model how to write the answer in a sentence that relates back to the problem.

Lesson 11

Independent Practice

MP2 **23.** Without subtracting, tell which subtraction equation will have the greater answer.

$$74 - 68 = \blacksquare \quad \text{or} \quad 83 - 68 = \blacksquare$$

Talk about your answer.

83 − 68; Answers may vary. Possible answer: 83 is greater than 74, so 74 is less than 83. Subtracting the same number, 68, from the greater number would leave more than subtracting it from the lesser number.

MP3 **24.** Marco says that he can use addition to check that his subtraction is correct. Marco's work is shown below. Finish what Marco started.

$$
\begin{array}{cc}
\overset{5\ 12}{\cancel{6}\,\cancel{2}} & \overset{1}{}3\,5 \\
-\ 2\,7 & +\ \underline{} \\
\hline
3\,5 &
\end{array}
$$

Is Marco's subtraction correct? Why can you use addition to check subtraction?

yes; Answers may vary. Possible answer: Marco's subtraction is correct. Addition and subtraction equations that have the same numbers are related to each other. If you start with the answer and add the 27 that you subtracted, the sum will be the number you started with.

Unit 2 ▪ Focus on Number and Operations in Base Ten **103**

Common Errors

Item 24

Children may place the incorrect value in the addition equation. Explain that since 27 was subtracted in the first equation, it must be added back in the second equation.

Teaching Tips

Item 23

Guide children to identify how the two equations are alike and how they differ. Children should notice that the same amount is subtracted in both. Explain that they need to compare 74 and 83 to determine their answer. If children have difficulty reasoning abstractly, place the values in a scenario that children are familiar with to provide a real-world context.

Mathematical Practices	
MP2	**Reason abstractly and quantitatively.**
Item 23: Children make sense of quantities and their relationships.	
MP3	**Construct viable arguments and critique the reasoning of others.**
Item 24: Children explain a way to check the solution to a problem.	

Common Core Focus:

2.NBT.6 Add up to four two-digit numbers using strategies based on place value and properties of operations.

OBJECTIVE

Add up to four 2-digit numbers using place value and regrouping of ones.

ESSENTIAL QUESTION

Focus children on the lesson objective by reading the Essential Question aloud, and then ask them to recall what they know about adding two 2-digit numbers. Children have already learned to add two 2-digit numbers using place value and regrouping of ones. Now they will expand on this skill by adding three or four 2-digit numbers using the same strategies.

PREREQUISITE SKILLS

Use Foundational Skills Handbook page 283, *Add 2-Digit Numbers,* to review adding with 2-digit numbers.

FLUENCY PRACTICE

Fluency practice is available at **sadlierconnect.com**.

Concept Development

Understand: You can add three 2-digit numbers using place value

■ Ask children to describe how the place-value models represent the digits in each number.

■ Prior to having children solve, ask them what they think they should do first. They should be able to reason that they should first add the ones and then add the tens.

■ Once the problem is completed, ask children to tell how solving this problem is both alike and different from adding two 2-digit numbers.

Lesson 12

Add More Than Two Numbers

Essential Question:
How can you add three or four 2-digit numbers?
2.NBT.6

In this lesson you will learn how to add up to four 2-digit numbers.

Understand: You can add three 2-digit numbers using place value

> Tia has 32 pennies.
> Leo has 23 pennies.
> Albert has 24 pennies.
> How many pennies do they have in all?

Write an addition equation.
$32 + 23 + 24 = $ ▨

Use models to show the tens and ones in each addend.

$32 = 30 + 2$
$23 = 20 + 3$
$24 = 20 + 4$

$30 + 2$ $20 + 3$ $20 + 4$

Add the ones.
$2 + 3 = 5$ and $5 + 4 = 9$

Add the tens.
$30 + 20 = 50$ and $50 + 20 = 70$

Put the tens and ones together: $70 + 9 = 79$
$32 + 23 + 24 = 79$

▷ They have 79 pennies in all.

Support English Language Learners

The word *sum* may be confusing to children as it is a homonym for the word *some*. Review the meaning of *sum* as the answer to an addition problem. Explain that the word *some* means just a few. Write these words in sentences on the board. Read each sentence aloud, pointing to *sum* or *some* as you say it. Discuss each meaning within the context of the sentence.

Have children write the word *sum* on one index card and *some* on another card. Say a sentence that uses either word in context. Have children hold up the index card that shows the correct word. If they have difficulty deciding which card to choose, guide children in a brief discussion about the meaning of the sentence.

Lesson 12

Guided Instruction

Understand: Grouping addends to add three 2-digit numbers

> There are 25 red marbles, 42 green marbles, and 15 blue marbles in a bag.
> How many marbles in all are in the bag?

Write an addition equation.

$25 + 42 + 15 =$ ▧

Break each addend into tens and ones.

$25 = 20 + 5 \qquad 42 = 40 + 2 \qquad 15 = 10 + 5$

Add the ones.

$5 + 2 + 5 =$ ▧

You can change the order of the addends and make 10.

Remember!
Changing the order of the addends does not change the sum.
$5 + 2 + 5 = 5 + 5 + 2$

$5 + 2 + 5$

$5 + 5 = 10$

$10 + 2 = 12$

$12 = 1$ ten 2 ones

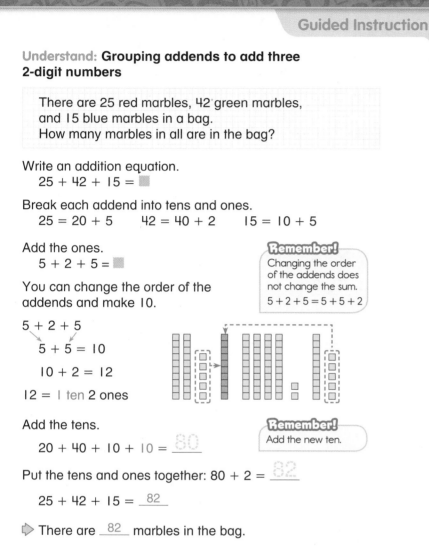

Add the tens.

$20 + 40 + 10 + 10 = \underline{80}$

Remember!
Add the new ten.

Put the tens and ones together: $80 + 2 = \underline{82}$

$25 + 42 + 15 = \underline{82}$

➪ There are $\underline{82}$ marbles in the bag.

Understand: Grouping addends to add three 2-digit numbers

■ Begin by having children read the problem and then underline the numbers.

■ For each of the three addends, call on children to tell which digit represents a number of tens or a number of ones. Use a place-value chart to demonstrate the reasoning if children cannot explain it.

■ Children may not understand that changing the order of the addends can be helpful. Explain that changing the order can make adding easier.

■ Make sure children understand, and can explain, the regrouping shown in the place-value model. Provide actual place-value models for children who need additional assistance.

Math-to-Math Connection

Adding Greater Numbers In order for children to successfully synthesize the number concepts taught in later grades, it is essential that they understand not only the algorithms for adding and subtracting multi-digit numbers, but the reasoning behind the algorithms. Encouraging children to take various approaches to problem solving gives them the opportunity to strengthen their mathematical reasoning skills, to make sense of the problem-solving process, and to rationally critique the work and reasoning of others.

Connect: Connect adding three 2-digit numbers to adding four 2-digit numbers Use this page to help children extend their understanding of adding 2-digit numbers by adding four 2-digit numbers using the same strategies.

■ Point out that while the problem is written horizontally at the top of the page, in the place-value chart, it is written vertically. Confirm that, whether children add across or down, the sum will be the same. Have children explain which way they think is easier to add the four numbers, across or down.

■ Explain the addition at the right of the place-value charts. Tell children that this shows how to keep track of which ones have already been added and which tens have already been added.

■ Have children explain why they had to regroup and how the regrouping is represented in the place-value chart.

■ Finally, ask children to explain how solving this problem compares to adding two or three 2-digit numbers. They should be able to express that the methods are the same, but that it takes more time to add the fourth number.

Guided Instruction

Connect: Connect adding three 2-digit numbers to adding four 2-digit numbers

Add: $21 + 23 + 19 + 26 =$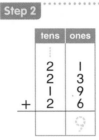

Step 1

Write the addition in a place-value chart.

Step 2

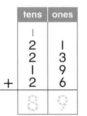

Add the ones.

1 one + 3 ones = 4 ones

4 ones + 9 ones = 13 ones

13 ones + 6 ones = 19 ones

Make a new ten: 19 = 1 ten 9 ones

Add the tens.

2 tens + 2 tens = 4 tens

4 tens + 1 ten = 5 tens

5 tens + 2 tens = 7 tens

7 tens + 1 ten = 8 tens

Remember!
Add the ten you made to the other tens.

8 tens 9 ones = ___89___

▷ $21 + 23 + 19 + 26 =$ ___89___

Math-to-Business Connection

Bake Sales Discuss that schools sometimes hold bake sales to raise money. To keep costs down, children and their families may bake the items to be sold. Provide several scenarios that ask children to find the total number of items for sale, such as the following: *Lincoln Elementary School is holding a bake sale. Ms. Smith's class bakes 24 items. Mr. Deaver's class brings in 36 items. Ms. Michaels's class provides 15 items, and Ms. Long's class contributes 12 items. How items in all does Lincoln Elementary School have to sell at the bake sale?*

Have children work in pairs to solve this problem. After they have found the sum, ask pairs to explain how they solved, being sure to explain their regrouping. Model how to write the answer in a sentence that relates to the question asked.

Lesson 12

Guided Practice

1. Add: $12 + 36 + 25 + 14 =$ ■

Step 1

Write the addition in a place-value chart.

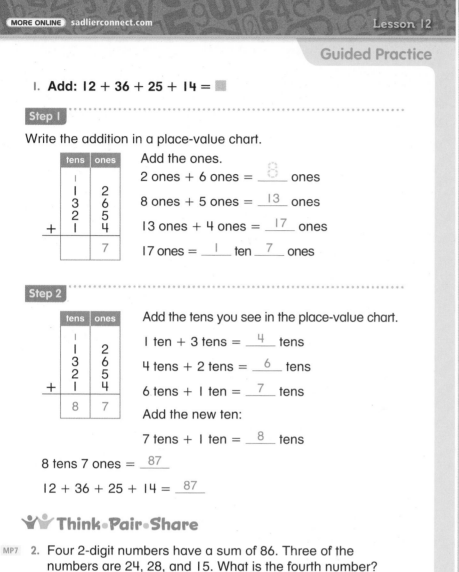

Add the ones.

2 ones + 6 ones = ___8___ ones

8 ones + 5 ones = ___13___ ones

13 ones + 4 ones = ___17___ ones

17 ones = ___1___ ten ___7___ ones

Step 2

Add the tens you see in the place-value chart.

1 ten + 3 tens = ___4___ tens

4 tens + 2 tens = ___6___ tens

6 tens + 1 ten = ___7___ tens

Add the new ten:

7 tens + 1 ten = ___8___ tens

8 tens 7 ones = ___87___

$12 + 36 + 25 + 14 =$ ___87___

Think·Pair·Share

MP7 2. Four 2-digit numbers have a sum of 86. Three of the numbers are 24, 28, and 15. What is the fourth number? Talk about how you know. See Additional Answers.

Mathematical Practices

Mathematical Practice Standards underline the teaching and understanding of all concepts and skills presented. The emphasis of specific practices is noted throughout the guided and independent practice of this lesson.

MP7 **Look for and make use of structure.**

Item 2: Children look at and use the structure of adding four 2-digit numbers to determine the missing addend for a given sum.

Observational Assessment

Use page 107 to assess children's understanding of how to add four 2-digit numbers. Take note of those children who are not regrouping correctly. They may need additional practice using place-value models to strengthen their understanding of regrouping.

Think·Pair·Share

Peer Collaboration Have children work with a partner to answer the question. Remind children that there may be more than one way to solve the problem. Children should be able to explain why the way they chose results in a correct solution. Suggest that partners discuss questions such as these:

- *What did you do first? Why?*

- *How did you find the fourth number, which is the missing addend?*

- *Can you think of another method to solve this problem?*

To summarize, confirm that children could subtract the sum of the first three addends from 86 to find the missing addend.

Return to the Essential Question

Reread the Lesson 12 Essential Question on page 104: *How can you add three or four 2-digit numbers?*

Tell children to think about what they learned in this lesson to answer this question.
(Possible responses: I can break the number into tens and ones. First, add the ones. If there are 10 or more ones, regroup 10 ones as 1 ten. Then add the tens, being sure to include the regrouped ten, to find the sum.)

Additional Answers

Item 2: 19; Answers may vary. Possible answer: I added the 24, 28, and 15. The sum was 67. Then I subtracted 67 from 86 to get the fourth number. $86 - 67 = 19$.

Independent Practice

Concept Application

Children may work independently on these pages in the classroom or at home. They may refer to the first four pages of the lesson to revisit the instruction or to see a worked-out example.

Common Errors and **Teaching Tips** may help you support learning either in the classroom or as a follow-up for work done at home.

Common Errors

Items 2-3

Children may forget to regroup the 10 ones as 1 ten. Allow children to use place-value blocks if they have difficulty explaining their regrouping or remembering to regroup.

Independent Practice

Add.

1. $42 + 25 + 22 = $ ▓

   $2 + 5 + \underline{\ 2\ } = \underline{\ 9\ }$

   $40 + 20 + \underline{\ 20\ } = \underline{\ 80\ }$

   $42 + 25 + 22 = \underline{\ 89\ }$

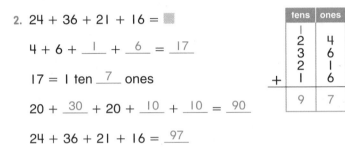

2. $24 + 36 + 21 + 16 = $ ▓

   $4 + 6 + \underline{\ 1\ } + \underline{\ 6\ } = \underline{\ 17\ }$

   $17 = 1$ ten $\underline{\ 7\ }$ ones

   $20 + \underline{\ 30\ } + 20 + \underline{\ 10\ } + \underline{\ 10\ } = \underline{\ 90\ }$

   $24 + 36 + 21 + 16 = \underline{\ 97\ }$

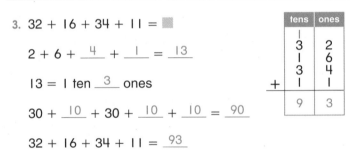

3. $32 + 16 + 34 + 11 = $ ▓

   $2 + 6 + \underline{\ 4\ } + \underline{\ 1\ } = \underline{\ 13\ }$

   $13 = 1$ ten $\underline{\ 3\ }$ ones

   $30 + \underline{\ 10\ } + 30 + \underline{\ 10\ } + \underline{\ 10\ } = \underline{\ 90\ }$

   $32 + 16 + 34 + 11 = \underline{\ 93\ }$

108 Unit 2 ▪ Focus on Number and Operations in Base Ten

Talking About Math

Comparing Addition Problems Ask children to recall the strategies they used when adding two 2-digit numbers. Have them work in pairs to create and solve a problem that involves adding two 2-digit numbers. Then have children talk about how the way they solved their problem is like, and different from, the way they solved problems in this lesson.

MORE ONLINE sadlierconnect.com

Lesson 12

Independent Practice

Teaching Tips

Items 4–9

Ensure that children remember to add each new ten they made to the other tens in the problem. Explain that forgetting to add this ten will result in an incorrect answer.

Add.

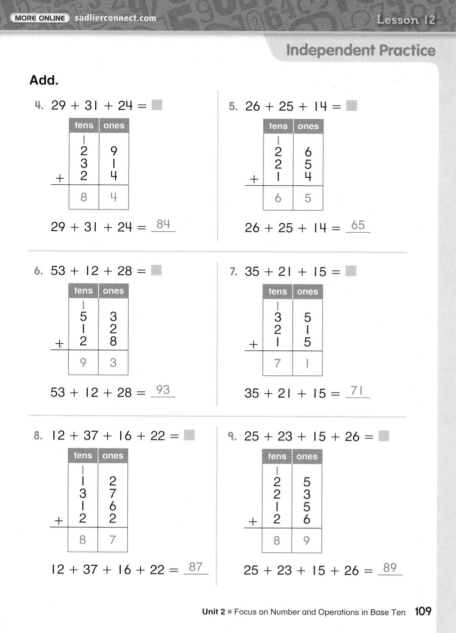

4. 29 + 31 + 24 = ■

tens	ones
1	
2	9
3	1
2	4
8	4

29 + 31 + 24 = __84__

5. 26 + 25 + 14 = ■

tens	ones
1	
2	6
2	5
1	4
6	5

26 + 25 + 14 = __65__

6. 53 + 12 + 28 = ■

tens	ones
1	
5	3
1	2
2	8
9	3

53 + 12 + 28 = __93__

7. 35 + 21 + 15 = ■

tens	ones
1	
3	5
2	1
1	5
7	1

35 + 21 + 15 = __71__

8. 12 + 37 + 16 + 22 = ■

tens	ones
1	
1	2
3	7
1	6
2	2
8	7

12 + 37 + 16 + 22 = __87__

9. 25 + 23 + 15 + 26 = ■

tens	ones
1	
2	5
2	3
1	5
2	6
8	9

25 + 23 + 15 + 26 = __89__

Unit 2 ■ Focus on Number and Operations in Base Ten **109**

Digital Connection

Addition-Practice Web Site Use a search engine to find a Web site that allows children to practice adding up to four 2-digit numbers with sums to 99. Have children work in pars to determine the sum for each problem.

Independent Practice

Teaching Tips

Items 10-13

Suggest that children underline each digit in the ones place, and then add mentally. Remind them that they need to add the new ten to the other three tens.

Items 14-21

Remind children to record the regrouped ones as a new ten at the top of the tens column and then add it to the other tens.

Independent Practice

Circle the correct answer.

10. $51 + 10 + 19 = $ ▪   70   (80)   89

11. $43 + 17 + 29 = $ ▪   (89)   79   70

12. $23 + 31 + 16 = $ ▪   60   (70)   80

13. $20 + 18 + 24 = $ ▪   52   60   (62)

Add.

14.
```
  41
  28
+ 17
----
  86
```

15.
```
  32
  13
+ 27
----
  72
```

16.
```
  41
  17
+ 24
----
  82
```

17.
```
  34
  16
+ 29
----
  79
```

18.
```
  36
  17
  23
+ 12
----
  88
```

19.
```
  27
  15
  14
+ 33
----
  89
```

20.
```
  31
  24
  19
+ 25
----
  99
```

21.
```
  11
  28
  22
+ 35
----
  96
```

Math-to-Sports Connection

Football Scores Explain that football coaches keep track of the number of points their teams score in each game. Provide children with scores from the last three or four football games played by the local high school team or by a popular professional team. (Alternatively, make up scores for a fictional team.) Have children use the scores to write an equation to find the total number of points. Allow them to write the scores in a place-value chart or use place-value blocks to help organize the ones and tens. Remind children to regroup 10 ones as 1 ten. Challenge children to apply the strategies they know as they talk about what to do when the sum of the digits in the ones place is 10 or more.

Lesson 12

Independent Practice

MP1 **22.** A jar has 90 buttons in it. There are 21 red buttons, 19 yellow buttons, and 36 green buttons. The rest of the buttons are blue. How many blue buttons are there? Talk about how you found your answer.

14 blue buttons; Answers may vary. Possible answer: I know that there are 90 buttons in all. I added the numbers for the red, yellow, and green buttons and found that there were 76. So I subtracted the 76 from 90 to find the number of blue buttons.

MP3 **23.** Rod added $38 + 13 + 22$. His answer was 63. Was his answer correct? If not, talk about what mistake he made.

no; Answers may vary. Possible answer: The correct answer is 73. Rod's answer has the correct digit in the ones place, but the digit in the tens place is not correct. Rod probably added the ones and found that there were 13, but then forgot to add the regrouped ten to the other tens.

MP1 **24.** Make up a word problem for which you need to add three or four 2-digit numbers to solve. Write and solve an equation for your word problem.

Answers may vary. Possible answer: Sam had 11 grapes, 20 cherries, and 15 apple pieces in his fruit salad. How many pieces of fruit were in his fruit salad? $11 + 20 + 15 = 46$; Sam had 46 pieces of fruit in his fruit salad.

Unit 2 ■ Focus on Number and Operations in Base Ten **111**

Common Errors

Item 22

Be sure children are reading carefully and do not use 90 as one of the addends. They should understand that 90 is the sum of all the buttons.

Teaching Tips

Item 24

Read the problem aloud with children and discuss what they are to do to complete the work. Allow children to brainstorm ideas for their word problems.

Mathematical Practices	
MP1	**Make sense of problems and persevere in solving them.**

Item 22: Children analyze and plan a solution to a problem.

Item 24: Children use what they know about solving similar problems to write and solve a new problem.

MP3	**Construct viable arguments and critique the reasoning of others.**

Item 23: Children share their reasoning with others.

Common Core Focus:

2.NBT.7 Add and subtract within 1,000, using concrete models or drawings and strategies based on place value, properties of operations, and/or the relationship between addition and subtraction; relate the strategy to a written method. Understand that in adding or subtracting three-digit numbers, one adds or subtracts hundreds and hundreds, tens and tens, ones and ones; and sometimes it is necessary to compose or decompose tens or hundreds.

OBJECTIVE

Add three-digit numbers within 1,000.

ESSENTIAL QUESTION

Read the Essential Question aloud to the class. This lesson will help children learn to add three-digit numbers with and without regrouping. They will use both models and place-value charts to assist them.

FLUENCY PRACTICE

Fluency practice is available at **sadlierconnect.com**.

Concept Development

Understand: Adding 3-digit numbers without regrouping

■ Ask children to explain why they must add in the ones place first, in the tens place next, and in the hundreds place last.

Understand: Adding 3-digit numbers by regrouping ones

■ Have children explain why the sum of 15 ones cannot be written in the ones place in the chart. Then discuss why 10 of the ones are written in the tens place in the chart.

Lesson 13 Add Three-Digit Numbers within 1,000

Guided Instruction

In this lesson you will learn how to add three-digit numbers.

Understand: Adding 3-digit numbers without regrouping

Add: 134 + 125 = ▇

Use models and a place-value chart.

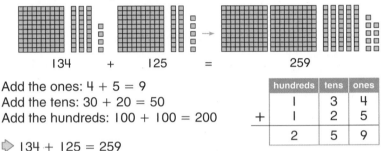

134   +   125   =   259

Add the ones: 4 + 5 = 9
Add the tens: 30 + 20 = 50
Add the hundreds: 100 + 100 = 200

	hundreds	tens	ones
	1	3	4
+	1	2	5
	2	5	9

▷ 134 + 125 = 259

Understand: Adding 3-digit numbers by regrouping ones

Add: 156 + 239 = ▇

Add the ones: 6 + 9 = 15
Make 1 ten from 10 ones: 15 = 1 ten 5 ones
Add the tens: 50 + 30 + 10 = 90
Add the hundreds: 100 + 200 = 300

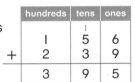

	hundreds	tens	ones
		1	
	1	5	6
+	2	3	9
	3	9	5

▷ 156 + 239 = 395

Support English Language Learners

English language learners may be familiar with the word *group*. However, the word *regroup* may cause some confusion. Explain that *regrouping* means "grouping again in a different way."

Use place-value models to help children understand the meaning of *regroup*. Count out 13 ones. Call on a volunteer to trade 10 of the ones for 1 ten. Make sure children understand that 10 ones have the same value as 1 ten. Review that this process is called *regrouping* because the group of 13 ones was used to make a different, equivalent group of 1 ten and 3 ones. Point out that after regrouping, the value of the regrouped model, 1 ten and 3 ones, has the same value as the original group of 13 ones.

MORE ONLINE sadlierconnect.com

Guided Instruction

Understand: Adding two 3-digit numbers with regrouping tens to make a hundred

Lisa has 183 seashells.
Kendra has 142 seashells.
How many seashells do they have in all?

Write an equation.
183 + 142 = ▨

Use models and a place-value chart to show the addition.

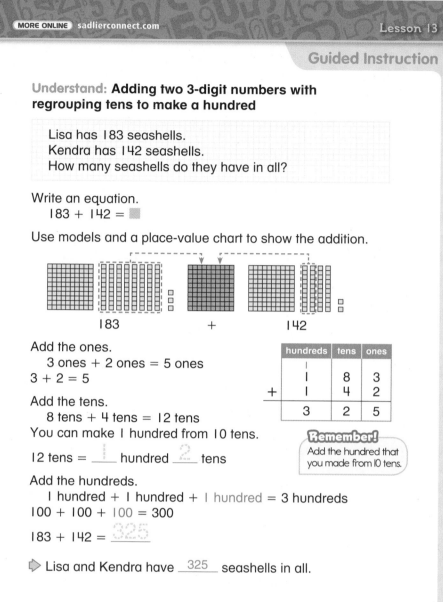

183   +   142

Add the ones.
   3 ones + 2 ones = 5 ones
3 + 2 = 5

hundreds	tens	ones
1	8	3
+ 1	4	2
3	2	5

Add the tens.
   8 tens + 4 tens = 12 tens
You can make 1 hundred from 10 tens.

12 tens = __1__ hundred __2__ tens

Remember!
Add the hundred that
you made from 10 tens.

Add the hundreds.
   1 hundred + 1 hundred + 1 hundred = 3 hundreds
100 + 100 + 100 = 300

183 + 142 = _325_

▷ Lisa and Kendra have __325__ seashells in all.

Understand: Adding two 3-digit numbers with regrouping tens to make a hundred

■ Have children use place-value models to represent each number in the problem.

■ Direct children to put all the ones together and then count the total number of ones. Relate this to what is shown in the ones column in the chart to help children transfer their knowledge from the concrete to the abstract.

■ Ask children to explain whether or not they think that they will need to regroup the tens.

■ Have children discuss the similarities and differences between adding tens in this problem and adding ones that they had to regroup in other problems. Children should recognize that they previously regrouped 10 ones as 1 ten. In this problem, they need to regroup 10 tens as 1 hundred.

■ Show how to line up 10 of the tens above the 1 hundred in the model. Have children do this with their models. Demonstrating this equality can help them understand and justify the regrouping process.

Math-to-Real-World Connection

Interviews Have children interview adults to gather examples of when people use 3-digit addition in everyday life. Encourage children to ask specific questions and record the real-world examples that adults may give, such as working with a budget, paying bills, or taking inventory at work. Have children fold and staple together sheets of paper to make a book. Children should write or draw about four of the real-world examples they learned about in their interviews. Encourage children to share their interview experiences and books with the class.

Connect: Addition with regrouping both tens and ones

Use this page to help children strengthen their understanding of adding 3-digit numbers with regrouping.

■ Review what it means to regroup ones to add. Then discuss what it means to regroup tens to add.

■ You may wish to have children use place-value models as they follow steps 1–4.

■ Have children explain why they need to write a 1 in the tens column after adding 6 and 5. Make sure they understand that the 1 represents 10 ones regrouped as 1 ten. Engage children in a similar discussion for the 1 that they need to write in the hundreds column.

■ Ask children what might happen if they do not write the 1s in the tens and hundreds columns. Children should recognize that those digits affect the sums in their respective columns. Without them, the answer would not be correct.

Connect: Addition with regrouping both tens and ones

Blake read 186 pages of one book and 175 pages of another book. How many pages was that altogether?

$186 + 175 = \blacksquare$

Step 1

Write the addition in a place-value chart.

Step 2

Add the ones.
6 ones + 5 ones = 11 ones

Make a ten:
11 ones = 1 ten 1 one

hundreds	tens	ones
	1	
1	8	6
+ 1	7	5
		1

Step 3

Add the tens.
8 tens + 7 tens + 1 ten = 16 tens

Make a hundred:
16 tens = 1 hundred 6 tens

hundreds	tens	ones
	1	
1	8	6
+ 1	7	5
	6	1

Step 4

Add the hundreds.
100 + 100 + 100 = 300
$186 + 175 = 361$

hundreds	tens	ones
1	1	
1	8	6
+ 1	7	5
3	6	1

▷ Blake read 361 pages altogether.

Math-to-Social Studies Connection

Making a Wish List Encourage a class discussion on costly items that children might want to put on their wish lists. Explain that people sometimes save their money over period of time in order to buy things that cost a lot. Use Internet resources to find popular items that cost more than $100, such as tennis shoes. Round the price of each item to the nearest dollar. Ask children to choose their two favorite items and add to find the total cost of both of them. If time allows, allow children to share their wish lists with a partner.

Lesson 13

Guided Practice

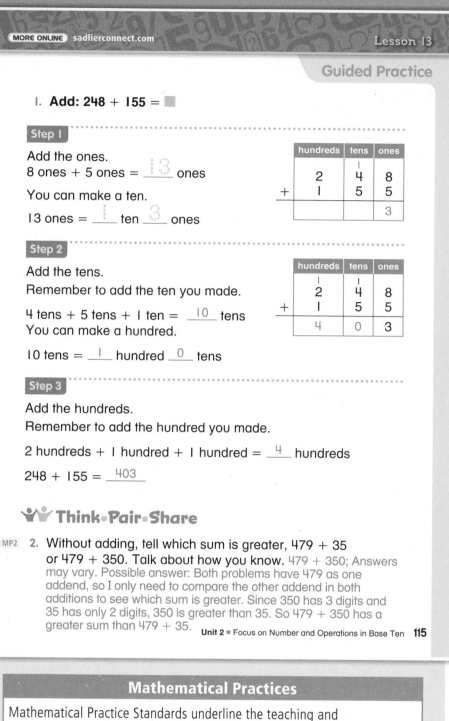

I. Add: 248 + 155 = ▓

Step 1

Add the ones.

8 ones + 5 ones = ___13___ ones

You can make a ten.

13 ones = __1__ ten __3__ ones

	hundreds	tens	ones
		1	
	2	4	8
+	1	5	5
			3

Step 2

Add the tens.
Remember to add the ten you made.

4 tens + 5 tens + 1 ten = ___10___ tens
You can make a hundred.

10 tens = __1__ hundred __0__ tens

	hundreds	tens	ones
	1	1	
	2	4	8
+	1	5	5
	4	0	3

Step 3

Add the hundreds.
Remember to add the hundred you made.

2 hundreds + 1 hundred + 1 hundred = ___4___ hundreds

248 + 155 = ___403___

👑 Think•Pair•Share

MP2 **2.** Without adding, tell which sum is greater, 479 + 35
or 479 + 350. Talk about how you know. 479 + 350; Answers
may vary. Possible answer: Both problems have 479 as one
addend, so I only need to compare the other addend in both
additions to see which sum is greater. Since 350 has 3 digits and
35 has only 2 digits, 350 is greater than 35. So 479 + 350 has a
greater sum than 479 + 35. **Unit 2 ▪ Focus on Number and Operations in Base Ten 115**

Mathematical Practices

Mathematical Practice Standards underline the teaching and
understanding of all concepts and skills presented. The emphasis of
specific practices is noted throughout the guided and independent practice
of this lesson.

MP2 **Reason abstractly and quantitatively.**

Item 2: Children make sense of quantities and their relationships.

Observational Assessment

Use page 115 to assess children's
understanding of adding 3-digit
numbers with regrouping. Take note of
those children who do not understand
how and when to regroup. If children
have difficulty, suggest they use place-
value models to show their work.

👑 Think•Pair•Share

Peer Collaboration Ask pairs to work
together to discuss possible answers.
Listen for children to share the reasoning
behind their answers. Encourage them
to think about how to answer questions
such as these:

- *How are the numbers in the first
  expression alike and different
  from the numbers in the
  second expression?*

- *How does a place-value help you to
  find the answer?*

To summarize, point out that comparing
the digits in each place-value position
and using number sense can help
identify the greater sum.

Return to the Essential Question

Reread the Lesson 13 Essential Question
on page 112: *How can you add two
3-digit numbers?*

Tell children to think about what they
learned in this lesson to answer
this question.

(Possible response: I can add the
numbers in each place beginning with
the ones. If the sum is greater than 9,
I need to regroup into the next place to
the left.)

Independent Practice

Concept Application

Children may work independently on these pages in the classroom or at home. They may refer to the first four pages of the lesson to revisit the instruction or to see a worked-out example.

Common Errors and **Teaching Tips** may help you support learning either in the classroom or as a follow-up for work done at home.

Common Errors

Items 1 and 2

Children may forget to regroup. Remind them that only one digit can be written for the sum in each column. Therefore, if the sum in any column is a 2-digit number, they should regroup.

Teaching Tips

Item 1

Children may try to use the models and count to find the answer. Make sure they understand that they will still need to regroup 10 tens as 1 hundred.

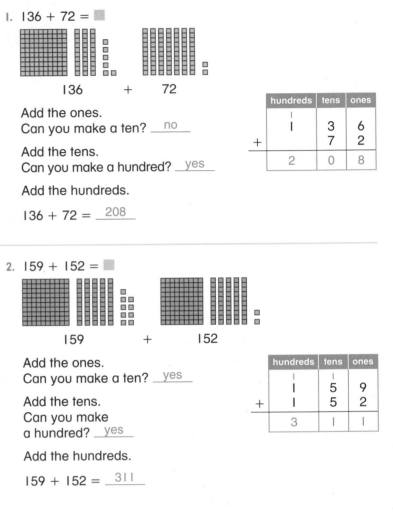

Independent Practice

Add. Show your work on the place-value chart.

1. 136 + 72 = ▩

136 + 72

Add the ones.
Can you make a ten? __no__

Add the tens.
Can you make a hundred? __yes__

Add the hundreds.

136 + 72 = __208__

	hundreds	tens	ones
	1	3	6
+		7	2
	2	0	8

2. 159 + 152 = ▩

159 + 152

Add the ones.
Can you make a ten? __yes__

Add the tens.
Can you make a hundred? __yes__

Add the hundreds.

159 + 152 = __311__

	hundreds	tens	ones
	1	5	9
+	1	5	2
	3	1	1

Talking About Math

Collaborative Conversations Have children work in pairs to discuss the solution to problem 1. Ask them to explain why the digit in the tens place is 0 even though there are numbers to add in the tens place. Children should be able to express the partial sum and explain how they know when to regroup.

Lesson 13

Independent Practice

Add.

3.

hundreds	tens	ones
1	4	2
+ 2	3	6
3	7	8

4.

hundreds	tens	ones
1	1	5
+ 3	2	7
4	4	2

5.

hundreds	tens	ones
1		
4	7	3
+	3	4
5	0	7

6.

hundreds	tens	ones
1		
1	4	6
+ 4	9	2
6	3	8

7.

hundreds	tens	ones
	1	
4	8	9
+ 2	0	5
6	9	4

8.

hundreds	tens	ones
1		
2	7	8
+ 3	4	1
6	1	9

9.

hundreds	tens	ones
1	1	
2	4	2
+ 6	9	9
9	4	1

10.

hundreds	tens	ones
1	1	
7	5	6
+ 1	4	6
9	0	2

Teaching Tips

Item 3
Remind children that they do not need to regroup in every problem.

Item 10
Point out that, after 12 ones are regrouped as 1 ten 2 ones, the 1 ten needs to be written in the tens place. Then the addition in the tens place is 5 tens + 4 tens + 1 ten, which equals 10 tens. Since 10 tens is equal to 1 hundred, now the 10 tens need to be regrouped as 1 hundred.

Digital Connection

Digital Manipulatives Have children use digital manipulatives to solve 3-digit addition problems. Ask one volunteer to make up a 3-digit addition problem. Have another volunteer use the digital manipulatives to show the models for each number and to use them to model and record the partial sums. Have the rest of the class write down the problem and work along with the demonstration to solve it. Using the manipulatives to explain the problem-solving process will help children reason about when they need to regroup and when they do not.

Independent Practice

Common Errors

Items 14 and 16–22

Some children may neglect to regroup, writing the 2-digit partial sum in the answer. These children may still need to use place-value charts or models to help them identify when and how to regroup.

Teaching Tips

Items 11–13

Children do not necessarily have to add to rule out impossible answer choices, such as 383 in problem 11. In this case, using good number sense is an effective strategy for recognizing that with one addend having 3 hundreds and the other addend having 1 hundred, the correct answer has to be one of the choices that has 4 hundreds. This strategy is also helpful when taking standardized tests.

Independent Practice

Circle the correct answer.

11. $302 + 181 =$ ▧   383   (483)   493

12. $245 + 229 =$ ▧   (474)   464   574

13. $159 + 222 =$ ▧   391   (381)   371

Add.

14.
```
  438
+ 381
―――
  819
```

15.
```
  342
+ 227
―――
  569
```

16.
```
  283
+ 241
―――
  524
```

17.
```
  178
+ 443
―――
  621
```

18.
```
  156
+ 336
―――
  492
```

19.
```
  552
+ 267
―――
  819
```

20.
```
  504
+ 268
―――
  772
```

21.
```
  197
+ 336
―――
  533
```

22.
```
  604
+ 198
―――
  802
```

Math-to-Math Connection

Estimates and Exact Answers Explain that some math problems can be answered with an estimate instead of an exact answer. To model estimation, count out 100 large, dried beans. Place the beans into a plastic sandwich bag and seal the bag. Then pour visibly different amounts of the same kind of beans into two plastic containers. Each container should contain more than 100 beans but fewer than about 450. Have pairs of children take turns using the bag of 100 beans to estimate, or get an idea of, the number of beans in each container. Then have pairs find the sum of their two estimates. Lead them to express their results as: *We think there are about [number] beans in the two containers.* Have pairs compare their estimates.

Lesson 13

Independent Practice

Solve each problem.

23. Mr. Kent drives 214 miles on Monday. On Tuesday, he drives 258 miles. How many miles does Mr. Kent drive in all?

Mr. Kent drives _472_ miles in all.

24. Alex has 345 soccer cards and 365 baseball cards. How many cards does he have altogether?

Alex has _710_ cards altogether.

MP1 25. There are three grades at the Clark School.
There are 268 children in the first grade.
There are 324 children in the second grade.
There are 297 children in the third grade.
How many children go to the Clark School?
Talk about how to solve the problem.

889; Answers may vary. Possible answer: First I added 268 + 324. The total is 592. Then I added 297 to that total and found 592 + 297 = 889. So 889 children go to the Clark School.

MP3 26. Bradley added 163 + 428. His work is shown below.

$$
\begin{array}{r}
163 \\
+428 \\
\hline
581
\end{array}
$$

What did Bradley do wrong? Show the correct way to solve the problem. Answers may vary. Possible answer: Bradley added the ones and got 11. He wrote the 1 one in the ones place in the answer. But he forgot to write the new 1 ten with the other tens. So, when he added tens, he got 8 instead of 9. He needs to add one more to the tens. So 163 + 428 = 591.

Unit 2 ■ Focus on Number and Operations in Base Ten **119**

Common Errors

Items 23–25

Children may not correctly align the place values when writing the equations. Suggest they draw and use a place-value chart.

Mathematical Practices

MP1	Make sense of problems and persevere in solving them.
Item 25: Children analyze and plan a solution to a problem.	
MP3	Construct viable arguments and critique the reasoning of others.
Item 26: Children share their reasoning with others.	

Common Core Focus:

2.NBT.7 Add and subtract within 1,000, using concrete models or drawings and strategies based on place value, properties of operations, and/or the relationship between addition and subtraction; relate the strategy to a written method. Understand that in adding or subtracting three-digit numbers, one adds or subtracts hundreds and hundreds, tens and tens, ones and ones, and sometimes it is necessary to compose or decompose tens or hundreds.

OBJECTIVE

Subtract three-digit numbers.

ESSENTIAL QUESTION

Read the question aloud to the children. Ask them to describe how they subtract two-digit numbers and discuss what they remember about regrouping.

FLUENCY PRACTICE

Fluency practice is available at **sadlierconnect.com**.

Concept Development

Understand: Subtracting two 3-digit numbers without regrouping

■ Earlier this year, children learned to subtract two-digit numbers with and without regrouping. Encourage children to access and apply their previous knowledge and skills as they work through this lesson.

Understand: Subtracting two 3-digit numbers regrouping a ten

■ Have children explain how they know when they need to regroup.

■ Remind children to rename the tens after regrouping but before subtracting in the tens column.

Lesson **14** **Subtract Three-Digit Numbers within 1,000**

Essential Question:
How can you subtract three-digit numbers?
2.NBT.7

Guided Instruction

In this lesson you will learn how to subtract three-digit numbers.

Understand: Subtracting two 3-digit numbers without regrouping

Subtract: 287 − 135 = ▨

Use a place-value chart.
Subtract the ones: 7 − 5 = 2
Subtract the tens: 80 − 30 = 50
Subtract the hundreds:
    200 − 100 = 100

	hundreds	tens	ones
	2	8	7
−	1	3	5
	1	5	2

▷ 287 − 135 = 152

Understand: Subtracting two 3-digit numbers regrouping a ten

Subtract: 252 − 113 = ▨

Use a place-value chart.
You cannot subtract 3 ones from 2 ones.
Make 10 ones from 1 ten.
    1 ten 2 ones = 12 ones
Now 4 tens are left.
Subtract the ones: 12 − 3 = 9
Subtract the tens: 40 − 10 = 30
Subtract the hundreds: 200 − 100 = 100

	hundreds	tens	ones
	2	⁴5̶	¹²2̶
−	1	1	3
	1	3	9

▷ 252 − 113 = 139

Support English Language Learners

Write *regroup a ten* and *regroup a hundred* on the board. Circle the words *regroup*. Have children use their previous knowledge to explain that to regroup means to group again. Use place-value blocks to model the difference between tens and hundreds. Have children show how to regroup a ten. They should start with 1 tens block and model how to regroup it as 10 ones. Then have children show how to regroup a hundred. They should start with 1 hundreds block and model how to regroup it as 10 tens.

Lesson 14

Guided Instruction

Understand: Subtracting two 3-digit numbers regrouping a hundred

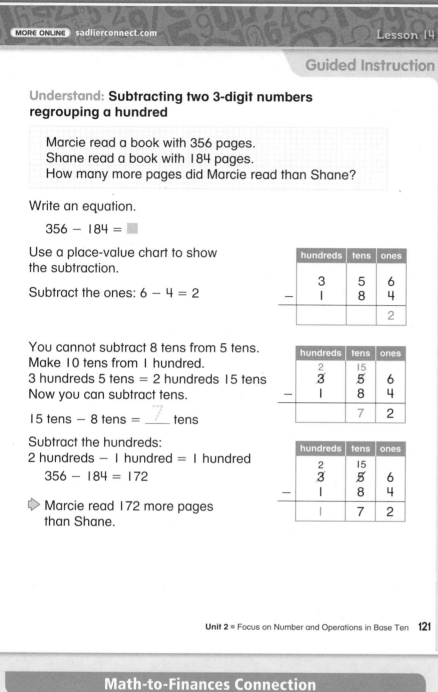

Marcie read a book with 356 pages.
Shane read a book with 184 pages.
How many more pages did Marcie read than Shane?

Write an equation.

356 − 184 =

Use a place-value chart to show the subtraction.

Subtract the ones: 6 − 4 = 2

hundreds	tens	ones
3	5	6
− 1	8	4
		2

You cannot subtract 8 tens from 5 tens.
Make 10 tens from 1 hundred.
3 hundreds 5 tens = 2 hundreds 15 tens
Now you can subtract tens.

15 tens − 8 tens = ___ tens

hundreds	tens	ones
2	15	
3	5	6
− 1	8	4
	7	2

Subtract the hundreds:
2 hundreds − 1 hundred = 1 hundred
356 − 184 = 172

hundreds	tens	ones
2	15	
3	5	6
− 1	8	4
1	7	2

▷ Marcie read 172 more pages than Shane.

Unit 2 ■ Focus on Number and Operations in Base Ten **121**

Understand: Subtracting two 3-digit numbers regrouping a hundred

■ It is critical that children understand that subtraction is not commutative. That is, the order of the numbers in a subtraction problem cannot be changed without changing the result.

■ Before they begin to solve the problem, ask children to predict where they will need to regroup based on the digits in each column of the place-value chart.

■ Make sure children understand that the digits they subtract must have the same place value. Grid paper can be used to help children vertically align the digits in the problem.

Math-to-Finances Connection

Banking Explain that, when you have a bank account, you need to keep track of the total amount of money in the account. Money saved is put into the bank account. The amount put in is added to the amount already in the account. To spend money, it is taken out of the account. The amount taken out is subtracted from the amount already in the account. It is important to add and subtract correctly so the total amount of money in the bank account is correctly recorded. Ask a volunteer to act as a bank teller and name the balance of an imaginary bank account in hundreds of dollars. Have another volunteer act as the account holder and name an amount in hundreds of dollars to take out of the account. Model and discuss regrouping a ten or a hundred as children subtract to find how much money remains in the account.

Connect: Subtraction with regrouping both a ten and a hundred
Use this page to help children strengthen their understanding of subtracting 3-digit numbers with regrouping.

■ Remind children that the greater number in the problem is the total, and the other number is how many are taken away.

■ A place-value chart helps children organize their work. It aids in the alignment of the digits, and it is a visual reminder of the value of each digit.

■ Explain that it may be necessary to regroup more than once in a problem. Ask children to explain where they will need to regroup in this problem.

■ Ask children to recall their previous knowledge about subtraction to explain the importance of subtracting from right to left.

Connect: Subtraction with regrouping both a ten and a hundred

Emile has 320 pennies. He gives 195 to his sister. How many pennies does Emile have left?

Write an equation: $320 - 195 = $ ▢

Step 1

Write the subtraction in a place-value chart.
Make 10 ones from 1 ten.
Subtract the ones.

10 ones − 5 ones = _5_ ones

hundreds	tens	ones
	1	10
3	2	0̸
− 1	9	5
		5

Step 2

Make 10 tens from 1 hundred.
Add the new tens to the 1 ten you had left after making 10 ones.

1 ten + 10 tens = _11_ tens

Subtract the tens:

11 tens − 9 tens = _2_ tens

hundreds	tens	ones
	11	
2	1̸	10
3̸	2̸	0̸
− 1	9	5
	2	5

Step 3

Subtract the hundreds:

2 hundreds − 1 hundred = _1_ hundred

$320 - 195 = $ _125_

▷ Emile has _125_ pennies left.

hundreds	tens	ones
	11	
2	1̸	10
3̸	2̸	0̸
− 1	9	5
1	2	5

Math-to-Real-World Connection

World Records Explain that people are fascinated with world records. Records have been set for many different things. When people are interested in setting new world records, they must first find the numbers of the current records. With those numbers in mind, people subtract their records from the corresponding world records. The answers tell how far they have to go to set new records. Help children research world records particularly those expressed as 3-digit numbers. Tell children to make up a 3-digit number that they can subtract from one of the record numbers. After they subtract, have them announce how far they would need to go to set a new world record.

Lesson 14

Guided Practice

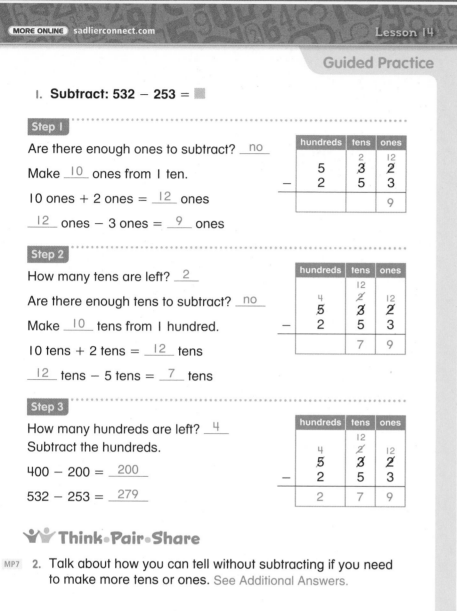

1. Subtract: 532 − 253 = ▣

Step 1

Are there enough ones to subtract? __no__

Make __10__ ones from 1 ten.

10 ones + 2 ones = __12__ ones

__12__ ones − 3 ones = __9__ ones

hundreds	tens	ones
5	3̶ (2)	2̶ (12)
− 2	5	3
		9

Step 2

How many tens are left? __2__

Are there enough tens to subtract? __no__

Make __10__ tens from 1 hundred.

10 tens + 2 tens = __12__ tens

__12__ tens − 5 tens = __7__ tens

hundreds	tens	ones
5̶ (4)	3̶ (12)(2̶)	2̶ (12)
− 2	5	3
	7	9

Step 3

How many hundreds are left? __4__

Subtract the hundreds.

400 − 200 = __200__

532 − 253 = __279__

hundreds	tens	ones
5̶ (4)	3̶ (12)(2̶)	2̶ (12)
− 2	5	3
2	7	9

Think•Pair•Share

MP7 **2.** Talk about how you can tell without subtracting if you need to make more tens or ones. See Additional Answers.

Mathematical Practices

Mathematical Practice Standards underline the teaching and understanding of all concepts and skills presented. The emphasis of specific practices is noted throughout the guided and independent practice of this lesson.

MP7 **Look for and make use of structure.**

Item 2: Children evaluate the structure of a problem.

Observational Assessment

Use page 123 to assess children's understanding of subtracting three-digit numbers. Be sure that children are able to regroup tens and hundreds. Ask them to use place value to describe their regrouping.

Think•Pair•Share

Peer Collaboration Ask pairs to share their ideas about regrouping. Children should explain specifically how they know when they need more tens or ones. Have children address these questions:

- *Why is regrouping sometimes necessary?*

- *Why would you need more ones?*

- *Why do you not need to subtract to tell if you need more tens?*

To summarize, point out that sometimes it is necessary to regroup in the ones place, the tens place, or in both places in order to subtract.

Return to the Essential Question

Reread the Lesson 14 Essential Question on page 120: *How can you subtract three-digit numbers?*

Tell children to think about what they learned in this lesson to answer this question.

(Possible responses: You can use a place-value chart. You can regroup if the number being subtracted is greater than the number being subtracted from. Always subtract from right to left.)

Additional Answers

Item 2: Possible answer: I can look at the tens and ones places of the two numbers. If the number I am subtracting from has fewer ones than the number I am subtracting, then I know that I need to make more ones. If the number I am subtracting from has fewer tens than the number I am subtracting, then I know that I need to make more tens.

Concept Application

Children may work independently on these pages in the classroom or at home. They may refer to the first four pages of the lesson to revisit the instruction or to see a worked-out example.

Common Errors and **Teaching Tips** may help you support learning either in the classroom or as a follow-up for work done at home.

Teaching Tips

Items 1–2

Point out that the place-value model represents the first number in the subtraction problem. Discuss how children can use the model to see whether they need to regroup. Children should see that if they are subtracting a greater number than the model shows, they need to regroup from the next place to the left.

Independent Practice

Subtract.

1. 254 − 137 = ▨

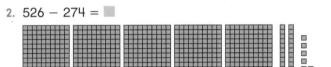

Are there enough ones to subtract 7 ones? __no__

Regroup 1 ten as 10 ones.

    4 ones + 10 ones = __14__ ones

Subtract the ones, tens, and hundreds.

    254 − 137 = __117__

hundreds	tens	ones
	4	14
2	5	4
− 1	3	7
1	1	7

---

2. 526 − 274 = ▨

Subtract the ones.

Are there enough tens to subtract 7 tens? __no__

Regroup 1 hundred as 10 tens.

    2 tens + 10 tens = __12__ tens

Subtract the tens and hundreds.

    526 − 274 = __252__

hundreds	tens	ones
4	12	
5	2	6
− 2	7	4
2	5	2

Talking About Math

Tell A Story Ask children to work in small groups to act out a story that involves subtracting three-digit numbers. Challenge them to create numbers that would require regrouping in at least one place. Encourage them to be creative in their situations. Their story should include the answer. As groups perform their stories, guide the class to record and solve the subtraction problems.

Lesson 14

Independent Practice

Subtract.

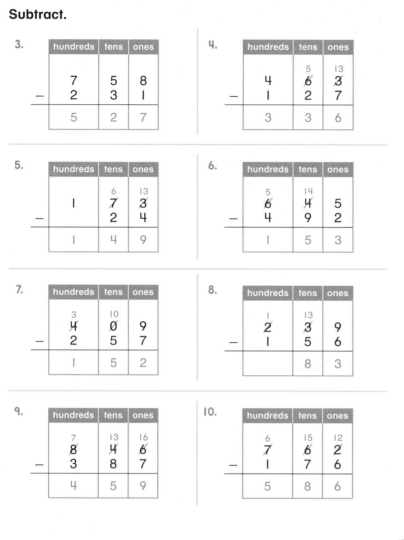

3.
hundreds	tens	ones
7	5	8
− 2	3	1
5	2	7

4.
hundreds	tens	ones
4	⁵6̸	¹³3̸
− 1	2	7
3	3	6

5.
hundreds	tens	ones
1	⁶7̸	¹³3̸
−	2	4
1	4	9

6.
hundreds	tens	ones
⁵6̸	¹⁴4̸	5
− 4	9	2
1	5	3

7.
hundreds	tens	ones
³4̸	¹⁰0̸	9
− 2	5	7
1	5	2

8.
hundreds	tens	ones
¹2̸	¹³3̸	9
− 1	5	6
	8	3

9.
hundreds	tens	ones
⁷8̸	¹³4̸	¹⁶6̸
− 3	8	7
4	5	9

10.
hundreds	tens	ones
⁶7̸	¹⁵6̸	¹²2̸
− 1	7	6
5	8	6

Unit 2 ■ Focus on Number and Operations in Base Ten **125**

Common Errors

Items 3-10

Children may subtract the lesser digit from the greater digit in each place. If they do this, guide them to highlight each digit that requires regrouping.

Digital Connection

Whiteboard Encourage children to drag place-value blocks together to model a three-digit number. Then ask other children to write three-digit numbers that could be subtracted from the number that is modeled, but that would require regrouping. Have children complete the subtraction to check their reasoning.

Teaching Tips

Items 11-12

Encourage children to use a place-value chart if they struggle to subtract numbers written horizontally. Encourage those who can to analyze the numbers and subtract without rewriting them.

Independent Practice

Circle the correct answer.

11. $239 - 129 =$ ▨   100   (110)   210

12. $345 - 182 =$ ▨   (163)   243   263

Subtract.

13.
$$\begin{array}{r} 634 \\ -519 \\ \hline 115 \end{array}$$

14.
$$\begin{array}{r} 388 \\ -263 \\ \hline 125 \end{array}$$

15.
$$\begin{array}{r} 582 \\ -265 \\ \hline 317 \end{array}$$

16.
$$\begin{array}{r} 724 \\ -445 \\ \hline 279 \end{array}$$

17.
$$\begin{array}{r} 628 \\ -283 \\ \hline 345 \end{array}$$

18.
$$\begin{array}{r} 427 \\ -289 \\ \hline 138 \end{array}$$

Solve each problem.

19. Zach is flying 723 miles on an airplane. The plane makes a stop after going 472 miles. How far is the rest of the flight?

The rest of the flight is

___251___ miles.

20. Isabelle has 856 stamps in her stamp collection. Akeem has 512 stamps in his collection. How many more stamps does Isabelle have?

Isabelle has ___344___ more stamps.

Math-to-Math Connection

Inverse Operations Review the relationship between addition and subtraction. Addition and subtraction are inverse operations. Addition puts two lesser groups together to make a new greater group. Subtraction takes one lesser group from a greater group and leaves the other lesser group. Use this relationship to prompt children to find a way to use addition to check the answers to the subtraction problems. Encourage children to use this strategy to check their answers for problems 19 and 20.

Lesson 14

Independent Practice

Common Errors

Item 23

Children may misinterpret the problem to mean all numbers, including 1- and 2-digit numbers, that can be subtracted from 210. Ask children to summarize a rule for finding digits that do not require regrouping. The digits chosen for each place must be equal to or less than the given digit.

MP3 **21.** Drew started with a 3-digit number and made 10 tens from 1 hundred. He then had 8 hundreds 14 tens 7 ones. Megan said that Drew must have started with the number 747. Is Megan correct? Talk about why or why not.

No. Answers may vary. Possible answer: If Drew made 10 tens from a hundred, then he would have had more hundreds when he started. So, if Drew's regrouping was done correctly, he must have started with 9 hundreds 4 tens 7 ones. His starting number would have been 947, not 747.

MP2 **22.** Show what you know about regrouping. Write and solve a problem for subtracting a 3-digit number from 653 by regrouping 1 hundred as 10 tens. Talk about why the number you chose involves regrouping 1 hundred as 10 tens.

Answers may vary. Possible answer: $653 - 472 = 181$. The number in the tens place of 472 is 7, which is greater than the 5 in the tens place of 653. 7 tens are more than 5 tens, so there are not enough tens to subtract. That means that I have to regroup 1 hundred as 10 tens in order to subtract the tens.

MP7 **23.** List all the 3-digit numbers that can be subtracted from 210 that do not involve any regrouping. Talk about how you know that these numbers do not need to be regrouped.

100, 110, 200, 210; Answers may vary. Possible answer: The numbers in the ones place are not greater than 0, which is in the ones place of 210. So there will be enough ones to subtract. The numbers in the tens place are not greater than 1, which is in the tens place of 210. So there will be enough tens to subtract.

Unit 2 ■ Focus on Number and Operations in Base Ten **127**

Mathematical Practices

MP2	**Reason abstractly and quantitatively.**

Item 22: Children make sense of quantities and their relationships in problem situations.

MP3	**Construct viable arguments and critique the reasoning of others.**

Item 21: Children analyze situations and justify their conclusions.

MP7	**Look for and make use of structure.**

Item 23: Children search for patterns to solve a problem.

Common Core Focus:

2.NBT.8 Mentally add 10 or 100 to a given number 100–900, and mentally subtract 10 or 100 from a given number 100–900.

OBJECTIVE

Use mental math to add or subtract 10 or 100.

ESSENTIAL QUESTION

Focus children on the lesson objective by reading the Essential Question aloud. Children have already learned to mentally add and subtract 10 from a 2-digit number. Now they will expand on this skill by mentally adding or subtracting 10 or 100 from a 3-digit number.

FLUENCY PRACTICE

Fluency practice is available at **sadlierconnect.com**.

Concept Development

Understand: When you add or subtract 10, the digit in the tens place changes

■ Children should describe how the place-value charts represent the numbers from the problem. They should understand that the chart with 246 represents the total number of pages that Evan read. The chart with 226 represents the total number of pages that Marta read.

■ Stress that, because 10 has a zero in the ones place, when adding or subtracting 10, the value of the digit in the ones place in the other number does not change.

■ Once the problem is complete, ask children to tell how the three numbers of pages read are alike and different.

Lesson 15

Mentally Add and Subtract 10 or 100

Essential Question:
How can you use mental math to add or subtract 10 or 100?
2.NBT.8

Guided Instruction

In this lesson you will learn how to use mental math to add or subtract 10 or 100.

Understand: When you add or subtract 10, the digit in the tens place changes

> Jamie read 236 pages last month.
> Evan read 10 more pages than Jamie.
> How many pages did Evan read?
> Marta read 10 fewer pages than Jamie.
> How many pages did Marta read?

> **Remember!**
> You can add to find more.
> You can subtract to find fewer or less.

Find the number of pages Evan read.

Add: $236 + 10 =$ ▪

When you add 10, the digit in the tens place changes. In 236, the 3 that shows **30** changes to a 4 that shows **40**.
$236 + 10 = 246$

hundreds	tens	ones
2	**3**	6

↓ $30 + 10 = 40$

hundreds	tens	ones
2	**4**	6

Find the number of pages Marta read.

Subtract: $236 - 10 =$ ▪

When you subtract 10, the digit in the tens place changes. In 236, the 3 that shows **30** changes to a 2 that shows **20**.
$236 - 10 = 226$

hundreds	tens	ones
2	3	6

↓ $30 - 10 = 20$

hundreds	tens	ones
2	**2**	6

▷ Evan read 246 pages. Marta read 226 pages.

128　Unit 2 ■ Focus on Number and Operations in Base Ten

Suppport English Language Learners

The term *mental math* may be difficult for English language learners to understand. Define the word *mental* as having to do with a person's mind or brain. Say that children usually solve math problems by writing them on paper. Then point to your own head as you say that children can solve some math problems *mentally,* or "in your head."

To help children understand what this means, have them do a number of tasks mentally. Such tasks might involve reviewing basic facts and their solutions without counting or describing a place children know well, such as their bedroom, from memory.

Lesson 15

Guided Instruction

Understand: When you add or subtract 100, the digit in the hundreds place changes

> Clark has 348 trading cards.
> Jesse has 100 more trading cards than Clark.
> How many trading cards does Jesse have?
> Saher has 100 fewer trading cards than Clark.
> How many trading cards does Saher have?

Find the number of trading cards Jesse has.

Add: $348 + 100 = $ ▨

When you add 100, the digit in the hundreds place changes. In 348, the 3 that shows **300** changes to a 4 that shows **400**.

$348 + 100 = 448$

hundreds	tens	ones
3	4	8

↓ $300 + 100 = 400$

hundreds	tens	ones
4	4	8

Find the number of trading cards Saher has.

Subtract: $348 - 100 = $ ▨

When you subtract 100, the digit in the hundreds place changes. In 348, the 3 that shows **300** changes to a 2 that shows **200**.

$348 - 100 = 248$

hundreds	tens	ones
3	4	8

↓ $300 - 100 = 200$

hundreds	tens	ones
2	4	8

▷ Jesse has 448 trading cards.
  Saher has 248 trading cards.

Unit 2 ■ Focus on Number and Operations in Base Ten **129**

Understand: When you add or subtract 100, the digit in the hundreds place changes

■ Prior to solving, have children predict how many trading cards Jesse and Saher will have after adding or subtracting 100. Children may express that only the digit in the hundreds place will change. The digits in the tens and ones places will stay the same.

■ Ask children to explain why 448 is written below the first place-value chart. They should recognize that number as being 100 more than 348.

■ Ask why 248 is written in the last place-value chart. Children should recognize that number as being 100 less than 348.

■ Once the problem is complete, have children compare the answers to this problem with those of the problem on page 128. They should see that when 0 is in a particular place-value position, the original digit does not change, regardless of whether the 0 is being added or subtracted.

■ Have children discuss why these problems are easier to do mentally than some others that they have solved recently.

Math-to-Industry Connection

Factory Production Tell children that most things we use every day, like cars, clothing, and furniture, are made in factories. Some people who work in factories keep track of how many items are made and sold.

Place a set of 0-to-9 number cards face down in front of three children. Have children each turn over a card to create a three-digit number. The number tells how many items their "factory" made. Then have children roll a number cube to find how many items their factory sold. Rolling an even number means the factory sold 10 items, so children subtract 10 from their number. Rolling an odd number means the factory sold 100 items, so they subtract 100. Tell children to use mental math to find how many items their factory has left.

Guided Instruction

Connect: What you know about adding and subtracting 10 or 100

Use this page to help children extend their understanding of mentally adding or subtracting 10 or 100 to a 3-digit number.

■ Have children align a sheet of paper below Pattern A so that the paper covers the rest of the page. Focusing only on Pattern A, ask children to talk about how the numbers in the pattern are alike and different. Using a place-value chart may help some children see the change in the tens place in the pattern more clearly.

■ Ask children whether the pattern is increasing or decreasing and how they know. Then ask what operation would cause that kind of change. In this case, because the pattern is decreasing, subtraction was used to find the next number.

■ Have children apply these strategies to complete the question about Pattern B.

Lesson 15   **Mentally Add and Subtract 10 or 100**

Guided Instruction

Connect: What you know about adding and subtracting 10 or 100

La Vae wrote these two number patterns.
Pattern A: 277, 267, ▆, 247, 237, 227
Pattern B: 451, 551, ▆, 751, 851, 951
Each pattern is missing one number.
What number is missing from each pattern?

Step 1

Look at Pattern A.
The digit in which place changes each time?

The digit in the ___tens___ place changes each time.

The pattern rule is ___subtract 10___.

Subtract 10. Find the missing number.

The missing number is ___257___.

Remember!
A number pattern shows numbers arranged according to a rule.

Step 2

Look at Pattern B.
The digit in which place changes each time?

The digit in the ___hundreds___ place changes each time.

The pattern rule is ___add 100___.

Add 100. Find the missing number.

The missing number is ___651___.

▷ The missing number in Pattern A is ___257___.

The missing number in Pattern B is ___651___.

130   Unit 2 ■ Focus on Number and Operations in Base Ten

Math-to-Business Connection

Saving and Spending Discuss jobs that children can do to earn money, like walking dogs, raking leaves, and delivering newspapers. Have pairs talk about what kind of job they would each like to do.

Direct partners to take turns rolling a number cube three times to each create a 3-digit number. Have them record this number to represent how much money they have already saved. Using a weekly pay rate of $10, have children record their increasing pattern of savings over 6 weeks and the final amounts saved. Now tell children to pretend to spend $100 each month for 6 months. Ask them to find how much money they will each have left after 6 months. Encourage children to share their number patterns and explain how they used mental math to find the increasing and decreasing amounts.

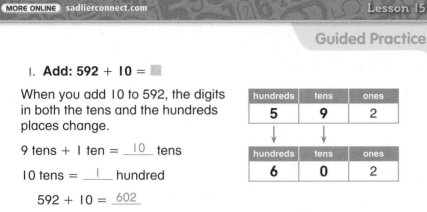

MORE ONLINE sadlierconnect.com   Lesson 15

Guided Practice

1. **Add: 592 + 10 =** ■

When you add 10 to 592, the digits in both the tens and the hundreds places change.

9 tens + 1 ten = __10__ tens

10 tens = __1__ hundred

592 + 10 = __602__

hundreds	tens	ones
5	9	2

hundreds	tens	ones
6	0	2

2. **Subtract: 407 − 10 =** ■

When you subtract 10 from 407, the digits in both the tens and the hundreds places change.

407 = 4 hundreds 7 ones

There are not enough tens to subtract,

so change 1 hundred to __10__ tens.

407 = 3 hundreds __10__ tens 7 ones

10 tens − 1 ten = __9__ tens

407 − 10 = __397__

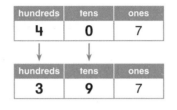

hundreds	tens	ones
4	0	7

hundreds	tens	ones
3	9	7

♕ Think•Pair•Share

MP3 3. Otto starts at 197. He adds a number to 197 to make 207. What number does he add? How can you tell? Answers may vary. Possible answer: Otto adds 10 to 197 to make 207. I can tell because the digits in both the tens and the hundreds places change and the digit in the ones place stays the same.

Unit 2 ■ Focus on Number and Operations in Base Ten **131**

Mathematical Practices

Mathematical Practice Standards underline the teaching and understanding of all concepts and skills presented. The emphasis of specific practices is noted throughout the guided and independent practice of this lesson.

MP3	**Construct viable arguments and critique the reasoning of others.**

Item 3: Children analyze a problem situation and share their reasoning with others.

Observational Assessment

Use page 131 to assess children's understanding of how to mentally add or subtract 10 or 100. Take note of children who are struggling to use mental math. These children may need additional practice to strengthen their understanding of place value, the value of zero, and regrouping.

♕ Think•Pair•Share

Peer Collaboration Ask pairs to share their work after determining their answer. Have them consider questions such as these:

- *Which digit or digits changed between the two numbers?*
- *What do you know about the sum of 1 + 9? How does what you know affect your reasoning?*
- *Which digits would change if 100 were added instead of 10?*

To summarize, point out that when 10 is added to or subtracted from a number, the hundreds place may change if the value already in the tens place was 9 or 0, respectively. This is because when we add 1 to 9 the sum is 10, which means we must regroup, and if we need to subtract 1 from 0 we must also regroup.

Return to the Essential Question

Reread the Lesson 15 Essential Question on page 128: *How can you use mental math to add or subtract 10 or 100?*

Tell children to think about what they learned in this lesson to answer this question.

(Possible responses: When adding or subtracting 10, the tens place increases or decreases by 1. The same is true when adding or subtracting 100. If I am adding 10 to 90, I will need to regroup 10 tens as 1 hundred. If I am subtracting 10 from 0 tens, I will first need to regroup 1 hundred as 10 tens.)

Encourage children to share their reasoning and examples with the class.

Concept Application

Children may work independently on these pages in the classroom or at home. They may refer to the first four pages of the lesson to revisit the instruction or to see a worked-out example.

Common Errors and **Teaching Tips** may help you support learning either in the classroom or as a follow-up for work done at home.

Teaching Tips

Items 1–16

Remind children to read the direction line for each set of problems. You may suggest that children circle the word *add* and underline the word *subtract* to remind them that the operation changes from one set of problems to the next.

Independent Practice

Add 10.

1. $173 + 10 = \underline{183}$

2. $215 + 10 = \underline{225}$

3. $741 + 10 = \underline{751}$

4. $693 + 10 = \underline{703}$

Subtract 10.

5. $283 - 10 = \underline{273}$

6. $486 - 10 = \underline{476}$

7. $591 - 10 = \underline{581}$

8. $204 - 10 = \underline{194}$

Add 100.

9. $315 + 100 = \underline{415}$

10. $482 + 100 = \underline{582}$

11. $638 + 100 = \underline{738}$

12. $195 + 100 = \underline{295}$

Subtract 100.

13. $782 - 100 = \underline{682}$

14. $459 - 100 = \underline{359}$

15. $264 - 100 = \underline{164}$

16. $158 - 100 = \underline{58}$

Talking About Math

Step-by-Step Instructions Tell children that an algorithm is a set of steps used to solve a kind of problem. Assign each pair of children a 3-digit number. Have the pair record their number, decide whether to add 10 or 100 to it or subtract 10 or 100 from it. Tell partners to work together to agree on an algorithm to use in solving the problem mentally. Have pairs share their algorithms with the class, and demonstrate how they used them to solve their problems.

Teaching Tips

Items 17-20

Ask children to summarize the pattern they see in the number chart after adding and subtracting by 10s.

Use the number chart below for questions 17–20.

1	2	3	4	5	6	7	8	9	10
11	12	13	14	15	16	17	18	19	20
21	22	23	24	25	26	27	28	29	30
31	32	33	34	35	36	37	38	39	40
41	42	43	44	45	46	47	48	49	50
51	52	53	54	55	56	57	58	59	60
61	62	63	64	65	66	67	68	69	70
71	72	73	74	75	76	77	78	79	80
81	82	83	84	85	86	87	88	89	90
91	92	93	94	95	96	97	98	99	100

17. Start at 3. Add 10s. Circle each number as you add.

Children should circle 3, 13, 23, 33, 43, 53, 63, 73, 83, 93.

18. Start at 9. Add 10s. Draw a triangle around each number as you add.

Children should draw a triangle around 9, 19, 29, 39, 49, 59, 69, 79, 89, 99.

19. Start at 95. Subtract 10s. Draw an X on each number as you subtract.

Children should draw an X on 95, 85, 75, 65, 55, 45, 35, 25, 15, 5.

20. Start at 91. Subtract 10s. Draw a square around each number as you subtract.

Children should draw a square around 91, 81, 71, 61, 51, 41, 31, 21, 11, 1.

Unit 2 ■ Focus on Number and Operations in Base Ten **133**

Digital Connection

Random-Number Generator Have children take turns calling out *add 10* (or *100*) or *subtract 10* (or *100*). Then use a random-number generator to create a 3-digit number and have the child add or subtract 10 or 100 using mental math to say the solution. If others disagree with the answer, have them raise their hand and give their solutions. Take time to discuss strategies and reasoning as necessary. Repeat the activity, allowing another child to call out the operation along with *10* or *100*.

Independent Practice

Teaching Tips

Items 25-26

Encourage children to circle the key words *more than* and *less than*. Before having children solve, tell them to write an equation that represents each problem.

Independent Practice

Add or subtract.

21. $112 + 10 =$ ___122___

22. $318 - 10 =$ ___308___

23. $828 + 10 =$ ___838___

24. $106 - 10 =$ ___96___

Circle the correct answer.

25. 100 more than 838 is ____.   848   (938)   948

26. 10 less than 117 is ____.   217   127   (107)

Solve each problem. Show your work.

27. Ms. Clarkson has 325 crayons.
Ms. Turner has 100 more crayons than Ms. Clarkson.
How many crayons does Ms. Turner have?

    Ms. Turner has ___425___ crayons.

28. Diego has 286 postcards.
Paul has 10 fewer postcards than Diego.
How many postcards does Paul have?

    Paul has ___276___ postcards.

Math-to-Games Connection

Bingo Use an online program to create Bingo-like boards that show 3-digit numbers instead of words or pictures. Make a variety of call cards that include expressions equal to the numbers on the boards. For example, if the board includes 426, your call cards can show $416 + 10$, $326 + 100$, $436 - 10$, and $526 - 100$.

Name a column—B, I, N, G, or O. Then draw a call card and read the expression aloud or write it on the board. Have children use mental math to determine the sum or difference for that expression. Allow them time to find the answer in the correct column on their board and mark it in the correct box. Whoever is first to mark five boxes horizontally, vertically, or diagonally wins.

Independent Practice

MP1 **29.** Demi wrote the two addition patterns below.
How did she add for each pattern?
Talk about how you know.

Pattern A: 485, 585, 685, 785, 885, 985

Pattern B: 137, 147, 157, 167, 177, 187

Answers may vary. Possible answer: For Pattern A, Demi added by 100s. I know because the digit in the hundreds place goes up by 1 each time. The other digits do not change. For Pattern B, Demi added by 10s. I know because the digit in the tens place goes up by 1 each time. The other digits do not change.

MP8 **30.** Timmy and Brian were both asked to subtract 100 from 472. Timmy says the answer is 372. Brian says the answer is 462.

Which boy is correct?
Explain your thinking.

Answers may vary. Possible answer: Timmy is correct. 472 − 100 = 372. The digit in the hundreds place changes by 1. No other digits change. Brian is not correct because he subtracted 10, not 100, and got 462.

Unit 2 ■ Focus on Number and Operations in Base Ten **135**

Teaching Tips

Item 29

Children may want to write the pattern vertically and circle the place of the digit that is changing. Be sure to remind them to identify whether the pattern is increasing or decreasing before explaining their reasoning.

Item 30

Encourage children to solve the subtraction problem themselves. This will help them identify which child is correct and what error the other child made.

Return to the

Progress Check

Remind children to return to the Progress Check self-assessment, page 53, to check off additional items they have mastered during the unit.

Mathematical Practices

MP1	**Make sense of problems and persevere in solving them.**

Item 29: Children analyze the relationship between given numbers to identify a pattern.

MP8	**Look for and express regularity in repeated reasoning.**

Item 30: Children evaluate the reasonableness of results.

The Common Core Review covers all the standards presented in the unit. Use it to assess your children's mastery of the unit's concepts and skills.

Depth of Knowledge

The depth of knowledge is a ranking of the content complexity of assessment items based on Webb's Depth of Knowledge (DOK) levels. The levels increase in complexity as shown below.

Level 1: Recall and Reproduction
Level 2: Basic Skills and Concepts
Level 3: Strategic Reasoning and Thinking
Level 4: Extended Thinking

Item	Standard	DOK
1	2.NBT.1	2
2	2.NBT.2	2
3	2.NBT.2	2
4	2.NBT.3	2
5	2.NBT.3	2
6	2.NBT.4	2
7	2.NBT.4	2
8	2.NBT.5	2
9	2.NBT.5	2
10	2.NBT.5	2
11	2.NBT.5	2
12	2.NBT.6	2
13	2.NBT.6	2
14	2.NBT.8	1
15	2.NBT.8	1
16	2.NBT.7	2
17	2.NBT.7	2
18	2.NBT.2	2
19	2.NBT.1	3
20	2.NBT.9	4

Unit 2 Common Core Review

1. Write how many hundreds, tens, and ones. Then write the number.

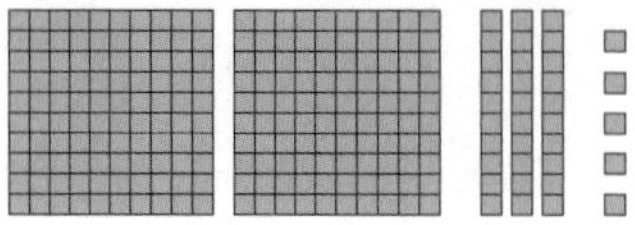

__2__ hundreds __3__ tens __5__ ones   __235__

2. Skip-count by 5s.

900, __905__, 910, 915, __920__, __925__, 930, __935__, 940

3. Skip-count by 10s.

265, __275__, __285__, 295, __305__, __315__, 325, __335__, 345

Write the number and the expanded form for the number name.

4. one hundred thirty-nine   __139__   __100 + 30 + 9__

5. six hundred eight   __608__   __600 + 8__

Compare. Write >, <, or =.

6. 410 (>) 401

7. 340 (<) 434

Unit 2 Common Core Review

Add or subtract.

8.
```
  3 5
+ 4 4
-----
  7 9
```

9.
```
  7 8
- 2 3
-----
  5 5
```

10.
```
  9 2
- 6 5
-----
  2 7
```

Circle the correct answer.

11. 23 + 57 = ▨   70   (80)   710

12. 34 + 47 + 10 = ▨   71   83   (91)

13. 26 + 14 + 32 = ▨   62   (72)   76

Add or subtract.

14. 892 + 10 = __902__

15. 115 − 100 = __15__

Add or subtract.

16.
```
  6 3 2
+ 1 1 8
-------
  7 5 0
```

17.
```
  4 5 7
-   8 3
-------
  3 7 4
```

18. Write the numbers that come next.

828, __829__, __830__, __831__, __832__, __833__

This chart correlates the Common Core Review items with the lessons in which the concepts and skills are presented.

Item	Lesson
1	6
2	7
3	7
4	8
5	8
6	9
7	9
8	10
9	11
10	11
11	10
12	12
13	12
14	15
15	15
16	13
17	14
18	7
19	6
20	11

Talking About Math

Direct children to respond to the Unit 2 Essential Question. (This can also be found on page 55.)

Essential Question:
How does place value help you add and subtract?

Possible responses:
- Place value helps you remember to add or subtract the ones first, the tens next, and then the hundreds.
- Place-value models show you how to make sense of adding and subtracting greater numbers.

Unit Assessment

- Unit 2 Common Core Review, *pp. 136–138*
- Unit 2 Performance Task (ONLINE)

Additional Assessment Options

- Performance Task 1, *pp. 139–142*
  (ALSO ONLINE)

Optional Purchase:
- iProgress Monitor (ONLINE)
- Progress Monitor Student Benchmark Assessment Booklet

MP3 19. Use the digits 5, 6, and 7 to write three different 3-digit numbers. How are your numbers alike? How are they different?

Answers may vary. Possible answer: 567, 675, 756; all the numbers I wrote have the digits 5, 6, and 7, but the digits are in different places. The 6 means 6 tens in 567, 6 hundreds in 675, and 6 ones in 756. The 7 means 7 hundreds in 756, 7 ones in 567, and 7 tens in 675. The 5 means 5 ones in 675, 5 tens in 756, and 5 hundreds in 567.

MP3 20. Kate says that she can use addition to check that her subtraction is correct. Here is Kate's work:

$$
\begin{array}{r}
\overset{4\ \ 14}{5\ 4} \\
-\ 2\ 6 \\
\hline
2\ 8
\end{array}
\qquad
\begin{array}{r}
\overset{1}{2\ 8} \\
+\ 2\ 6 \\
\hline
5\ 4
\end{array}
$$

Is Kate's subtraction correct? Why can she use addition to check her subtraction?

Yes; Answers may vary. Possible answer: Kate's subtraction is correct. Addition and subtraction are inverse operations (addition undoes the subtraction). If she starts with the difference and adds the 26 she subtracted, the result should be the number she started with.

Mathematical Practices	
MP3	**Construct viable arguments and critique the reasoning of others.**

Item 19: Children make conjectures and build a logical progression of statements to explore the validity of their conjectures.

Item 20: Children reason inductively about data, making reasonable arguments and responding to the arguments of others.

Performance Task I

2.OA.1, 2.OA.2, 2.OA.3, 2.OA.4,
2.NBT.1, 2.NBT.3, 2.NBT.4

Performance Tasks

Performance Tasks show your understanding
of the math that you have learned.

Beginning This Task

This is the beginning of a Performance Task.
The next three pages have problems for
you to solve.

As you work, you will:

1. Show that you can use math skills
   and concepts

2. Decide how to solve a problem

3. Use different ways to model and solve
   real-world problems

Tips to help you!

- Read each problem carefully.
- Plan how you will solve the problem.
- Check your work.
- Be ready to show your work or explain
  your thinking.

ONLINE Customize Performance Task 1

Performance Task 1 in *Common Core Progress
Mathematics* also provides children with additional
practice. You can use the online items of Performance
Task 1 to customize the amount and kind of
performance task practice based on your ongoing
evaluation of your children. You may choose to
challenge some children, to give extra experience
with a particular kind of task for other children, or to
extend exposure to performance assessment for the
entire class.

Go to **sadlierconnect.com** to download the following
resources for Performance Task 1.

- Additional Items

- Additional Teacher Support

- Additional Scoring Rubrics

Performance Task 1 Overview

Performance Task 1 in *Common Core Progress
Mathematics* provides children with practice for the
types of items that may be found on standardized
performance assessments.

Various item formats, including short- and extended-
response items and technology-enhanced items, are
included in the tasks. All items connect mathematical
content correlated to the Mathematical Practices.

Items in Performance Task 1 are based on three
primary types of tasks:

Type I Mastery of mathematical concepts, skills
and procedures

Type II Using and explaining mathematical
reasoning

Type III Modeling problem situations in a real-world
context

Performance Task 1 begins with a collection of
three self-contained items in the Student Book
and continues with additional items online at
sadlierconnect.com.

Introduce Performance Task 1 Read page 139 to
children. Explain that Performance Task 1 may cover
any of the math they have learned in Units 1 and 2.
Orient children to each item and communicate helpful
reminders that will enable children to approach each
item successfully. Once children have completed each
item, go over the correct responses with them.

Recommended Pacing Administer Performance
Task 1 on Student Book pages 140–142 over three
15-minute sessions.

Teacher Resources For each task, the teacher
materials include:

- Item types and purposes

- Correlations to Common Core State Standards for
  Mathematical Content and Practice, and Depth of
  Knowledge (DOK) levels

- Suggested administration procedure

- Scoring Rubric

Item 1: Riding the Bus

Item	Type	Purpose
1.a.	II	Solve and explain a real-world word problem.
1.b.	III	Solve and explain a multistep word problem that uses more than one operation.

Item	CCSS	MP	DOK
1.a.	2.OA.1	3	Level 3
1.b.	2.OA.1	3	Level 3

Administering Item 1 (Pacing: 15 minutes)

Ask a volunteer to read the introductory paragraph. Have others describe the situation in their own words.

Item 1.a. (7 minutes)

Read the problem aloud to children. Explain that some information given in the problem is not needed to answer Item 1.a. Lead children to realize that the number of people that got off the bus is not needed to solve this part of the problem.

Item 1.b. (8 minutes)

Encourage children to draw a picture to show the situation. If children did not answer Item 1.a. correctly, they will likely not find a correct answer for this problem. Children should understand that here they need to find the difference of 39 – 29.

Riding the Bus

1. Alice takes the bus to school with her mom. After they got on the bus one morning, Alice counted 36 people in all on the bus.

   At the first stop, 3 people got on the bus. At the second stop, some people got off the bus. Then there were 29 people on the bus.

   a. How many people were on the bus after the first stop? Tell how you know.

   39 people; Answers may vary. Possible answer: I know that there were 36 people on the bus before the first stop. So if 3 people got on the bus at the first stop, there would be 36 + 3, or 39, people on the bus.

   b. How many people got off the bus after the second stop? Tell how you know.

   10 people; Answers may vary. Possible answer: There were 39 people on the bus after the first stop. There were 29 people on the bus after the second stop. Since 39 – 10 = 29, 10 people must have gotten off the bus after the second stop.

Scoring Rubric

Item	Points	Student Responses
1.a.	2	Correctly identifies 39 people and explains it as a result of 36 + 3.
	1	Correctly answers 39 but does not provide an explanation.
	0	Does not provide correct answer or explanation.
1.b.	2	Demonstrates logical reasoning and working backward to solve and explain a solution of 10 people.
	1	Either correctly answers 10 or explains a correct process.
	0	Does not provide correct answer or explanation.

Performance Task I

Bus Station

2. At Gate A, 4 rows of are buses are parked. There are 3 buses in each row.

At Gate B, there are 5 rows of buses with 2 buses in each row.

a. Draw an array to show the buses parked at each gate.

Sample arrays:

Gate A	Gate B
Row 1 ● ● ●	Row 1 ● ●
Row 2 ● ● ●	Row 2 ● ●
Row 3 ● ● ●	Row 3 ● ●
Row 4 ● ● ●	Row 4 ● ●
	Row 5 ● ●

b. Write an addition equation for each array.

Gate A: $\underline{\quad 3 + 3 + 3 + 3 = 12 \quad}$

Gate B: $\underline{\quad 2 + 2 + 2 + 2 + 2 = 10 \quad}$

c. How many buses are parked at Gate A and Gate B in all? Write an addition equation to help you solve the problem.

$\underline{\ 12\ } + \underline{\ 10\ } = \underline{\ 22\ }$

There are $\underline{\ 22\ }$ buses parked at Gates A and B in all.

d. There are 17 buses parked in two rows at Gate C. Can you draw an array to show the buses parked at Gate C? Tell how you know. Answers may vary. Possible answer: No, I cannot draw an array to show the 17 buses. An array must have equal rows and equal columns, and I cannot make 2 equal rows with 17. That's because 17 is an odd number.

Performance Task I **141**

Scoring Rubric

Item	Points	Student Responses
2.a.	2	Correctly draws two arrays to show 12 and 10 respectively.
	1	Correctly draws one of the arrays.
	0	Does not draw a correct array.
2.b.	2	Correctly writes two equations.
	1	Correctly writes one equation.
	0	Does not correctly write an equation.
2.c.	2	Writes a correct equation and sum.
	1	Writes a correct equation or sum.
	0	Does not write equation or sum.
2.d.	2	Shows understanding that 17 cannot be drawn as an array and tells why.
	1	Answers without explanation.
	0	Does not answer, draw, or explain.

Item 2: Bus Station

Item	Type	Purpose
2.a.	III	Draw arrays to match given data.
2.b.	II	Write addition equations for arrays.
2.c.	I	Add two 2-digit numbers to solve a word problem.
2.d.	III	Explain and justify a conjecture.

Item	CCSS	MP	DOK
2.a.	2.OA.4	4	Level 1
2.b.	2.OA.2, 2.OA.3, 2.OA.4	7	Level 1
2.c.	2.OA.1	1	Level 1
2.d.	2.OA.3	3	Level 1

Administering Item 2 (Pacing: 15 minutes)

Ask a volunteer to read the introductory paragraph. Have others describe the situation in their own words.

Item 2.a. (5 minutes)

Help children understand that they need to draw separate arrays to represent the buses at different gates. If children are having difficulty with this task, provide them with counters to help model the problem.

Item 2.b. (3 minutes)

Make sure children understand that they will use patterns in an array to complete each addition equation. If needed, provide prompts such as asking how counting the number in each row shows addition.

Item 2.c. (3 minutes)

Have children complete the addition sentence to combine the sums they found in Item 2.b.

Item 2.d. (4 minutes)

Encourage children to talk about whether 17 can be shown as an array. Provide counters for children's use if they cannot mentally determine that no combination with a sum of 17 results in equal rows of any length.

Item 3: At the Parking Garage

Item	Type	Purpose
3.a.	III	Complete a table to show numbers in numeric, word, and expanded forms.
3.b.	I	Identify the greatest value in a table.
3.c.	I	Identify the least value in a table.
3.d.	II	Compare 3-digit numbers in a table and explain drawn conclusions.
3.e.	I	Add 3-digit numbers from data in a table.

Item	CCSS	MP	DOK
3.a.	2.NBT.1, 2.NBT.3	7	Level 2
3.b.	2.NBT.4	2	Level 2
3.c.	2.NBT.4	2	Level 2
3.d.	2.NBT.1, 2.NBT.4	7	Level 3
3.e.	2.NBT.6, 2.NBT.7	7	Level 2

Administering Item 3 (Pacing: 15 minutes)

Ask a volunteer to read the introductory paragraph.

Item 3.a. (5 minutes)
Guide children to see that each row shows a number written in three different ways.

Item 3.b. (1 minute)
Children should start by comparing the digits in the greatest place-value positions.

Item 3.c. (1 minute)
Check that children understand that they should write a letter, rather than a number, on the line after the word "Garage."

Item 3.d. (5 minutes)
Encourage children to include their process and reasoning strategies as they write their explanations.

Item 3.e. (3 minutes)
Children should recognize that the phrase *How many buses in all* tells them to add to find the total.

At the Parking Garage

3. The table shows the number of buses parked at three garages.

Garage	Number	Number Name	Expanded Form
A	299	two hundred ninety-nine	200 + 90 + 9
B	374	three hundred seventy-four	300 + 70 + 4
C	380	three hundred eighty	300 + 80

a. Complete the table by writing the missing number, number name, or expanded form.

b. Which garage has the most buses? Garage __C__

c. Which garage has the fewest buses? Garage __A__

d. Talk about how you found the garage with the most buses and the garage with the fewest buses.

Answers may vary. Possible answer: I compared the digits in the hundreds places and the tens places to find the garage with the most buses. I compared the digits in the hundreds places to find the garage with the fewest buses.

e. How many buses in all are parked at Garage A and Garage B?

__673__ buses

Scoring Rubric

Item	Points	Student Responses
3.a.	2	Correctly completes entire table.
	1	Completes most data in the table.
	0	Completes less than half of the table.
3.b.	2	Correctly identifies Garage C.
	0	Writes incorrect or no answer.
3.c.	2	Correctly identifies Garage A.
	0	Writes incorrect or no answer.
3.d.	2	Shows clear understanding of comparing numbers by place value.
	1	Shows partial understanding of comparing numbers by place value.
	0	Does not show understanding of comparing numbers or place value.
3.e.	2	Correctly adds to find sum 673.
	0	Writes incorrect or no answer.

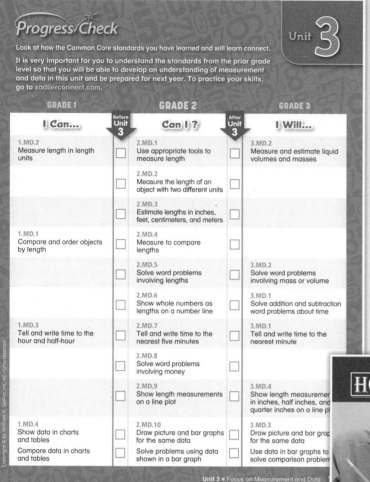

Progress Check

Look at how the Common Core standards you have learned and will learn connect.

It is very important for you to understand the standards from the prior grade level so that you will be able to develop an understanding of measurement and data in this unit and be prepared for next year. To practice your skills, go to sadlierconnect.com.

Unit 3

	GRADE 1			GRADE 2			GRADE 3
	I Can...	Before Unit 3		Can I?	After Unit 3		I Will...
	1.MD.2 Measure length in length units	☐	2.MD.1 Use appropriate tools to measure length	☐	3.MD.2 Measure and estimate liquid volumes and masses	
			2.MD.2 Measure the length of an object with two different units	☐		
			2.MD.3 Estimate lengths in inches, feet, centimeters, and meters	☐		
	1.MD.1 Compare and order objects by length	☐	2.MD.4 Measure to compare lengths	☐		
			2.MD.5 Solve word problems involving lengths	☐	3.MD.2 Solve word problems involving mass or volume	☐
			2.MD.6 Show whole numbers as lengths on a number line	☐	3.MD.1 Solve addition and subtraction word problems about time	☐
	1.MD.3 Tell and write time to the hour and half-hour	☐	2.MD.7 Tell and write time to the nearest five minutes	☐	3.MD.1 Tell and write time to the nearest minute	☐
			2.MD.8 Solve word problems involving money	☐		
			2.MD.9 Show length measurements on a line plot	☐	3.MD.4 Show length measurements in inches, half inches, and quarter inches on a line plot	☐
	1.MD.4 Show data in charts and tables	☐	2.MD.10 Draw picture and bar graphs for the same data	☐	3.MD.3 Draw picture and bar graphs for the same data	☐
	Compare data in charts and tables	☐	Solve problems using data shown in a bar graph	☐	Use data in bar graphs to solve comparison problems	☐

Unit 3 ■ Focus on Measurement and Data

Student Page 143

Progress Check

Progress Check is a self-assessment tool that children can use to gauge progress. Research shows that motivation increases as children gradually become accountable for their own learning.

Before children begin work on Unit 3, have them check the boxes in front of any standards they think they can know well. Tell them it is okay if they cannot check any boxes. They will have a chance to learn and practice all the standards as they work through this unit.

Let children know that, after they complete Lesson 27, they will review the boxes they checked today. Before having them begin the Common Core Review, you will be prompted to have them revisit this page. Remind them to keep this page in a safe place where they can find it later.

HOME ◆ CONNECT...

The Home Connect feature keeps parents or other adult family members apprised of what their children are learning. The key learning objectives are listed, and some ideas for related activities and discussions are included.

Tell children that there is an activity connected to their classroom learning that they can do at home with their families.

Encourage children and their families to share their experiences using the ideas on the Home Connect page. Afterward, you may wish to invite children to share the work they did at home with the class.

HOME ◆ CONNECT...

Your child will learn to solve problems involving money. He or she is learning the value of coins and bills up to $10 and will be able to add money amounts, compare amounts of money, and subtract money amounts. Understanding the value of money is an important and empowering skill for children.

Your child is learning the value of the following coins and bills.

Coin or Bill	Value
Penny	1¢
Nickel	5¢
Dime	10¢
Quarter	25¢
One-dollar bill	$1
Five-dollar bill	$5
Ten-dollar bill	$10

On the Go: The next time you are shopping with your child, choose an item in the store. Ask your child to determine if you have enough money in your wallet to purchase the item. Use the coins and bills that he or she has learned about in this unit to purchase the item.

In this unit, your child will:

- Measure length in inches and feet or centimeters and meters.
- Use different units to measure length.
- Estimate, compare, add, and subtract lengths.
- Read and make number-line diagrams.
- Tell and write time to five-minute intervals.
- Solve problems involving money.
- Read and make line plots, picture graphs, and bar graphs.

NOTE: All of these learning goals for your child are based on the Grade 2 Common Core State Standards for Mathematics.

Ways to Help Your Child

In this unit, your child will estimate the length of objects. Work with your child to estimate the length of objects in your home. Then have your child use a ruler to find the actual measurements. You might also have your child compare the length of two objects to determine which is longer or shorter. Encourage your child to estimate lengths as part of your daily routine to practice this important skill.

ONLINE
For more Home Connect activities, continue online at sadlierconnect.com

144   Unit 3 ■ Focus on Measurement and Data

Student Page 144

UNIT PLANNER

	Lesson	Standard(s)	Objective
16	Measure Length: Inches and Feet	**2.MD.1**	Measure length in inches, feet, and yards using the appropriate unit.
17	Measure Length: Centimeters and Meters	**2.MD.1**	Measure lengths in centimeters and meters using the appropriate unit.
18	Measure Length with Different Units	**2.MD.2**	Measure an object using two different units of length and then compare the measurements.
19	Estimate Length	**2.MD.3**	Estimate lengths of objects using standard units of measure.
20	Compare Lengths	**2.MD.4**	Compare the lengths of two objects.
21	Add and Subtract Lengths	**2.MD.5**	Add or subtract lengths to solve a problem.
22	Number Line Diagrams	**2.MD.6**	Use a number line to add and to subtract.
23	Tell and Write Time	**2.MD.7**	Read analog and digital clocks to the nearest five minutes.
24	Money	**2.MD.8**	Solve problems involving dollar bills, quarters, dimes, nickels, and pennies.
25	Line Plots	**2.MD.9**	Make and use line plots.
26	Picture Graphs	**2.MD.10**	Make and read picture graphs and solve problems using them.
27	Bar Graphs	**2.MD.10**	Interpret and create bar graphs.

Essential Question	Words to Know
How can you measure the length of objects using inches or feet?	inch, foot (feet), yard
How can you measure the length of objects using centimeters or meters?	centimeter, meter
How can you measure the same length with different-size units?	
How do you estimate the length of an object?	estimate
How can you compare the lengths of two objects?	
How can you add or subtract lengths to solve a problem?	
How do you use a number line to add and subtract?	number line
How do you tell time to the nearest five minutes?	hour, minute, midnight, noon, A.M., P.M.
How do you solve problems with money?	dime, cents, penny, dollars, quarter, nickel
How do you make and read a line plot?	line plot, data
How do you read and make a picture graph?	picture graph, data, key
How do you read and make a bar graph?	bar graph

Unit Assessment

- Unit 3 Common Core Review, *pp.242–244*
- Unit 3 Performance Task ONLINE

Additional Assessment Options

Optional Purchase:

- iProgress Monitor ONLINE
- Progress Monitor Student Benchmark Assessment Booklet

ONLINE Digital Resources

- Home Connect Activities
- Unit Performance Tasks
- Additional Practice
- Fluency Practice
- Teacher Resources
- iProgress Monitor (optional purchase)

Go to SadlierConnect.com to access your Digital Resources.

SadlierConnect

Log In

If you do not know your login information, contact your teacher or school technology coordinator.

Username Enter your Username

Password Enter your Password

Forgot Password?

☐ Remember Me

Log In

Teacher Registration
Teacher, if you do not have an account you can create one to gain access to an abundance of program resources.

Get Started!

Student & Family Resources
Get free program resources for both you and your family. You may need an Access Code to gain access to these materials.

Let's Go!

For more detailed instructions see page T3.

LEARNING PROGRESSIONS

This page provides more in-depth detail on the development of the standards across the grade levels. See also the unit Progress Check page in the Student Edition for a roadmap of the Learning Progressions.

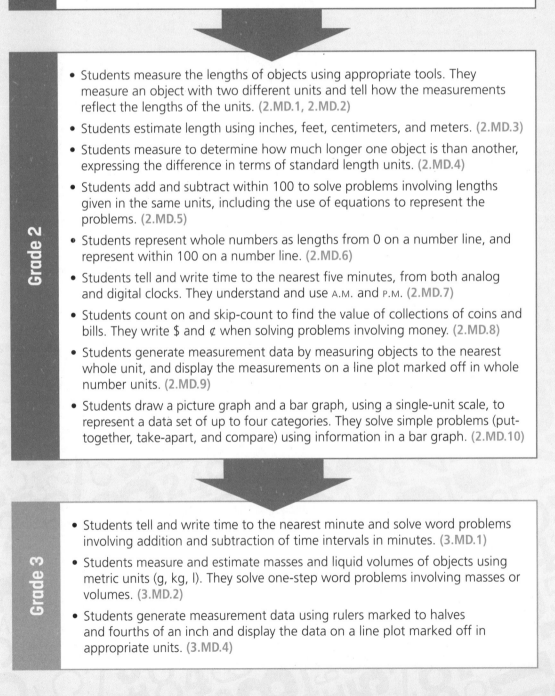

Grade 1

- Students order three objects by length and compare the lengths of two objects indirectly by using a third object as a benchmark. (**1.MD.1**)
- When measuring the length of an object using multiple copies of a shorter object (the length unit), students must be careful not to leave gaps or create overlaps. (**1.MD.2**)
- Students tell and write time to the hour and half-hour. (**1.MD.3**)

Grade 2

- Students measure the lengths of objects using appropriate tools. They measure an object with two different units and tell how the measurements reflect the lengths of the units. (**2.MD.1, 2.MD.2**)
- Students estimate length using inches, feet, centimeters, and meters. (**2.MD.3**)
- Students measure to determine how much longer one object is than another, expressing the difference in terms of standard length units. (**2.MD.4**)
- Students add and subtract within 100 to solve problems involving lengths given in the same units, including the use of equations to represent the problems. (**2.MD.5**)
- Students represent whole numbers as lengths from 0 on a number line, and represent within 100 on a number line. (**2.MD.6**)
- Students tell and write time to the nearest five minutes, from both analog and digital clocks. They understand and use A.M. and P.M. (**2.MD.7**)
- Students count on and skip-count to find the value of collections of coins and bills. They write $ and ¢ when solving problems involving money. (**2.MD.8**)
- Students generate measurement data by measuring objects to the nearest whole unit, and display the measurements on a line plot marked off in whole number units. (**2.MD.9**)
- Students draw a picture graph and a bar graph, using a single-unit scale, to represent a data set of up to four categories. They solve simple problems (put-together, take-apart, and compare) using information in a bar graph. (**2.MD.10**)

Grade 3

- Students tell and write time to the nearest minute and solve word problems involving addition and subtraction of time intervals in minutes. (**3.MD.1**)
- Students measure and estimate masses and liquid volumes of objects using metric units (g, kg, l). They solve one-step word problems involving masses or volumes. (**3.MD.2**)
- Students generate measurement data using rulers marked to halves and fourths of an inch and display the data on a line plot marked off in appropriate units. (**3.MD.4**)

Focus on Measurement and Data

Unit 3

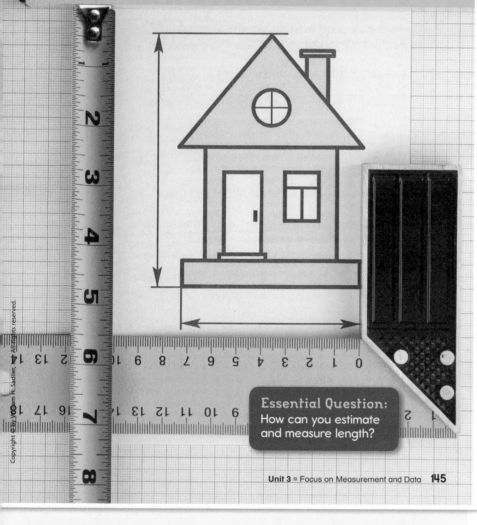

Essential Question:
How can you estimate and measure length?

Activity

Materials: 2 number cubes, half-inch or centimeter grid paper
Draw attention to the picture of the house. Then distribute the grid paper.

Tell children that they will draw houses on the grid paper. Explain that they will each roll the number cubes twice. The first roll will determine the height of the house. The second roll will determine the length of the house. Suggest that children first draw a rectangle on the grid paper to outline the space they can fill. Then have them draw any kind of house as long as it is as tall and as long as their rectangle. Conclude the activity by having children share their drawings and show the height and length that they used for their house.

Essential Question:
How can you estimate and measure length?

As children become involved with the Essential Question they will learn to use customary and metric measurement tools to measure objects in more than one unit. They will estimate and compare lengths, add and subtract lengths, and use number lines. Also in this unit, children will learn to tell and record time, combine coin and dollar values, and display data.

Conversation Starters

Have children discuss the photograph. Ask question such as: *What measurement tools do you see? Which measurement tools have you used before? How are measurement tools used in everyday life?*

Ask children to compare the scales on the tape measure and ruler shown in the picture. *Are the units of measure on the tape measure and the ruler the same or different? How can you tell?* (They are different. The numbers are farther apart on the tape measure than on the ruler.) *If the tape measure shows inches, is the house drawing closer to 4 inches high or 5 inches high? How do you know?* (The bottom of the house is close to the 5 on the tape measure, but the top is not lined up with the 0-mark on the tape measure. If I could move the tape measure down, I think the bottom would be closer to 4 inches.) Have children turn the page upside down to read the house measurement along the centimeter ruler. *About how many units long is the bottom of the house? Explain how you know.* (The arrow that shows the length of the house starts at 0 and ends a little past 7, so it is about 7 units long.)

Have a whole-class discussion on ways to estimate the length of the classroom.

Common Core Focus:

2.MD.1 Measure the length of an object by selecting and using appropriate tools such as rulers, yardsticks, meter sticks, and measuring tapes.

OBJECTIVE
Measure length in inches, feet, and yards using the appropriate unit.

ESSENTIAL QUESTION
Read the Essential Question to the class and discuss the concept of length. Ask children to tell what length means in their own words. Children may discuss the topic by describing how tall or how long something is.

PREREQUISITE SKILLS
Use Foundational Skills Handbook page 285, *Measure Length,* to review measuring using nonstandard units.

FLUENCY PRACTICE
Fluency practice is available at **sadlierconnect.com**.

Concept Development

Understand: You can use an inch ruler to find how long an object is

■ Explain that length is the measurement of the distance from one end of an object to the other end. The units used to express length measurements are inch, foot, and yard.

■ Tell children that we decide which unit to use based on the length of the object to be measured. Very short distances are measured in inches.

■ Have children find, and point to, the 0-mark on the ruler. Say that the 0-mark is close to, but not exactly at, the end of the ruler. Explain that the eraser end of the pencil is lined up above this mark on the ruler.

■ You may wish to display actual rulers some of which have 0-marks and others that do not.

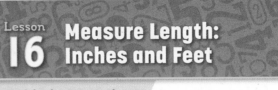

Essential Question:
How can you measure the length of objects using inches or feet?
2.MD.1

Words to Know
inch
foot (feet)
yard

Guided Instruction

In this lesson you will learn how to measure length using inches and feet.

Understand: You can use an inch ruler to find how long an object is

How long is Thea's pencil?

An **inch** is a unit of measure used to measure lengths. You can measure the length of the pencil using inches.

Use an inch ruler.
Line up one end of the pencil with the 0-mark on the ruler.
Find the number of inches that lines up with the tip of the pencil.

```
0      1      2      3      4      5      6
inches
```

The number of inches that lines up with the tip

of the pencil is ___5___.

▷ Thea's pencil is 5 inches long.

146 Unit 3 ■ Focus on Measurement and Data

Words to Know

inch: a unit of measure used to measure lengths

foot (feet): a unit of measure used to measure lengths; 12 inches = 1 foot

yard: a unit of measure used to measure lengths; 3 feet = 1 yard

Glossary can be found on pp. 293–304.

Lesson 16

Guided Instruction

Understand: You can measure objects using a yardstick or a tape measure

How long is the window in Greg's room?

Feet and yards are units used to measure longer lengths.
One foot is the same length as 12 inches.
One yard is the same length as 36 inches, or 3 feet.

Use a yardstick or a tape measure. Line up one end with the 0-mark.

The other end lines up with the 36-inch mark, which is the same as the 3-foot mark.

Since there are 3 feet in one yard, the window is also 1 yard long.

▷ The window in Greg's room is __36__ inches,

__3__ feet, or __1__ yard long.

Unit 3 ■ Focus on Measurement and Data **147**

Understand: You can measure objects using a yardstick or a tape measure

■ Make sure children understand that *foot* and *yard* are different ways to name lengths. Be sure they know that if something is 12 inches long, it is also 1 foot long. Check that they know that if something is 36 inches long, it is also both 3 feet long and 1 yard long.

■ Lead children to compare the way of measuring the window on this page with the way of measuring the pencil on page 146.

■ You may want to make sure that children understand that, while the pencil shown on page 146 can be the size of a real pencil, the window is a smaller drawing of a real window and the yardstick is a smaller drawing of a real yardstick.

Support English Language Learners

Children may have heard teachers tell their classes to *line up* meaning to form a line. Help them understand another meaning for these words. Explain that *line up* also means to put one object above another so the end of one is at the same place as the end of the other. Have children line up two connecting-cube trains at left to help solidify this meaning.

Connect: **What you know about measuring length** Use this page to help children strengthen their understanding of how to measure using inches.

■ Ask children why it is important to line up the end of the feather at the 0-mark on the ruler.

■ Point out that the red dashed lines that show where to measure do not appear in real life. They are on the page to help children see how to measure exactly. Have children discuss what they might in use in place of the dotted lines when measuring objects with a real ruler. They might suggest using their fingers or a sheet of paper or another straightedge to help them read the measurements.

■ Ask children to tell whether it would make sense to measure the feather in feet or yards and to explain their reasoning.

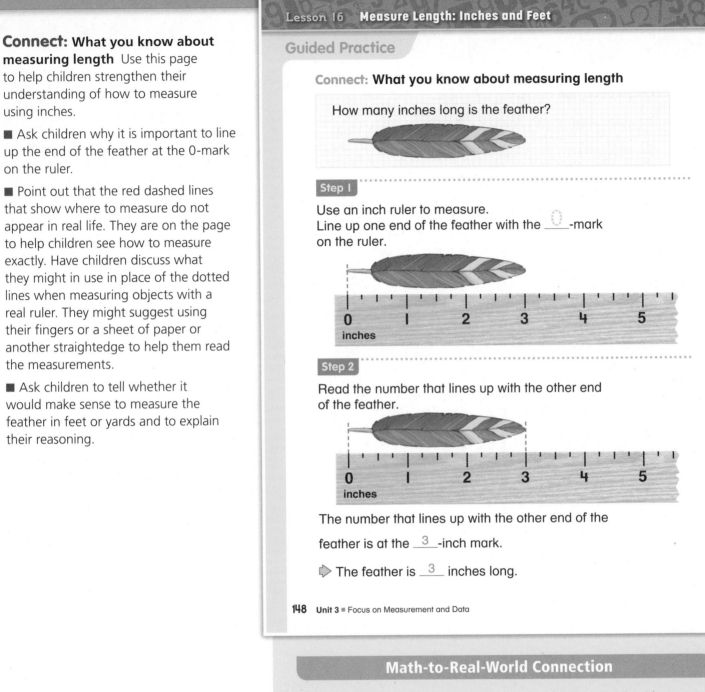

Lesson 16 **Measure Length: Inches and Feet**

Guided Practice

Connect: **What you know about measuring length**

How many inches long is the feather?

Step 1

Use an inch ruler to measure.
Line up one end of the feather with the ___0___-mark on the ruler.

0   1   2   3   4   5
inches

Step 2

Read the number that lines up with the other end of the feather.

0   1   2   3   4   5
inches

The number that lines up with the other end of the feather is at the ___3___-inch mark.

▷ The feather is ___3___ inches long.

148 Unit 3 ■ Focus on Measurement and Data

Math-to-Real-World Connection

Measuring Things in the Classroom Have children work with a partner to measure and record the lengths of different objects in the classroom. Provide rulers, yardsticks, and/or tape measures for children's use in measuring to the nearest inch. Have children share and compare their actual measurements with others in the class.

Guided Practice

I. **Zarny measures the length of his TV with a tape measure.**

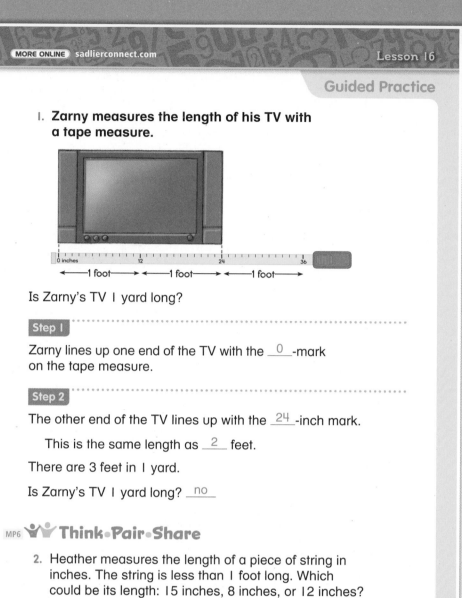

Is Zarny's TV I yard long?

Step 1

Zarny lines up one end of the TV with the __0__-mark on the tape measure.

Step 2

The other end of the TV lines up with the __24__-inch mark.

This is the same length as __2__ feet.

There are 3 feet in I yard.

Is Zarny's TV I yard long? __no__

MP6 ☙ **Think•Pair•Share**

2. Heather measures the length of a piece of string in inches. The string is less than I foot long. Which could be its length: 15 inches, 8 inches, or 12 inches? How do you know? See Additional Answers.

Unit 3 ▪ Focus on Measurement and Data **149**

Mathematical Practices

Mathematical Practice Standards underline the teaching and understanding of all concepts and skills presented. The emphasis of specific practices is noted throughout the guided and independent practice of this lesson.

MP6	**Attend to precision.**

Item 2: Children use a clue to identify an exact measurement.

Observational Assessment

Use page 149 to assess children's understanding of how to measure using a measurement tool. Watch for children who have difficulty reading the measurement. Provide additional practice as necessary.

☙ **Think•Pair•Share**

Peer Collaboration Ask pairs to share the reasoning they used to determine the length of the string. Ask children to consider questions such as:

• *If the string is less than a foot, what different lengths in whole inches could it be?*

• *What reasoning can you use to eliminate the incorrect answers?*

• *Explain how you could use the answer to the first question to answer the problem?*

To summarize, point out that you can use what you know about how many inches in one foot to answer the problem.

Return to the Essential Question

Reread the Lesson 16 Essential Question on page 146: *How can you measure the length of objects using inches or feet?*

Tell children to think about what they learned in this lesson to answer this question.
(Possible response: I choose the best measuring tool based on what I am measuring. Line up the end of the object with the 0 on the measuring tool. Find which number the other end of the object aligns with to determine the length.)

Additional Answers

Item 2: Possible response: One foot is equal to 12 inches. The string is less then 1 foot long, so it cannot measure 12 inches. Fifteen inches is greater than 12 inches, so the string cannot measure 15 inches. The string must be 8 inches long.

Concept Application

Children may work independently on these pages in the classroom or at home. They may refer to the first four pages of the lesson to revisit the instruction or to see a worked-out example.

Common Errors and **Teaching Tips** may help you support learning either in the classroom or as a follow-up for work done at home.

Common Errors

Items 1 and 3

Children may write the number at the end of the ruler rather than the measurement of the object. Remind children to only consider the number closest to the end of the object, regardless of the length of the measuring tool.

Independent Practice

Write the length of each object.

1.

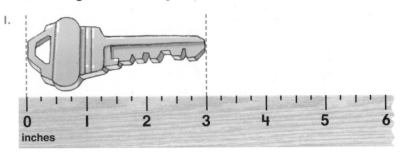

___3___ inches

2.

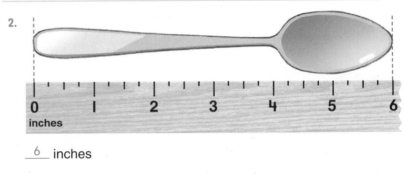

___6___ inches

3.

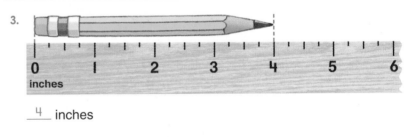

___4___ inches

Talking About Math

Collaborative Conversations Have children work in pairs. Have one partner choose one object in the classroom to measure. Have the other partner decide on the best measuring tool to use to find the length of that object. Children should use the measuring tool to find and record the actual length of the object. Allow children to share their work with the class talking about how they found the actual measurements.

Circle the correct answer.

4. The paintbrush is _____ long.

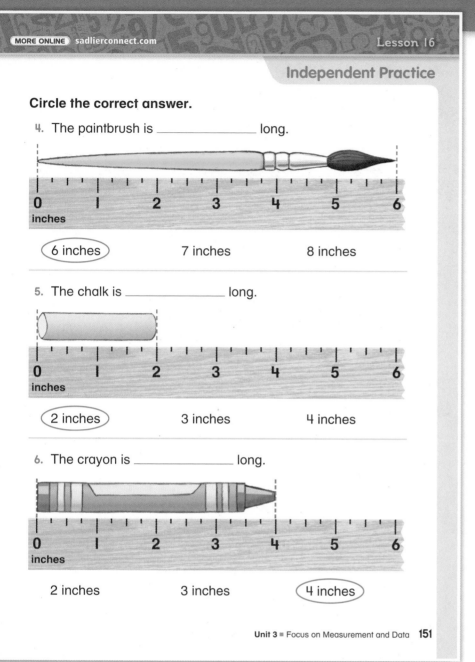

   (6 inches)   7 inches   8 inches

5. The chalk is _____ long.

   (2 inches)   3 inches   4 inches

6. The crayon is _____ long.

   2 inches   3 inches   (4 inches)

Unit 3 ■ Focus on Measurement and Data **151**

Teaching Tips

Items 4-6
To help children develop good measuring habits, ask them to verify that one end of the object is lined up with the 0-mark on the ruler below it.

Digital Connection

Digital Measuring Devices Children may be interested to know that there are measuring tools that use digital lasers to measure objects. There are digital tape measures, digital rulers worn on the fingers, and digital measurement wheels used to measure greater lengths. Several videos are available on the Internet that describe how this technology works. Research such videos and have children view those that are appropriate.

Independent Practice

Common Errors

Items 7–9

Before measuring, have children point to the 0-mark on their rulers. Then, if they seem to be having trouble measuring, help them align the 0-mark on their rulers below one end of the objects.

Teaching Tips

Item 7

The toothbrush is curved, so the ruler will not align perfectly with the bottom of the illustration. Make sure children place the 0-mark on the ruler at the left end of the toothbrush.

Item 10

Children may have little concept of the length of 20 yards. Allow children to find 20 inches on a yardstick. By eliminating one length as a possibility, children can reason that the other length must be the correct answer.

Independent Practice

Use an inch ruler to measure each object.

7. How long is the toothbrush?

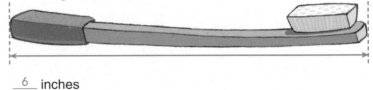

___6___ inches

8. How long is the comb?

___4___ inches

9. How long is the marker?

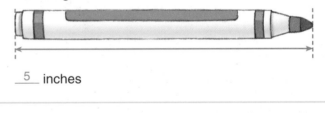

___5___ inches

10. Which of these might be the measure of a soccer field: 20 inches or 20 yards?

_____20 yards_____

Math-to-Language Connection

Riddles To provide children practice with reasoning about measurement, give them a measurement riddle such as this one: *I have 4 wheels outside and one wheel inside. I can beep and roll, but not by myself. My length is measured in feet. What am I?* (a car) Have children work in small groups to write their own riddles that include measurement clues. Then have groups challenge the rest of the class to answer their riddles.

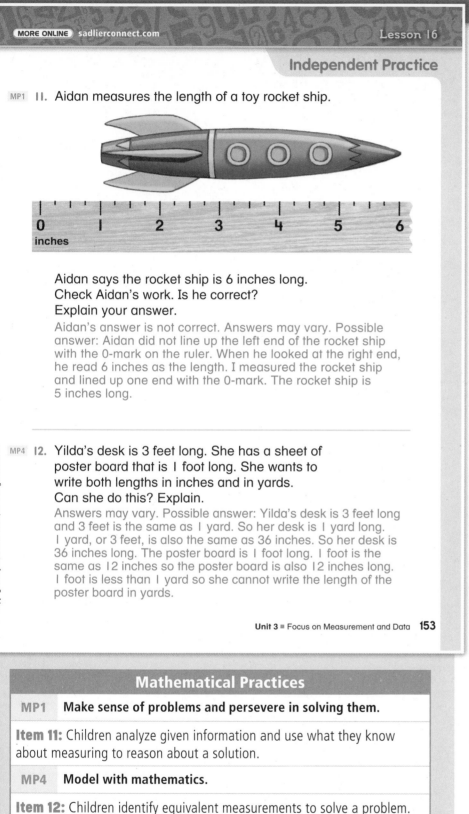

MP1 **11.** Aidan measures the length of a toy rocket ship.

0 1 2 3 4 5 6
inches

Aidan says the rocket ship is 6 inches long.
Check Aidan's work. Is he correct?
Explain your answer.

Aidan's answer is not correct. Answers may vary. Possible
answer: Aidan did not line up the left end of the rocket ship
with the 0-mark on the ruler. When he looked at the right end,
he read 6 inches as the length. I measured the rocket ship
and lined up one end with the 0-mark. The rocket ship is
5 inches long.

MP4 **12.** Yilda's desk is 3 feet long. She has a sheet of
poster board that is 1 foot long. She wants to
write both lengths in inches and in yards.
Can she do this? Explain.

Answers may vary. Possible answer: Yilda's desk is 3 feet long
and 3 feet is the same as 1 yard. So her desk is 1 yard long.
1 yard, or 3 feet, is also the same as 36 inches. So her desk is
36 inches long. The poster board is 1 foot long. 1 foot is the
same as 12 inches so the poster board is also 12 inches long.
1 foot is less than 1 yard so she cannot write the length of the
poster board in yards.

Unit 3 ■ Focus on Measurement and Data **153**

Common Errors

Item 11

Some children may answer this problem
incorrectly because they begin counting
from 1. Help them recall that when
measuring, they have to align one
end of the object with the 0-mark
on the ruler.

Teaching Tips

Item 12

It may be helpful for children to make a
chart to organize the information about
each item.

Mathematical Practices	
MP1	**Make sense of problems and persevere in solving them.**
Item 11: Children analyze given information and use what they know about measuring to reason about a solution.	
MP4	**Model with mathematics.**
Item 12: Children identify equivalent measurements to solve a problem.	

Guided Instruction

Common Core Focus:

2.MD.1 Measure the length of an object by selecting and using appropriate tools such as rulers, yardsticks, meter sticks, and measuring tapes.

OBJECTIVE

Measure lengths in centimeters and meters using the appropriate unit.

ESSENTIAL QUESTION

Focus children on the lesson objective by reading the Essential Question aloud. Explain to children that they have been using customary units of measurement, inches, feet, and yards. Now they will measure length with centimeters and meters, part of the metric system of measurement.

PREREQUISITE SKILLS

Use Foundational Skills Handbook page 285, *Measure Length,* to remind children how to measure length using nonstandard units.

FLUENCY PRACTICE

Fluency practice is available at **sadlierconnect.com**.

Concept Development

Understand: You can use a centimeter ruler to find how long an object is

■ Tell children that they can use what they have learned about measuring in inches for measuring in centimeters.

■ Ask everyone to point to the 0-mark on the centimeter ruler. Then have them trace along the ruler to the right as they count the centimeters to determine the length of the crayon.

■ Explain that one dotted line shows that the end of the crayon lines up with the 0-mark on the ruler. The other dotted line shows that the tip of the crayon lines up with the 6-centimeter mark on the ruler.

Lesson 17 Measure Length: Centimeters and Meters

Guided Instruction

Essential Question:
How can you measure the length of objects using centimeters or meters?
2.MD.1
Words to Know
centimeter
meter

In this lesson you will learn how to measure length using centimeters and meters.

Understand: You can use a centimeter ruler to find how long an object is

How long is Avery's crayon?

A centimeter is a unit of measure used to measure length. You can measure the length of the crayon in centimeters.

Use a centimeter ruler.
Line up one end of the crayon with the 0-mark on the ruler.
Find the number of centimeters that lines up with the tip of the crayon.

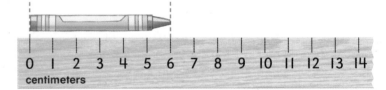

Read the number of centimeters that lines up with the tip of the crayon.

▷ Avery's crayon is 6 centimeters long.

Words to Know

centimeter: a unit of measure used to measure lengths

Example: 1 centimeter

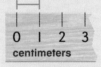

meter: a unit of measure used to measure lengths

Example:

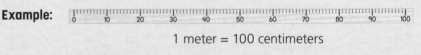

1 meter = 100 centimeters

Glossary can be found on pp. 293–304.

Guided Instruction

Understand: Use a meter stick to measure longer objects

How long is Ms. Warren's desk?

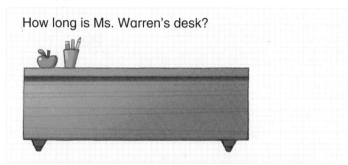

A meter stick can be used to measure longer lengths. One meter is the same length as 100 centimeters.

Ms. Warren can use a meter stick to measure her desk. She lines up one end of the desk with the 0-mark on the meter stick.

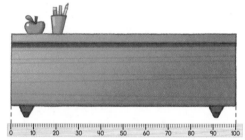

She sees that the other end of the desk lines up with the 100-centimeter mark, which is the same as the 1-meter mark.

▷ The desk is __100__ centimeters, or __1__ meter, long.

Unit 3 ■ Focus on Measurement and Data **155**

Support English Language Learners

Many English Language Learners will be familiar with the metric system since most countries use it as their official system of measurement. Write the word *meter* on the board. Say the word and have children repeat it. Then ask children if they know what the word means. Build from there to help children understand the metric terms in this lesson.

Understand: Use a meter stick to measure longer objects

■ Explain to children that 1 meter is equal in length to 100 centimeters. Draw the connection between this equality and the fact that 1 hundred is the same as 100 ones.

■ Discuss with children that measuring with a meter stick is similar to measuring with a centimeter ruler. They should know to line up one end of the object being measured above 0-mark on the meter stick and then find the point where the other end of the object lines up above the meter stick.

■ Discuss why it sometimes makes more sense to report a distance in meters than centimeters. For example, it might be easier for someone to imagine a distance of 3 meters than 300 centimeters even though these two measurements are the same length.

Guided Practice

Connect: What you know about measuring length This example models how to measure with a centimeter ruler.

■ Remind children why it is important to line up one end of the object being measured with the 0-mark on the ruler.

■ Review how to measure by lining up one end of the object exactly above the 0-mark on the centimeter ruler. Tell children that they may need to use a straightedge—the edge of a book, for example—to help them line up an object they want to measure above the ruler.

■ Mention that some centimeter rulers, like some inch rulers, may not have 0-marks. Explain that if a centimeter ruler has no "0," then the left end of the ruler serves as the 0-mark.

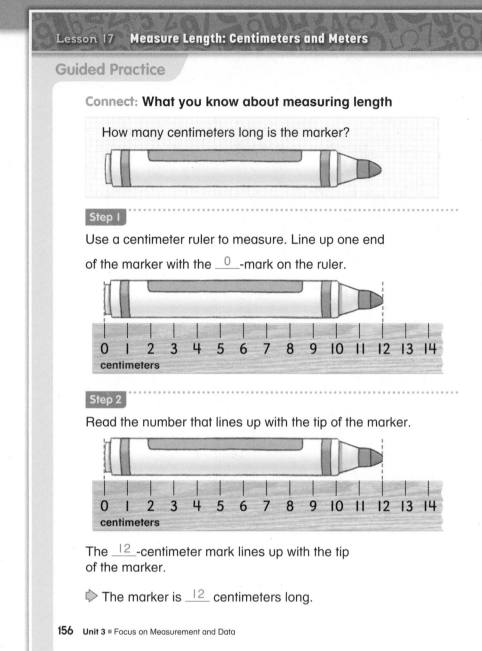

Guided Practice

Connect: What you know about measuring length

How many centimeters long is the marker?

Step 1

Use a centimeter ruler to measure. Line up one end of the marker with the __0__-mark on the ruler.

Step 2

Read the number that lines up with the tip of the marker.

The __12__-centimeter mark lines up with the tip of the marker.

▷ The marker is __12__ centimeters long.

156 Unit 3 ■ Focus on Measurement and Data

Math-to-Real-World Connection

Measuring Things Outside the Classroom Ask children to list some lengths they could measure outside of the classroom. Provide some examples, such as the length of a wall in a room at home and the length, or distance, between two cities on a map. Have volunteers share some of the items on their lists. Explain that all objects have lengths that can be measured using different units.

Guided Practice

I. **Mason uses a shovel to help his dad in the garden. He uses a meter stick to find the length of his shovel.**

Is Mason's shovel 1 meter long?

Step 1

Mason lines up one end of the shovel with the __0__-mark on the meter stick.

Step 2

He sees that the other end of the shovel lines up with

the __90__-centimeter mark.

Is a length of 90 centimeters the same as a length

of 100 centimeters? __no__

Is Mason's shovel 1 meter long? __no__

✌ Think·Pair·Share

MP6 **2.** Sariah has a kite with a long tail. She measures the tail with a meter stick. The tail is 1 meter long. Sariah says that the tail is also 200 centimeters long. Is she correct? Talk about how you know. See Additional Answers.

Mathematical Practices

Mathematical Practice Standards underline the teaching and understanding of all concepts and skills presented. The emphasis of specific practices is noted throughout the guided and independent practice of this lesson.

MP6 **Attend to precision.**

Item 2: Children explain whether or not two given measurements are equivalent.

Observational Assessment

Use page 157 to assess children's understanding of how to measure length using a meter stick. Make sure children understand that a meter is 100 centimeters long. If an object measures less than 100 meters, then it is less than 1 meter long.

✌ Think·Pair·Share

Peer Collaboration Ask pairs to share their work to determine whether or not Sarah is correct. Ask each pair of children questions such as:

- *Measure 200 centimeters along your wall using a meter stick? How many meters long is that? Explain.*

- *How did measuring 200 meters help you answer the question? Explain.*

To summarize, point out to children that they can use a meter stick to check how many meters are in 200 centimeters. They can also use what they know about comparing numbers to know that 200 centimeters is more than 100 centimeters, or 1 meter.

Return to the Essential Question

Reread the Lesson 17 Essential Question on page 154: *How can you measure the length of objects using centimeters or meters?*

Tell children to think about what they learned in this lesson and answer this question.
(Possible responses: I first pick the best tool to measure, either the centimeter ruler or the meter stick. I then line up the start of the object at 0 and see where the end of the object lines up on the measuring device.)

Additional Answers

Item 2: Answers may vary. Possible answer: 200 centimeters is not the same as 1 meter. 100 centimeters is the same as 1 meter. So, Sarah is not correct. The kite's tail is 100 centimeters long.

Concept Application

Children may work independently on these pages in the classroom or at home. They may refer to the first four pages of the lesson to revisit the instruction or to see a worked-out example.

Common Errors and **Teaching Tips** may help you support learning either in the classroom or as a follow-up for work done at home.

Common Errors

Item 3

The flashlight is drawn using perspective. Part of the front of it was made visible so children would recognize it as a flashlight. Children who realize this may measure to the start of the circle at the end or to the middle of the circle. However, the guideline suggests that they measure to the farthest point.

Teaching Tips

Item 2

Discuss with children how the leaf appears on the page. Have them compare the position of this leaf with the position of the feather on page 148. Stress that, as long as an object is positioned so that its length can be measured, the direction in which it faces does not affect its length.

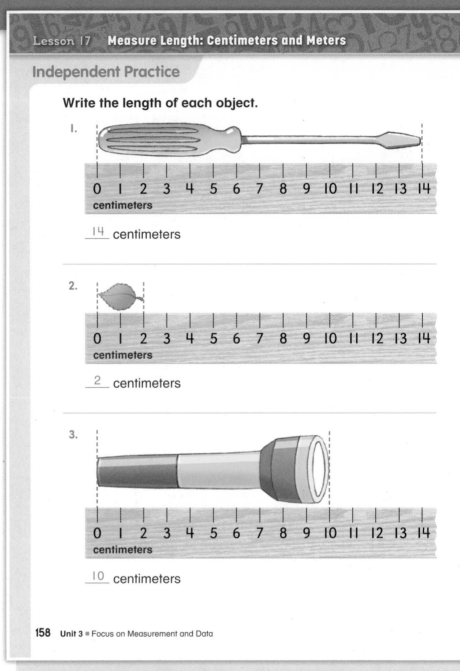

Independent Practice

Write the length of each object.

1.

_14_ centimeters

2.

_2_ centimeters

3.

_10_ centimeters

158   Unit 3 ■ Focus on Measurement and Data

Talking About Math

Collaborative Conversations Have children work in pairs. Ask one partner to name a classroom object that he or she thinks is less than 1 meter long. The other partner should choose an object that he or she thinks is more than 1 meter long. The pairs should discuss which one measuring tool they can use to check if they were each correct. Have them measure and then tell their measurements explaining why they chose that particular measuring tool.

Lesson 17

Independent Practice

Circle the correct answer.

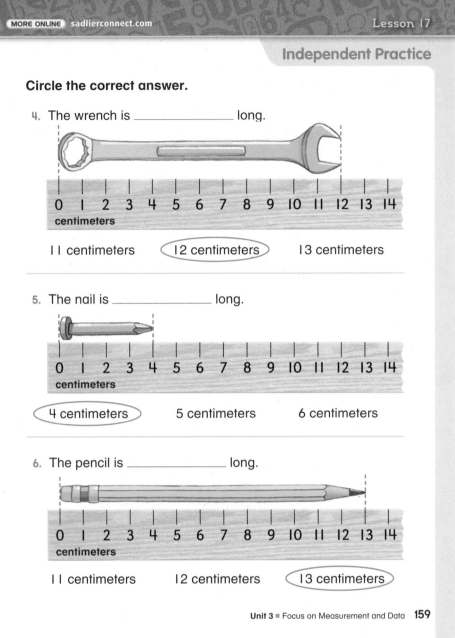

4. The wrench is _____ long.

11 centimeters   (12 centimeters)   13 centimeters

5. The nail is _____ long.

(4 centimeters)   5 centimeters   6 centimeters

6. The pencil is _____ long.

11 centimeters   12 centimeters   (13 centimeters)

Unit 3 ■ Focus on Measurement and Data **159**

Common Errors

Item 4
Children may have difficulty finding the end point of the wrench and think that it is 11, instead of 12, centimeters long.

Teaching Tips

Items 5 and 6
You may wish to discuss with children the similarity between the two items to be measured. Both items are flat on one end. Each flat end is lined up with the 0-mark on the ruler below. Both items have points at the other end. The points line up with the marking that shows the length of the item in centimeters.

Digital Connection

Digital Programs Have children use a digital manipulatives program to measure pictured items in centimeters. Have them place the item on the screen. Then have them maneuver the centimeter ruler to measure the item. Check to be sure that children are lining up the ruler below the left end of each item. Have them repeat the measuring process for other items.

Independent Practice

Common Errors

Item 7

Some children may have difficulty determining the beginning of the straw since it is drawn in perspective to show the opening. Make sure children know to measure the length starting from the left end as indicated by the guideline.

Teaching Tips

Item 8

The key has many jagged edges and a hole in it. Help children to see that these do not affect the length of the key.

Independent Practice

Use a centimeter ruler to measure each object.

7. How long is the straw?

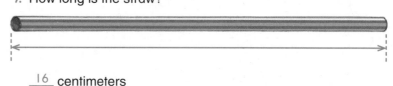

   16 centimeters

8. How long is the key?

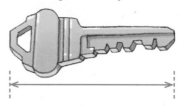

   7 centimeters

9. How long is the phone?

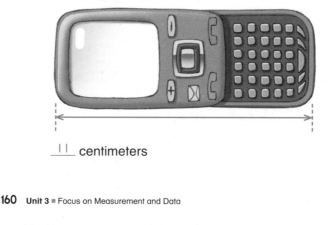

   11 centimeters

Math-to-Art Connection

Measuring Crayons Have children gather the crayons they have been using. Tell them to compare the lengths of their crayons. Then have them measure the lengths of their longest and shortest crayons in centimeters. Tell children to record and share their results.

Children may be interested in knowing that a new, unused regular-size crayon is 8 centimeters long. A new, unused large-size crayon is 10 centimeters long.

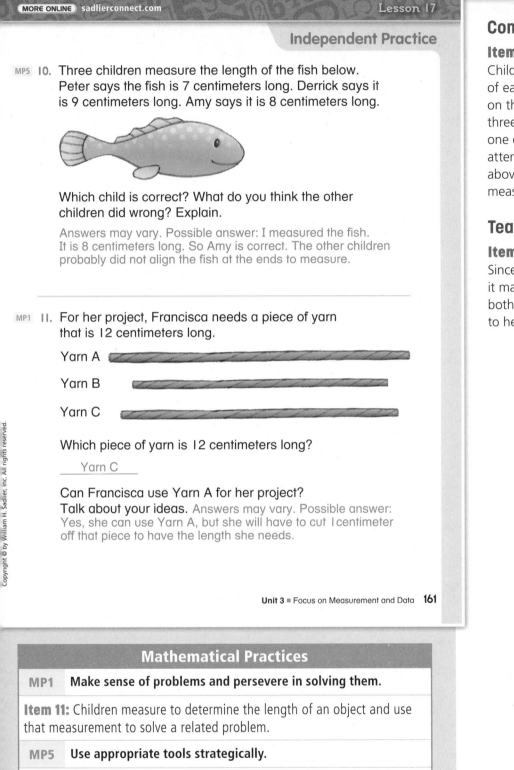

Independent Practice

MP5 **10.** Three children measure the length of the fish below. Peter says the fish is 7 centimeters long. Derrick says it is 9 centimeters long. Amy says it is 8 centimeters long.

Which child is correct? What do you think the other children did wrong? Explain.

Answers may vary. Possible answer: I measured the fish. It is 8 centimeters long. So Amy is correct. The other children probably did not align the fish at the ends to measure.

MP1 **11.** For her project, Francisca needs a piece of yarn that is 12 centimeters long.

Yarn A

Yarn B

Yarn C

Which piece of yarn is 12 centimeters long?

_____Yarn C_____

Can Francisca use Yarn A for her project?
Talk about your ideas. Answers may vary. Possible answer: Yes, she can use Yarn A, but she will have to cut 1 centimeter off that piece to have the length she needs.

Unit 3 ■ Focus on Measurement and Data **161**

Common Errors
Item 11
Children may fail to line up the left end of each piece of yarn with the 0-mark on the ruler. If so, point out that the three pieces of yarn are not lined up at one end. So, they need to pay careful attention to how to line up each piece above the 0-mark on the ruler as they measure it.

Teaching Tips
Item 10
Since the fish is curved at both ends, it may help children to make a mark at both the beginning and end of the fish to help them line up the ruler.

Mathematical Practices

MP1	**Make sense of problems and persevere in solving them.**

Item 11: Children measure to determine the length of an object and use that measurement to solve a related problem.

MP5	**Use appropriate tools strategically.**

Item 10: Children must measure an object in centimeters and use the measurement to solve the problem.

Common Core Focus:

2.MD.2. Measure the length of an object twice, using length units of different lengths for the two measurements; describe how the two measurements relate to the size of the unit chosen.

OBJECTIVE

Measure an object using two different units of length and then compare the measurements.

ESSENTIAL QUESTION

Review the different units of length that children have used to measure so far. Tell them to think about measuring a desk in inches and in feet. Have them share ideas about whether the desk would be the same number of inches long as feet long. Discuss why the measurements would be different.

FLUENCY PRACTICE

Fluency practice is available at **sadlierconnect.com**.

Concept Development

Understand: You can use inches and feet to measure the same object

■ Children should be able to measure an item using two different units, for example inches and feet. Then they need to be able to describe how the different units relate in size. Help them understand that it takes more inches than feet to measure an object because 1 inch is smaller, or shorter, than 1 foot.

■ Have children describe how the picnic bench is being measured in their own words. Make sure they know that a tape measure is being used and that they can identify the inch markings along the tape.

■ Children have learned that 1 foot is the same length as 12 inches. Tell them to look at the markings on the tape measure to help them find how many inches are in 2 feet, 3 feet, and 4 feet.

In this lesson you will learn how to measure the same length with different-size units.

Understand: You can use inches and feet to measure the same object

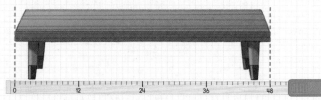

Lucille uses a tape measure to find the length of a picnic bench.

Does it take more inches or more feet to measure the length of the bench?

Lucille measured the length of the bench using inches.

    The bench is 48 inches long.

Then Lucille measured the length of the bench using feet.

    The bench is 4 feet long.

Inches are smaller units than feet.

▷ It takes more inches than feet to measure the bench.

162   Unit 3 ■ Focus on Measurement and Data

Support English Language Learners

English language learners may be confused by the sentence "It takes *more* inches than feet to measure the bench." Help them understand that the word *more* does not mean that the bench is longer when it is measured in inches. Instead it means that its length in inches, 48, is greater than, or more than, its length in feet, 4.

Lesson 18

Guided Instruction

Understand: You can use inches and centimeters to measure the same object

Does it take more inches or more centimeters to measure the length of this fish?

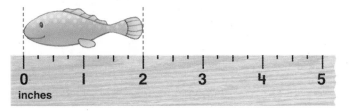

Use an inch ruler to measure the length of the fish.

The fish is 2 inches long.

Use a centimeter ruler to measure the length of the fish.

The fish is a little more than 5 centimeters long.

▷ It takes more ___centimeters___ than ___inches___ to measure the length of the fish.

Unit 3 ■ Focus on Measurement and Data **163**

Understand: You can use inches and centimeters to measure the same object

■ Discuss the fact that the fish is exactly 2 inches long, but it is not exactly 5 centimeters long. Instead, it is a little longer than 5 centimeters. Discuss with children that often items are a little longer or shorter than the markings on rulers.

■ Discuss with children why it takes more centimeters than inches to measure the fish.

Math-to-Science Connection

Measuring Snowfall Explain to children that after a snowstorm, scientists routinely measure how much snow fell. They poke a measuring tool into a snow pile. The mark on the measuring tool at the top of the pile tells them how deep the snow is.

Point out that scientists also measure amounts of rainfall. They do this by using a measuring tool called a rain gauge. This tool is a kind of long, thin cup. It is kept outdoors to catch rain as it falls. Scientists find out how much rain fell by checking the level of the rain inside the rain gauge and reading the mark along the side.

Guided Instruction

Connect: Measuring length with different size units Use this page to help strengthen children's understanding of measuring length using different-size units.

■ Discuss with children why Louis and Marie used different kinds of rulers to measure the length of the same stick.

■ Some children may struggle to understand that it takes more of a small unit than a large unit to measure the same object. To help such children, say that you want to measure the length of the classroom using two different units of measure. Explain that one child will walk along the length of the room by stepping heel to toe. Another child will take giant steps along the length. Have children predict who will take more steps. After having children perform the activity, review children's predictions. Again, point out that the smaller the unit, the more it takes of them to cover the same distance.

Guided Instruction

Connect: Measuring length with different-size units

Louis has an inch ruler and Marie has a centimeter ruler. They want to know if it will take more inches or more centimeters to measure the length of a stick.

Step 1

Louis measures the length of the stick with an inch ruler.

The stick is close to ___6___ inches long.

Step 2

Marie measures the length with a centimeter ruler.

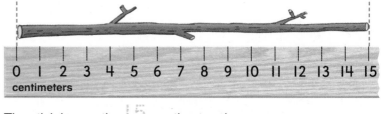

The stick is exactly ___15___ centimeters long.

▷ It takes more __centimeters__ than ___inches___ to measure the length of the stick.

Math-to-Construction Connection

Building Measurements Construction workers measure many different lengths in order to build. Discuss different objects that a construction worker might need to measure. Have children make a list of the different-size units that could be used to measure each object. Talk about whether it would take more or fewer of one listed unit than another to measure each object. For example, to measure the length of a window, a worker could use centimeters or inches. It would take more centimeters than inches to represent the length of the window.

Lesson 18

Guided Practice

I. **Jorge measures the length of his math book in inches and in feet. Does it take more inches or more feet to measure the math book?**

Step 1

Jorge measured the length using inches and feet.

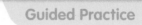

Math Book

1 foot

Step 2

How many inches long is the book? __12__

How many feet long is the book? __1__

Which unit is smaller, inches or feet? ____inches____

It takes more ____inches____ than ____feet____ to measure the book.

☻ Think•Pair•Share

MP4 2. **Marissa wants to measure the length of her classroom. Should she measure the length of her classroom in centimeters or in meters? Talk about why.**
Answers may vary. Possible answer: Marissa should use meters to measure the length of her classroom. Centimeters are used to measure shorter things. Meters are used to measure longer things.

Unit 3 ■ Focus on Measurement and Data **165**

Mathematical Practices

Mathematical Practice Standards underline the teaching and understanding of all concepts and skills presented. The emphasis of specific practices is noted throughout the guided and independent practice of this lesson.

MP4 **Model with mathematics.**

Item 2: Children apply their knowledge about units of length to determine the appropriate unit to use in a real-world application.

Observational Assessment

Use page 165 to assess children's understanding of which unit of measure requires more units to measure an object. Note children who think that it takes more of a longer unit than a shorter unit. Help them see that the smaller the unit, the more it takes of them to measure an object.

☻ Think•Pair•Share

Peer Collaboration Ask pairs to share their work to answer the question about whether or not they should use centimeters or meters to measure the classroom. Ask each pair of children questions such as:

• *Would it take more centimeters or meters to measure our classroom? Explain.*

• *Would you choose a centimeter ruler or a meter stick to measure the classroom? Explain.*

To summarize, point out that children need to think about the size of the unit before they measure an object. Children need to understand that it is often better to use a longer unit to measure longer objects and often better to use a shorter unit to measure shorter objects.

Return to the Essential Question

Reread the Lesson 18 Essential Question on page 162: *How can you measure the same length with different-size units?*

Tell children to think about what they learned in this lesson and answer this question.
(Possible responses: I know that I can use different-size units to measure the same length. When I do this, I will get a different number of units. If I measure the same item in both centimeters and inches, there will be more centimeters. Centimeters are shorter than inches, so there will be more of them.)

Concept Application

Children may work independently on these pages in the classroom or at home. They may refer to the first four pages of the lesson to revisit the instruction or to see a worked-out example.

Common Errors and **Teaching Tips** may help you support learning either in the classroom or as a follow-up for work done at home.

Common Errors

Item 2

Children may look at the label below the measuring tape, 4 feet, and then write 4 as the length of the table. Explain that dotted guidelines show the length to be measured.

Teaching Tips

Items 3 and 6

Remind children that they can check the answer to this question by asking themselves which unit is shorter. It will always take more of a shorter unit than a longer unit to measure an object.

Independent Practice

Hyun measured the table in inches and then in feet.

1. The table is __36__ inches long.

2. The table is __3__ feet long.

3. It takes more ____inches____ than ____feet____ to measure the length of the table.

Use an inch ruler to measure the pen. Then use a centimeter ruler to measure the pen.

4. The pen is close to __5__ inches long.

5. The pen is almost __13__ centimeters long.

6. It takes more ____centimeters____ than ____inches____ to measure the length of the pen.

Talking About Math

Collaborative Conversations Have children work in pairs to discuss how they can tell which unit it will take more of to measure an object.

Have pairs make a chart on which to write the following units in order of size: *inch, centimeter, foot, yard,* and *meter.* If chart paper is available, have children use it so they have enough space to include a actual-length drawing of each unit. Have pairs also state the general rule for telling which unit it takes more of to measure an object. They should know that the shorter the unit, the more units it will take to measure an object.

Liam measured the window in centimeters and then in meters. He knows that 100 centimeters is equal in length to 1 meter.

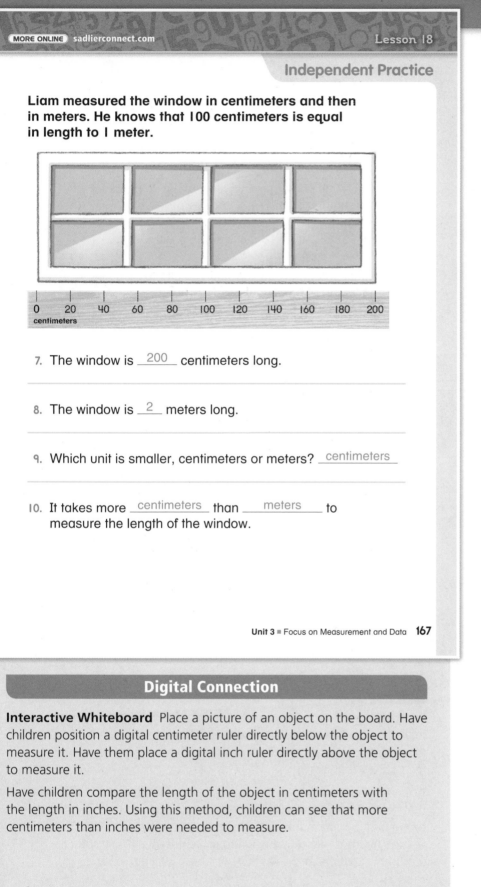

7. The window is __200__ centimeters long.

8. The window is __2__ meters long.

9. Which unit is smaller, centimeters or meters? __centimeters__

10. It takes more __centimeters__ than __meters__ to measure the length of the window.

Unit 3 ■ Focus on Measurement and Data **167**

Teaching Tips

Items 7–8

You may wish to discuss with children that these two measurements use the digit 2, but the 2 appears in different place-value positions. The centimeter measurement has the 2 in the hundreds place. The meter measurement has the 2 in the ones place. You might want to review that since 100 centimeters is the same as 1 meter, 200 centimeters is the same as 2 meters.

Digital Connection

Interactive Whiteboard Place a picture of an object on the board. Have children position a digital centimeter ruler directly below the object to measure it. Have them place a digital inch ruler directly above the object to measure it.

Have children compare the length of the object in centimeters with the length in inches. Using this method, children can see that more centimeters than inches were needed to measure.

Common Errors

Items 14–16

Some children may still have difficulty with these items. This may be because when they see the word *more,* they think of the larger measurement unit.

Teaching Tips

Items 11–13

Tell children to imagine that they are actually measuring each item using the units mentioned.

Independent Practice

11. Which unit of measure would you use to measure the length of a soccer field?

    inches   centimeters   (meters)

12. Which unit of measure would you use to measure the length of a car?

    (feet)   centimeters   inches

13. Which unit of measure would you use to measure the length of a baseball card?

    meters   (centimeters)   yards

14. Do you need more inches or more centimeters to measure the length of a sandbox?

    You need more ___centimeters___.

15. Do you need more feet or more yards to measure the length of a flagpole?

    You need more ___feet___.

16. Do you need more centimeters or more feet to measure the length of a garden?

    You need more ___centimeters___.

Math-to-Reading Connection

Length of a Book Tell children to select a book they are currently reading, or to take a book from the class library. Have them each measure one side of their book both in centimeters and in inches and record their results.

Arrange children in pairs. Have one partner indicate the side of the book that he or she measured and say the measurement numbers without telling whether the numbers represent centimeters or inches. The other partner needs to decide which number represents inches and which represents centimeters. Then have partners switch roles and repeat the activity.

Lesson 18

Independent Practice

MP1 **17.** Albert measures his violin in inches. He says that his violin is about 53 inches long. Then he measures his violin in centimeters. He says that his violin is also 21 centimeters long. What is wrong with Albert's measurements? What might he have done? Talk about it.

Answers may vary. Possible answer: Albert reported the measurements incorrectly because centimeters are smaller than inches. So his violin should be more centimeters long than inches. His violin could be 21 inches long and about 53 centimeters long. Maybe Albert wrote the wrong units with each measurement by mistake.

MP6 **18.** Maggie says that feet are shorter than yards. Lanie says that yards are shorter than inches. Regina says that inches are shorter than feet. Who is correct? Who is not correct? How do you know? Explain.

Answers may vary. Possible answer: Maggie and Regina are correct. I know that inches are shorter than feet because there are 12 inches in 1 foot. So, when I measure something, I use more inches than feet to find the length. I know that feet are shorter than yards because there are 3 feet in 1 yard. So, when I measure something, I use more feet than yards to find the length. Lanie is not correct. I know that yards are not shorter than inches because there are 36 inches in 1 yard. So, when I measure something, I use more inches than yards to find the length.

MP3 **19.** Which measurement is shorter, 15 inches or 15 centimeters? How do you know?

Answers may vary. Possible answer: 15 centimeters is shorter than 15 inches. I know this because centimeters are shorter than inches.

Common Errors
Item 18
Children may be confused by the amount of information in the problem. They may answer the questions based only on what Maggie and Lanie say. If so, tell them to organize the information by writing what each person in the problem says on a separate line on a sheet of paper.

Teaching Tips
Item 17
Many children may realize that Albert made a mistake in measuring his violin. However, they may not realize what the mistake may be. Have children line up a meter stick and a yardstick to help them see the relationship between meters and inches.

Mathematical Practices	
MP1	**Make sense of problems and persevere in solving them.**
Item 17: Children analyze a problem to determine what is wrong with it.	
MP3	**Construct viable arguments and critique the reasoning of others.**
Item 19: Children must construct an argument to answer the question.	
MP6	**Attend to precision.**
Item 18: Children explain specifically why they believe or disbelieve statements in the problem.	

Common Core Focus:

2.MD.3 Estimate lengths using units of inches, feet, centimeters, and meters.

OBJECTIVE

Estimate lengths of objects using standard units of measure.

ESSENTIAL QUESTION

Read the Essential Question aloud to the class. Lead children to analyze the difference between measuring to find the exact length of an object, and what they think is meant by estimating the length of the object.

FLUENCY PRACTICE

Fluency practice is available at **sadlierconnect.com**.

Concept Development

Understand: You can estimate length in inches.

■ In first grade, children learned to measure using non-standard, and then standard, measuring units.

■ Now, having learned to measure with inches, feet, centimeters, and meters, children should be able to identify these lengths by sight. They will need to imagine the length each represents in order to estimate length.

■ Discuss what *estimate* means and when estimation is a good strategy. Explain that when a problem does not need an exact answer, you can make an estimate. Also, if you do not have a ruler, estimation can be a useful means of getting an idea of the measurement.

■ Encourage children to identify objects that are *about* 1 inch long. Explain that they can use any of these objects to estimate length in inches; however, if they forget, a paper clip is a good estimate of 1 inch.

Essential Question:
How do you estimate the length of an object?
2.MD.3

Words to Know
estimate

Guided Instruction

In this lesson you will learn to estimate length.

Understand: You can estimate length in inches

About how many inches long is this paintbrush?

Peter does not have a ruler. He can estimate the length of the paintbrush to find about how long it is.

Peter says one small paper clip is about 1 inch long. He puts paper clips under the paintbrush to estimate its length.

The paintbrush is about six 1-inch paper clips long. Peter finds an inch ruler. He uses it to measure the paintbrush and check his estimate.

The paintbrush is almost 6 inches long. Compare the estimate to the measured length.

▷ The paintbrush is about 6 inches long.

Words to Know

estimate: tells about how long an object is

Example:

The straw is about 6 inches long.

Glossary can be found on pp. 293–304.

Guided Instruction

Understand: You can estimate length in centimeters

About how many centimeters long is this pencil?

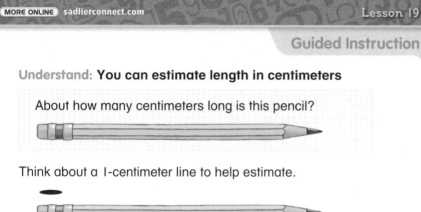

Think about a 1-centimeter line to help estimate.

The pencil is about twelve 1-centimeter lines long.

Your thumb is about 1 centimeter wide.

Now measure the pencil to check your estimate.
Use a centimeter ruler.

The pencil is a little more than 12 centimeters long.

Compare the estimate to the length.
The estimated length was about 12 centimeters.
The measured length was close to 12 centimeters.

▷ The pencil is about 12 centimeters long.

Unit 3 ▪ Focus on Measurement and Data **171**

Concept Development

Understand: You can estimate length in centimeters

■ Have children identify the word in the question that indicates that an estimate is required. Then have them identify the unit of length they will use.

■ Have children use a ruler to measure the 1-centimeter line and confirm that it is exactly 1 centimeter long.

■ Ask children to identify other objects that are about 1 centimeter in length. Have them compare the width of their thumbs to the 1-centimeter line. Then, have them use their thumbs to estimate the length of the pencil. Ask them to compare the results.

■ Discuss why a 1-centimeter line might not be the best tool to use for estimating.

■ Compare the two ways of estimating. To estimate a length, children can use an object that is the approximate length of one unit, or they can use the exact unit to measure an object. Be sure children see that the tip of the pencil is closer to the 12-centimeter mark than the 13-centimeter mark.

Support English Language Learners

Help children make a connection between the words *length* and *long*. Point out that both words can refer to the same measurement. Explain that we measure length to find out how long something is. *Length* refers to the distance from one end of an object to the other end, while *long* refers to the exact length of that object. Give examples and discuss other words that refer to length measurement, such as *width* and *wide*, *height* and *tall*, and *depth* and *deep*.

Connect: What you know about estimating length Use this page to help children strengthen their understanding about estimating length.

■ Ask children to show each of the measurements without using a measuring tool: 3 inches, 3 centimeters, 3 feet, and 3 meters. Children may use their fingers or arms to mark off each length. Reassure them that you do not expect their measurements to be exact, but that you are looking for an approximation of each length.

■ Point out that children will need to be able to explain whether they think the measurement is a good estimate. Remind children that the words "too long" and "too short" explain whether or not the estimate works.

Lesson 19   Estimate Length

Guided Instruction

Connect: What you know about estimating length

Which is the best estimate for the length of a classroom desk?

| 3 inches | 3 centimeters | 3 feet | 3 meters |

Step 1

Think about the size of a classroom desk.

Is a desk longer or shorter than this book? _____longer_____

Is a desk longer or shorter than a truck? _____shorter_____

Step 2

Look at each choice. Think about the size of each unit of length.

Is 3 inches a good estimate for the desk? _____no_____

3 inches is too _____short_____.

Is 3 centimeters a good estimate for the desk? _____no_____

3 centimeters is too _____short_____.

Is 3 feet a good estimate for the desk? _____yes_____

3 feet is a good estimate.

Is 3 meters a good estimate for the desk? _____no_____

3 meters is too _____long_____.

▷ The best estimate for the length of a classroom desk is _____3 feet_____.

Remember!
I foot is the same as 12 inches.
I meter is the same as 100 centimeters.

172   Unit 3 ■ Focus on Measurement and Data

Math-to-Sports Connection

Fishing Explain to the class that when people catch fish, they have to decide whether or not the fish is a *keeper*. A keeper is a fish that is big enough to keep. If a fish is too short to be a keeper, it has to be put back into the water where it can live and grow.

Explain that fishermen will estimate the length of a fish to tell if they can keep it or if they need to put it back. A fisherman who is not sure about the length of a fish might use a ruler to measure it. Most of the time, though, an estimate is good enough. Encourage children to suggest other situations where an exact measurement is not needed and an estimate of the measurement would be good enough.

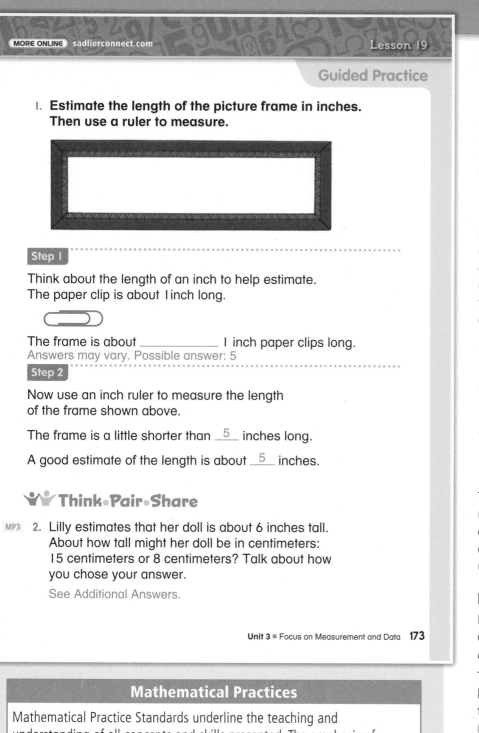

I. **Estimate the length of the picture frame in inches. Then use a ruler to measure.**

Step 1

Think about the length of an inch to help estimate. The paper clip is about 1 inch long.

The frame is about _____ 1 inch paper clips long.
Answers may vary. Possible answer: 5

Step 2

Now use an inch ruler to measure the length of the frame shown above.

The frame is a little shorter than __5__ inches long.

A good estimate of the length is about __5__ inches.

☺☺ Think•Pair•Share

MP3 2. Lilly estimates that her doll is about 6 inches tall. About how tall might her doll be in centimeters: 15 centimeters or 8 centimeters? Talk about how you chose your answer.

See Additional Answers.

Unit 3 ■ Focus on Measurement and Data **173**

Mathematical Practices

Mathematical Practice Standards underline the teaching and understanding of all concepts and skills presented. The emphasis of specific practices is noted throughout the guided and independent practice of this lesson.

MP3	**Construct viable arguments and critique the reasoning of others.**

Item 2: Children explain how to use an approximate number of inches to estimate an approximate number of centimeters.

Observational Assessment

Use page 173 to assess children's understanding of estimating length. Be sure that children understand that their measurements are not exact, but that they give a good idea of the length of the object.

☺☺ Think•Pair•Share

Peer Collaboration Ask pairs to explain how they chose the best estimate of the doll's height in centimeters. Children should include the comparison of inches and centimeters. Ask:

• *Can you use your fingers to show me about what 6 inches looks like?*

• *Which unit is bigger, inches or centimeters?*

• *Will it take a few more or a lot more centimeters than inches to measure the doll's height?*

To summarize, point out that you can use objects that are close to the length of the unit to estimate the length of an object. Sometimes you will use an exact unit to estimate the length of an object.

Return to the Essential Question

Reread the Lesson 19 Essential Question on page 170: *How do you estimate the length of an object?*

Tell children to think about what they learned in this lesson to answer this question.
(Possible responses: You can use paper clips to estimate one inch. You can check your estimate by measuring the object with a ruler.)

Additional Answers

Item 2: Answers may vary. Possible answer: Lilly's doll might be about 15 centimeters tall. I know this because centimeters are smaller than inches. 8 is too close to 6, so 8 would not be a good estimate.

Concept Application

Children may work independently on these pages in the classroom or at home. They may refer to the first four pages of the lesson to revisit the instruction or to see a worked-out example.

Common Errors and **Teaching Tips** may help you support learning either in the classroom or as a follow-up for work done at home.

Common Errors

Items 1–4

Children may forget to look at the units that they are supposed to use for estimating. Encourage them to read carefully to know whether to use inches or centimeters.

Estimate the length of the object. Then use a ruler to measure it. Estimates may vary.

1.

   estimate: _____ inches

   measurement: __4__ inches

2.

   estimate: _____ inches

   measurement: __5__ inches

3.

   estimate: _____ centimeter

   measurement: __1__ centimeter

4.

   estimate: _____ centimeters

   measurement: __6__ centimeters

174 Unit 3 ■ Focus on Measurement and Data

Talking About Math

Collaborative Conversations Ask children to look at the shovel in problem 2. Remind them that they are estimating the length of the picture of the shovel. Then, ask them to describe an actual shovel. They may tell about a shovel used for gardening, one used for shoveling snow, or one used at the beach for digging in the sand. Children should include an estimate of the length of the actual shovel they mention. Encourage them to give the estimate using two different units.

Lesson 19

Independent Practice

Circle the best estimate.

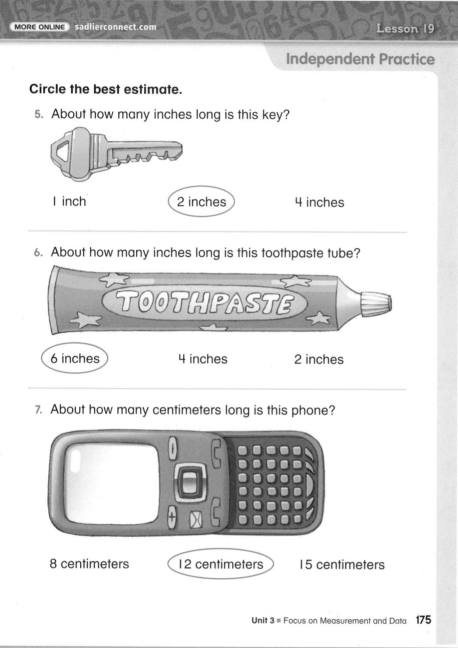

5. About how many inches long is this key?

   1 inch   (2 inches)   4 inches

6. About how many inches long is this toothpaste tube?

   (6 inches)   4 inches   2 inches

7. About how many centimeters long is this phone?

   8 centimeters   (12 centimeters)   15 centimeters

Unit 3 ■ Focus on Measurement and Data **175**

Teaching Tips

Items 5–7

Encourage children to check their estimates using a ruler. Discuss how they can eliminate answer choices that do not make sense by analyzing each choice.

Digital Connection

Interactive Whiteboard Write a specific length, like 12 inches, on the board. Then, have children use an interactive whiteboard and drag and stretch objects until they think the objects appear to be about the given length. Make sure children are estimating the length, and not using measuring tools at this stage. After children are confident about their estimates, ask them to use the ruler to measure to find out if their estimates were close to the actual measurements.

Teaching Tips

Items 8-11

For their use in estimating, encourage children to develop their own comparisons between a foot and a meter. They may say, for example, that 1 meter is about 3 feet. Be sure children understand that a given length can be measured using more short units or fewer long units.

Circle the best estimate.

8. Length of a bathtub　　2 feet　　4 feet　　(6 feet)

9. Length of a desk　　(1 meter)　　3 meters　　5 meters

10. Length of this book　　(1 foot)　　2 feet　　3 feet

11. Length of a car　　1 meter　　(4 meters)　　10 meters

Circle the correct answer.

12. Which is the best estimate for the length of a spoon?

　16 inches　　(16 centimeters)　　16 feet

13. Which is the best estimate for the length of a dollar bill?

　(6 inches)　　6 centimeters　　6 meters

14. Which is the best estimate for the length of your shoe?

　(20 centimeters)　　20 feet　　20 meters

Math-to-History Connection

Ancient Units of Measurement　As a class, use the Internet to investigate ancient units of measure. Explore how the length of the unit foot came to be a standardized measurement from once being the length of a king's actual foot.

Encourage a discussion of how measurements would differ if people still measured things with their feet and hands. Ask children to think about the sizes of their feet and the sizes of adults' feet. If time allows, have several children count their steps as they walk the distance from one doorway to another. Have them compare their numbers of steps to see whether or not everyone took the same number. Have children try to explain any differences in their measurements.

Lesson 19

Independent Practice

MP6 **15.** Tina and Gwen estimate the length of the playground slide. Tina thinks the slide is about 3 meters long. Gwen thinks it is about 8 meters long. They measure the slide and find that it is 350 centimeters long. Whose estimate was better? Explain your reasoning.

Answers may vary. Possible answer: Tina's estimate was better. She estimated that the slide is about 3 meters long. 3 meters is the same as 300 centimeters. Since the slide is 350 centimeters, Tina's estimate is closer to the actual length. 8 meters is the same as 800 centimeters, so Gwen's estimate is too long.

MP3 **16.** Use a centimeter ruler to measure the length of this crayon.

Explain how the measurement of the crayon would change if you used an inch ruler to measure it.

The crayon is 11 centimeters long. Answers may vary. Possible answer: 1 inch is a longer unit of measure than 1 centimeter. If I measure in inches it will measure fewer inches than if I measure in centimeters.

Common Errors

Item 16
Children may think that there would be more inches since inches are longer than centimeters. Remind them that because an inch is longer than a centimeter, there will be fewer of them used to measure the same length.

Mathematical Practices

MP3	Construct viable arguments and critique the reasoning of others.

Item 16: Children measure and then analyze how their measurement would change if it were measured with a different unit.

MP6	Attend to precision.

Item 15: Children compare estimates and communicate why one estimate is better than the other.

Common Core Focus:

2.MD.4 Measure to determine how much longer one object is than another, expressing the length difference in terms of a standard length unit.

OBJECTIVE
Compare the lengths of two objects.

ESSENTIAL QUESTION
Hold up two objects of different lengths several inches apart and ask children to tell which is longer. Have children explain how they compared the two objects. Read the Essential Question aloud and tell children that they will learn other ways to compare lengths in this lesson.

FLUENCY PRACTICE
Fluency practice is available at **sadlierconnect.com**.

Concept Development

Understand: You can find how much longer one object is than another

■ In first grade, children compared the lengths of objects by describing one object as being longer or shorter than the other. They did not determine how much longer one object was than the other. In this lesson, children will continue to apply their new skill in measuring in specific units. After they measure objects, they will find the difference in the measurements to determine how much longer one object is than another.

■ Review how to use a ruler. Remind children to line up one end of the object with the 0-mark on the ruler.

■ Have children look at the picture under the question. Have them identify the longer and shorter sticks. Then ask them how much longer the green stick is. Children should realize that they cannot tell how much longer it is. First, they do not know the actual length of either stick, but also because the ends of the sticks are not lined up.

Lesson 20 Compare Lengths

Essential Question:
How can you compare the lengths of two objects?
2.MD.4

Guided Instruction

In this lesson you will learn how to compare the lengths of two objects

Understand: You can find how much longer one object is than another

How many inches longer is the green stick than the blue stick?

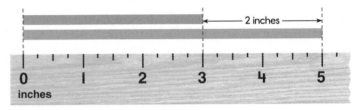

Line up one end of each stick with the 0-mark on an inch ruler.

The blue stick is 3 inches long.
The green stick is 5 inches long.

Find the difference in the lengths.
  5 inches − 3 inches = 2 inches

⇨ The green stick is 2 inches longer than the blue stick.

Support English Language Learners

Write the words *shorter* and *longer* on the board. Circle the suffix *–er*. Explain that when the suffix *–er* is added to a describing word, or adjective, the word compares two things. *Shorter* means more short, and *longer* means more long. Write some other examples on the board, such as bigger, larger, taller, and greater. Have children underline the *–er* suffix in each.

MORE ONLINE sadlierconnect.com

Lesson 20

**Understand: You can find how much shorter
one object is than another**

How many centimeters shorter is the yellow pencil
than the red pencil?

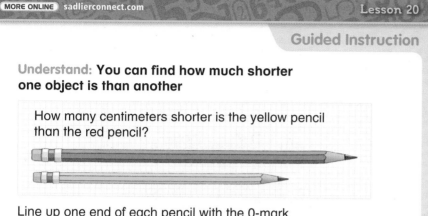

Line up one end of each pencil with the 0-mark
on a centimeter ruler.

←3 centimeters→

0 1 2 3 4 5 6 7 8 9 10 11 12 13 14
centimeters

The red pencil is 14 centimeters long.
The yellow pencil is 11 centimeters long.

Find the difference in the lengths.

14 centimeters − 11 centimeters = 3 centimeters

▷ The yellow pencil is 3 centimeters shorter
than the red pencil.

Unit 3 ▪ Focus on Measurement and Data **179**

Concept Development

Understand: You can find how
much shorter one object is
than another

■ In this presentation, children will
compare the lengths of two objects
using a centimeter ruler. They will also
determine how much longer one object
is than the other.

■ Have children read the question and
identify the unit of measure that they
will use to compare the lengths. Ask
children to identify the shorter pencil.
Discuss how they know it is shorter. Ask
them to identify the longer pencil if the
shorter pencil is yellow. Explain that if
one pencil is longer, the other pencil
is shorter.

■ Have children identify the exact
length of each pencil. Encourage them
to use the picture to find how much
shorter the yellow pencil is. Relate the
difference in length to the image on
the ruler. Children should see that they
could count the spaces from the end of
the yellow pencil to the end of the red
pencil to find how much shorter the
yellow pencil is.

■ Ask children what operation they will
use to determine how much shorter the
yellow pencil is.

Math-to-Driving Connection

Driving Distances Explain to children that when traveling in a car,
the driver may use a map or a GPS device to find the shorter route to
wherever he or she is going. Encourage children to discuss what reasons
the driver would have for wanting to choose a shorter route rather than
a longer route. Have children relate how this method of thinking can be
applied to comparing the lengths of two objects, as in this lesson.

Guided Instruction

Connect: What you know about comparing lengths Use this page to help children strengthen their understanding of comparing lengths.

■ Ask children to look at the picture of the two carrots. Ask them to identify the longer carrot and the shorter carrot.

■ Read the question aloud. Emphasize that the standard unit they should use is centimeters. Ask children to estimate how much shorter Jean's carrot is.

■ Have children describe how to use a ruler to measure the lengths of the carrots. Then, ask them to read the markings on the ruler and find the measurement of each carrot.

■ Have children identify the difference in the lengths of the carrots and compare the results to their estimates. Challenge children to say another way to summarize the results.

Guided Instruction

Connect: What you know about comparing lengths

Lisa and Jean each pick a carrot from the garden. How many centimeters shorter is Jean's carrot?

Lisa's carrot

Jean's carrot

Step 1

Line up both carrots with the __0__-mark on a centimeter ruler.

Step 2

Measure the length of each carrot.

Lisa's carrot

Jean's carrot

Lisa's carrot measures __9__ centimeters long.

Jean's carrot measures __8__ centimeters long.

0 1 2 3 4 5 6 7 8 9 10 11 12 13 14
centimeters

Subtract: 10 centimeters − 9 centimeters = __1__ centimeter

▷ Jean's carrot is __1__ centimeter shorter than Lisa's.

Math-to-Sports Connection

Trophies Athletes often collect trophies that they win at tournaments or in championships. Trophies come in all different shapes and sizes. Explain to children that they can use the same process shown in the lessons to compare the heights of trophies. Encourage children to think of how they would have to lay the trophy down on its side in order to measure its "length." Have children explain how they would measure the lengths of two different trophies and then subtract to find how much taller or how much shorter one is than the other.

Lesson 20

Guided Practice

I. **How many inches longer is the green yarn than the red yarn?**

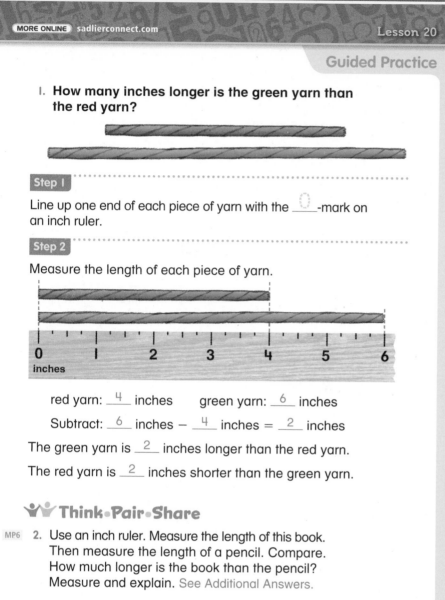

Step 1

Line up one end of each piece of yarn with the __0__-mark on an inch ruler.

Step 2

Measure the length of each piece of yarn.

red yarn: __4__ inches   green yarn: __6__ inches

Subtract: __6__ inches − __4__ inches = __2__ inches

The green yarn is __2__ inches longer than the red yarn.

The red yarn is __2__ inches shorter than the green yarn.

Think•Pair•Share

MP6 2. Use an inch ruler. Measure the length of this book. Then measure the length of a pencil. Compare. How much longer is the book than the pencil? Measure and explain. See Additional Answers.

Observational Assessment

Use page 181 to assess children's understanding of comparing lengths of objects. Be sure that they understand that it is important for their measurements to be precise.

Think•Pair•Share

Peer Collaboration Ask pairs to show their pencil and book and then share how much longer the book is. Remind them to follow the directions carefully. Ask:

- *What standard unit should you use to measure the book and pencil?*

- *How will you measure the lengths of the book and pencil?*

- *How will you find out how much longer the book is?*

Return to the Essential Question

Reread the Lesson 20 Essential Question on page 178: *How can you compare the lengths of two objects?*

Tell children to think about what they learned in this lesson to answer this question.

(Possible responses: You can measure the length of each object using the given measurement unit. Then you can subtract the length of one object from the length of another object to find which one is longer or shorter.)

Additional Answers

Item 2: Answers may vary. Possible answer: This book is 11 inches long. My pencil is 7 inches long. 11 − 7 = 4, so the book is 4 inches longer than my pencil.

Mathematical Practices

Mathematical Practice Standards underline the teaching and understanding of all concepts and skills presented. The emphasis of specific practices is noted throughout the guided and independent practice of this lesson.

MP6	Attend to precision.

Item 2: Children use a ruler to measure two objects and compare their lengths.

Concept Application

Children may work independently on these pages in the classroom or at home. They may refer to the first four pages of the lesson to revisit the instruction or to see a worked-out example.

Common Errors and **Teaching Tips** may help you support learning either in the classroom or as a follow-up for work done at home.

Teaching Tips

Items 1–2

Encourage children to write a subtraction equation to find the difference between the lengths of the objects. Help them recognize that the difference tells them both how much longer and how much shorter one object is than the other.

Measure each object. Find the difference between the lengths. Write how much longer. Then write how much shorter.

1.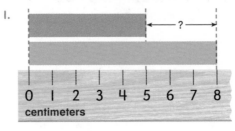

The purple tile is
_5_ centimeters long.

The green tile is
_8_ centimeters long.

The green tile is _3_ centimeters longer than the purple tile.
The purple tile is _3_ centimeters shorter than the green tile.

2.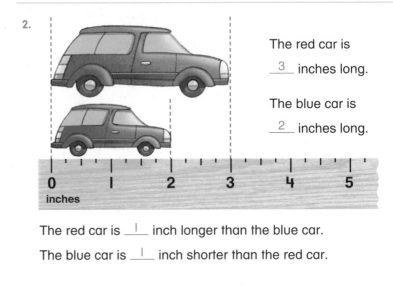

The red car is
_3_ inches long.

The blue car is
_2_ inches long.

The red car is _1_ inch longer than the blue car.
The blue car is _1_ inch shorter than the red car.

Talking About Math

Collaborative Conversations Divide the class into groups of 3 or 4. Provide each member of the group with an object and an inch ruler and ask children to measure their object. Then, ask the group to compare the lengths of their objects and tell how they can compare some of the lengths. A child might say, for example, "My truck is 4 inches shorter than Aiden's block, but it is 1 inch longer than Sara's eraser." Invite each group to share their objects and their results with the class.

MORE ONLINE sadlierconnect.com

Independent Practice

Measure each object. Find the difference between the lengths. Write how much longer. Then write how much shorter.

3. Use a centimeter ruler to measure the fork and the spoon.

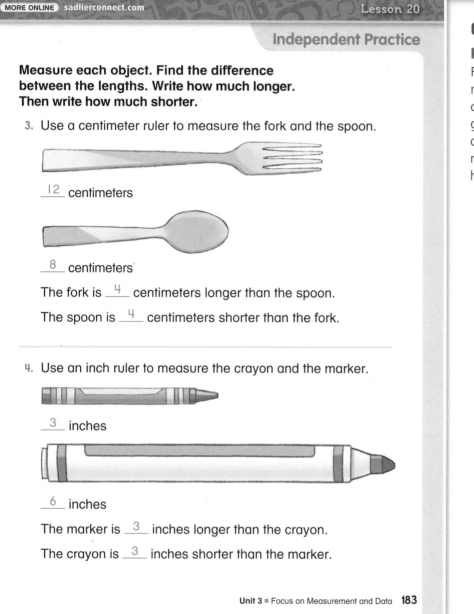

__12__ centimeters

__8__ centimeters

The fork is __4__ centimeters longer than the spoon.

The spoon is __4__ centimeters shorter than the fork.

4. Use an inch ruler to measure the crayon and the marker.

__3__ inches

__6__ inches

The marker is __3__ inches longer than the crayon.

The crayon is __3__ inches shorter than the marker.

Unit 3 ■ Focus on Measurement and Data **183**

Common Errors

Items 3–4

Remind children how to use a ruler to measure precisely. Be sure that they choose the appropriate ruler for the given unit. See that they align one end of the object with the 0-mark on the ruler or with the left end of a ruler that has no 0-mark.

Digital Connection

Interactive Whiteboard Activity Have children choose two different objects to place on the interactive whiteboard. Then, ask them to use the ruler to measure and then compare the lengths of the objects. Encourage children to tell how much longer or how much shorter one object is than the other.

Independent Practice

Teaching Tips

Items 5-6

Tell children that there is only one answer, but there are several steps that they must follow to get the answer. To help children compare the lengths, provide a list of steps for them to follow. Remind them to measure each object and then subtract one length from the other.

Independent Practice

Measure each object.
Find the difference between the lengths.

5. How many centimeters shorter is the paper clip than the feather?

The paper clip is __4__ centimeters shorter than the feather.

6. How many inches longer is the red block than the blue block?

blue

red

The red block is __2__ inches longer than the blue block.

Math-to-Sports Connection

Track and Field At a track-and-field event, some athletes participate in the long jump, where the object is to jump the farthest. Explain to children how the length of each competitor's jump is measured and how the lengths are compared. Explain that long-jump competitors may compare their performances by saying, for example, "My jump was 4 inches shorter than the winner's jump" or "I jumped 2 inches farther than the last record jump."

Tell children to think about how far they might be able to jump. Then mark a chalk line on the floor a measured distance from the wall. Allow children to take turns jumping and marking where they landed. Have them compare their results to find out who jumped the farthest.

MP3 **7.** Cindy's bracelet is 22 centimeters long. Emily's bracelet is 18 centimeters long. How many centimeters longer would Emily's bracelet need to be to make it the same length as Cindy's bracelet? Talk about your answer.

Answers may vary. Possible answer: Cindy's bracelet is 4 centimeters longer than Emily's. $22 - 18 = 4$. So Emily's bracelet would need to be 4 centimeters longer to be the same length as Cindy's bracelet.

MP5 **8.** Find two objects to measure in your classroom. Draw each object below. Choose one tool to measure the length of each. Write the length of each object below its picture.

Which object is longer? How much longer? Show your work.

Children's answers will vary. Check children's work to make sure appropriate units/tools were chosen, measurements were accurately done, and correct comparisons were made.

Teaching Tips

Item 7
Tell children that there is a hidden question in this problem. Ask them who has a longer bracelet. Then guide them to find how much longer Cindy's bracelet is.

Mathematical Practices	
MP3	**Construct viable arguments and critique the reasoning of others.**

Item 7: Children compare the lengths of two objects to determine how much longer one would need to be to match the length of the other.

MP5	**Use appropriate tools strategically.**

Item 8: Children choose an appropriate tool to measure two objects and find the difference in their lengths.

Common Core Focus:

2.MD.5 Use addition and subtraction within 100 to solve word problems involving lengths that are given in the same units and equations with a symbol for the unknown number to represent the problem.

OBJECTIVE

Add or subtract lengths to solve a problem.

ESSENTIAL QUESTION

Read the Essential Question aloud. Ask children to recall how to compare the lengths of two objects. Discuss key ideas, such as adding to find the sum of two lengths and subtracting to find the difference between two lengths.

FLUENCY PRACTICE

Fluency practice is available at **sadlierconnect.com**.

Concept Development

Understand: You can add lengths to solve a problem

■ Ask children to analyze the picture of the two trains and explain that the picture relates the lengths of the trains. Have children tell what they think they need to find.

■ Children should be encouraged to talk about which form of an addition equation they think is easier to solve.

■ Emphasize that the length unit, centimeters, must be included in the answer. Point out that, without the unit, the answer would not be complete.

Lesson 21

Add and Subtract Lengths

Guided Instruction

In this lesson you will learn how to add or subtract lengths to solve a problem.

Understand: You can add lengths to solve a problem

> Brad has a red toy train car that is 26 centimeters long. He has a green toy train car that is 11 centimeters longer. How long is the green toy train car?

You can use a picture to help solve the problem.

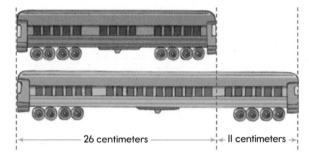

←——— 26 centimeters ———→ ←— 11 centimeters —→

Add to find the total length of the green toy train car.

Write an equation.

26 + 11 = ▩

Solve.
$$\begin{array}{r} 2\,6 \\ +\,1\,1 \\ \hline 3\,7 \end{array}$$

▷ The green toy train car is 37 centimeters long.

Support English Language Learners

English language learners may be confused by the multiple meanings of the word *left*. Ask children to hold up their left hands. Explain that *left* can refer to a direction or to a position. Also explain that *left* can refer to what remains after you subtract. Relate that you start with an amount, subtract some, and then what you get is what you have *left*.

Write a few subtraction equations on the board. Point to the corresponding numbers in one equation as you say, *I start with—. Then I take away—. Now I have—left.* Have volunteers use the same sentence frames to identify the numbers in each of the subtraction equations on the board.

Lesson 21

Guided Instruction

Understand: You can subtract lengths to solve a problem

> Moriah has a piece of yarn 50 centimeters long.
> She cuts off a piece that is 13 centimeters long.
> How much yarn does Moriah have left?

Draw a picture to show the yarn and label the parts.

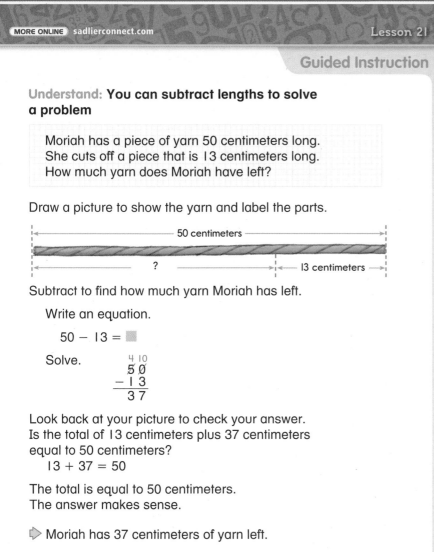

Subtract to find how much yarn Moriah has left.

Write an equation.

$$50 - 13 = \blacksquare$$

Solve.

$$\begin{array}{r} {\scriptstyle 4\ 10} \\ 5\,\cancel{0} \\ -\ 1\ 3 \\ \hline 3\ 7 \end{array}$$

Look back at your picture to check your answer.
Is the total of 13 centimeters plus 37 centimeters equal to 50 centimeters?

$$13 + 37 = 50$$

The total is equal to 50 centimeters.
The answer makes sense.

▷ Moriah has 37 centimeters of yarn left.

Unit 3 ▪ Focus on Measurement and Data **187**

Understand: You can subtract lengths to solve a problem

■ Use an actual piece of yarn or string to model the problem. Ask children if the yarn that is left will be longer or shorter than the yarn Moriah had at the start. Children should understand that the yarn that is left will be shorter.

■ Explain that the question mark in the drawing represents how much yarn is left. Ask children to tell which operation to use to find how much is left.

■ Relate the subtraction equation to both the picture and the problem. Make sure children understand why they are subtracting and what each number represents.

■ If necessary, review subtraction with regrouping. Remind children that they cannot always subtract the lesser digit from the greater digit. If the top digit is less than the bottom digit in the same place-value position, then regrouping is needed.

■ Have children talk about how they can check the answer to this subtraction problem by adding.

Math-to-Sports Connection

Football Explain that in order to score points in football, players have to move the ball forward a certain number of yards towards a goal line. Then explain that players can sometimes get called for a penalty, or a mistake, which means that the ball has to be moved away from the goal line a certain number of yards. Write the following problem on the board and have pairs of children work together to solve it. Then, have volunteers share their problem-solving methods with the class. *The Red Birds moved the football forward 23 yards. Then, they received a penalty and had to move the ball back 15 yards. Next, they moved the ball forward 7 yards. How many yards forward did the football travel in all?*

Connect: **What you know about adding and subtracting lengths to solve a problem** Use this page to help children strengthen their understanding of solving problems by adding and subtracting lengths.

■ Explain that children will sometimes have to complete more than one step to solve a problem. The steps could involve just addition, just subtraction, or both addition and subtraction.

■ Ask how to find the length of Boards 1 and 2 together. Discuss why adding the lengths of these boards makes sense in this problem.

■ Children should understand that in order to find the length of Board 3, they have to subtract the sum of the lengths of Boards 1 and 2 from the length of the whole shelf.

■ Ask if anyone has a different way to solve. Some children might start with the length of the whole shelf and then subtract the lengths of Board 1 and Board 2 individually.

■ Ask children to tell how they could check their answer.

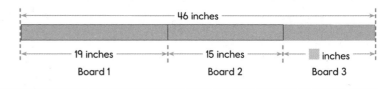

Lesson 21   **Add and Subtract Lengths**

Guided Instruction

Connect: **What you know about adding and subtracting lengths to solve a problem**

Connor is building a bookshelf using three boards.
He wants the shelf to be 46 inches long.
Board 1 is 19 inches long.
Board 2 is 15 inches long.
How long should Board 3 be?

Step 1

Draw a picture to model the problem.

46 inches
19 inches	15 inches	▮ inches
Board 1	Board 2	Board 3

Step 2

Add to find the total length of Boards 1 and 2.

19 inches + 15 inches = ? inches

$$\begin{array}{r} 1\ 9 \\ +\ 1\ 5 \\ \hline 3\ 4 \end{array}$$

The total length of Board 1 and Board 2 is 34 inches.

Step 3

Subtract to find how long Board 3 should be.

46 inches − 34 inches = ▮ inches

$$\begin{array}{r} 4\ 6 \\ -\ 3\ 4 \\ \hline 1\ 2 \end{array}$$

▷ Board 3 should be __12__ inches long.

Math-to-Sewing Connection

Piecing Fabric Explain that fabric to be used for sewing comes in certain widths. People who have fabric that is not wide enough for what they want to sew can put pieces of the fabric together to make a wider piece. Help children work in pairs to model this.

Give each pair four 3 in. × 8 in. strips of paper, four 3-in. squares of paper, a ruler, and tape. Tell children to pretend that the paper is their "fabric" for making a placemat. Direct them to arrange the pieces and tape them together to form a rectangle that is 12 inches long and 11 inches wide. Have volunteers explain how they arranged the pieces to form the placemat.

Lesson 21

Guided Practice

I. Mrs. Clarke's classroom is 32 feet long. Mr. Frank's classroom is 5 feet shorter than Mrs. Clarke's classroom. How long is Mr. Frank's classroom?

Step 1

Draw a picture to show the classrooms. Label the parts.

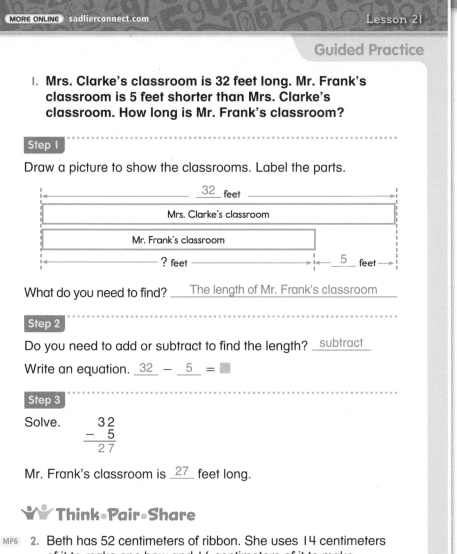

What do you need to find? _The length of Mr. Frank's classroom_

Step 2

Do you need to add or subtract to find the length? _subtract_

Write an equation. _32_ − _5_ = ■

Step 3

Solve.
$$\begin{array}{r} 3\,2 \\ -\ \ 5 \\ \hline 2\,7 \end{array}$$

Mr. Frank's classroom is _27_ feet long.

★ Think•Pair•Share

MP6 **2.** Beth has 52 centimeters of ribbon. She uses 14 centimeters of it to make one bow and 16 centimeters of it to make another bow. How much ribbon does Beth have left? Explain.
See Additional Answers.

Unit 3 ■ Focus on Measurement and Data **189**

Mathematical Practices

Mathematical Practice Standards underline the teaching and understanding of all concepts and skills presented. The emphasis of specific practices is noted throughout the guided and independent practice of this lesson.

MP6 | **Attend to precision.**

Item 2: Children add and subtract to solve a two-step measurement problem.

Observational Assessment

Use page 189 to assess children's understanding of adding and subtracting lengths to solve problems. Be sure they understand when to add and when to subtract. Continue to remind them to write the unit to label each answer.

★ Think•Pair•Share

Peer Collaboration Pair each child with a partner. Have pairs work together to solve the word problem. As they work, ask questions such as:

- *What are you trying to find?*
- *What is the first step you will take to solve the problem?*
- *What is the second step you will take to solve the problem?*

Ask pairs to explain their solution strategy to the rest of the class. To summarize, point out that there may be more than one way to find the correct answer and sometimes more than one operation can be used to solve.

Return to the Essential Question

Reread the Lesson 21 Essential Question on page 186: *How can you add or subtract lengths to solve a problem?*

Tell children to think about what they learned in this lesson to answer this question.
(Possible responses: I can add or subtract to solve a word problem in the same way I solve an equation. Then I write the unit of measure in the answer. If something gets longer, I know to add. To find out how much is left, I subtract.)

Additional Answers

Item 2: Beth has 22 centimeters of ribbon left. Possible explanation: I subtracted 14 from 52 and got 38. Then I subtracted 16 from 38 and got 22.

Concept Application

Children may work independently on these pages in the classroom or at home. They may refer to the first four pages of the lesson to revisit the instruction or to see a worked-out example.

Common Errors and **Teaching Tips** may help you support learning either in the classroom or as a follow-up for work done at home.

Common Errors

Item 2

Instead of subtracting, some children might add the given lengths to find how long Lonnie's banner is. If so, ask them if a length that is longer than Chelsea's banner would be a reasonable answer.

Solve the problem. Show your work.

1. Dmitri jumped 37 inches. Then he jumped another 32 inches. How far did Dmitri jump in all?

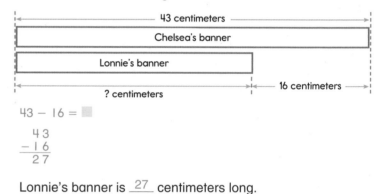

37 inches | 32 inches
? inches

$37 + 32 = \blacksquare$

$$\begin{array}{r} 37 \\ +32 \\ \hline 69 \end{array}$$

Dmitri jumped __69__ inches in all.

2. Chelsea made a banner that is 43 centimeters long. Lonnie made a banner that is 16 centimeters shorter than Chelsea's. How long is Lonnie's banner?

43 centimeters
Chelsea's banner
Lonnie's banner
? centimeters | 16 centimeters

$43 - 16 = \blacksquare$

$$\begin{array}{r} 43 \\ -16 \\ \hline 27 \end{array}$$

Lonnie's banner is __27__ centimeters long.

Talking About Math

Remind children that they had to add to solve problem 1. Now have them tell more about the story in problem 1 so that subtraction will be needed to solve. Children may provide any scenario that indicates that Dmitri's forward progress was cut back. For example, they might start by saying that after Dmitri jumped forward 69 inches, he jumped backward a given number of inches. Have volunteers share their problems and tell how to use subtraction to solve them.

Lesson 21

Independent Practice

Common Errors

Item 4

Some children may add, instead of subtract, because they think the word *farther* suggests addition. If so, explain that *How much farther...?* means the same as *How many more feet...?*

Draw and label a picture for the problem.
Then write an equation to solve the problem.
Solve your equation.

3. Sally has one string of beads that is 25 inches long. She has another string of beads that is 34 inches long. She puts the two together. How long is the string of beads after she puts them together?

After she puts the two together, the string of beads

is __59__ inches long.

4. William skates 56 feet across the ice rink. The ice rink is 80 feet long. How much farther does William need to skate to get all the way across the rink?

William needs to skate __24__ more feet.

Digital Connection

Interactive Whiteboard Have several children copy the pictures they drew for problems 3 and 4 onto the interactive whiteboard. Ask them to describe what they drew to show the parts of the problem. Call on others in the class to tell which drawings best describe the problems.

Common Errors

Item 7

Children may wonder how it is possible for a gate to join a fence that goes across the backyard with one that goes across a front yard. If so, explain that the "backyard fence" also goes around the sides of the house.

Teaching Tips

Items 5–7

Encourage children to draw a picture and write an equation for each problem. Consider having them also use a place-value chart to align the digits as they add or subtract.

Independent Practice

Solve the problem. Show your work.

5. A roll of ribbon is 45 meters long. Mikaela cuts off a piece of the ribbon that is 9 meters long. How much ribbon is left on the roll?

   There are __36__ meters of ribbon left on the roll.

6. Dominic is 42 inches tall. His father is 71 inches tall. How much taller is his father than Dominic?

   Dominic's father is __29__ inches taller than Dominic.

7. The backyard fence is 36 feet long. The front yard fence is 18 feet long. A gate that is 5 feet wide joins the fences together. How long are the fences and the gate altogether?

   The fences and gate are __59__ feet long altogether.

Math-to-Math Connection

Distances on a Map Explain that maps show distances, or how far it is, from one place to another. Ask children to help you draw a map of a town or city on the board. Call on volunteers to name several places that might be in the town. (They may name *supermarket, library, school, park,* and so on.) Record each place on the board. Then, draw straight lines connecting each of the places to the others. Suggest reasonable distances between the places and record these along the lines. Now have pairs of children write a word problem that involve three places and the distances between them. Have children share their word problems with the class.

MP6 **8.** Here is the path that Tommy takes when he walks from home to school. First he walks 32 meters. He turns right and walks 15 meters more. Then he turns left and walks another 20 meters. How many meters does Tommy walk to school?

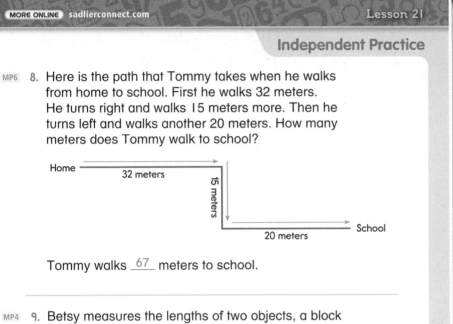

Home
32 meters
15 meters
20 meters
School

Tommy walks __67__ meters to school.

MP4 **9.** Betsy measures the lengths of two objects, a block of wood and a glue stick. The block is longer than the glue stick. One of the objects is 12 centimeters long. The sum of the two lengths is 30 centimeters. Find the length of each object. Show your work.

Answers may vary. Possible answer: I wrote the equation
12 + ■ = 30. I used a related subtraction fact to find the
missing measurement. 30 − 12 = ■ and 30 − 18 = 20.
So one object is 12 centimeters long and the other is
18 centimeters long. Since the block is longer than the glue
stick, the block must be 18 centimeters long and the glue
stick must be 12 centimeters long.

Unit 3 ■ Focus on Measurement and Data **193**

Common Errors

Item 8

Some children might think that because the path is not straight, they cannot add the lengths. Explain that lengths can be added even if they do not form a straight line. Point out that even though Tommy made two turns, he still walked all the way from home to school.

Mathematical Practices

MP4	**Model with mathematics.**

Item 9: Children model and solve a complex problem using mathematical sentences.

MP6	**Attend to precision.**

Item 8: Children read a map and then add to find the total distance walked from home to school.

Common Core Focus:

2.MD.6 Represent whole numbers as lengths from 0 on a number line diagram with equally spaced points corresponding to the numbers 0, 1, 2, ..., and represent whole-number sums and differences within 100 on a number line diagram.

OBJECTIVE
Use a number line to add and to subtract.

ESSENTIAL QUESTION
In this lesson, children will model forward jumps along a number line to represent addition and backward jumps to represent subtraction.

FLUENCY PRACTICE
Fluency practice is available at **sadlierconnect.com**.

Concept Development

Understand: Use a number line to add

■ Have children analyze and describe the number-line diagram. They should indicate that the tick marks along the number line are equally spaced. Moving from left to right, the numbers increase by 1s.

■ Lead children to explain that the arrow on the right end of the number line represents numbers greater than 20. Then explain that there are numbers less than 1 represented by the arrow on the left end of the number line.

■ Review that children solved this problem by starting at 10 on the number line and jumping forward 4. Challenge them to tell if the total number of jumps would be different if they started at 4 and jumped forward 10. Confirm that the order of the addends does not matter, so the answer would be the same. But starting at 4 would take 10 jumps. So it makes sense to start from the greater number, 10, so as to make fewer jumps.

---

22 Number Line Diagrams

Essential Question:
How do you use a number line to add and subtract?
2.MD.6

Words to Know
number line

In this lesson you will learn how to use a number line to add and to subtract.

Understand: Use a number line to add

> Maya read 10 pages of a book in the library. She read 4 more pages at home. How many pages of the book did she read in all?

Use a number line to add 10 and 4. Start at 10. To add 4, make four jumps forward.

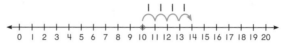

When you start at 10, and make four forward jumps of 1, you land on 14.

$$10 + 4 = 14$$

▷ Maya read 14 pages of the book in all.

You can also show 10 + 4 with one jump.
Start at 10.
Jump forward 4.

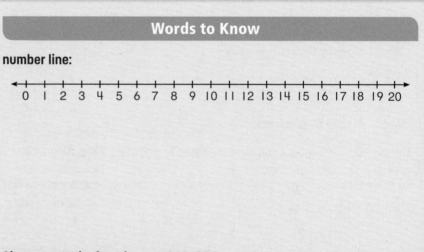

$$10 + 4 = \underline{14}$$

Words to Know

number line:

$$\underset{0 \ 1 \ 2 \ 3 \ 4 \ 5 \ 6 \ 7 \ 8 \ 9 \ 10 \ 11 \ 12 \ 13 \ 14 \ 15 \ 16 \ 17 \ 18 \ 19 \ 20}{\longleftrightarrow}$$

Glossary can be found on pp. 293–304.

MORE ONLINE sadlierconnect.com

Lesson 22

Guided Instruction

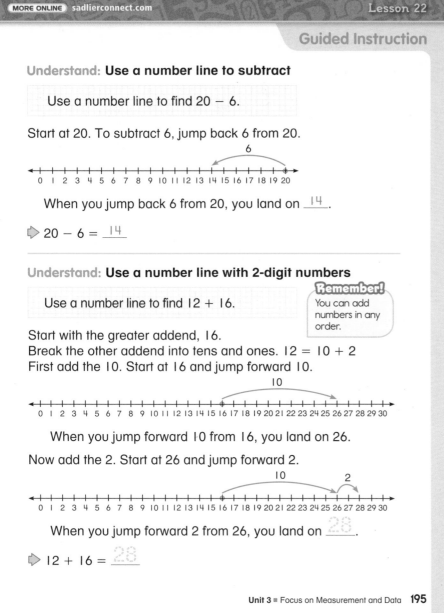

Understand: Use a number line to subtract

Use a number line to find 20 − 6.

Start at 20. To subtract 6, jump back 6 from 20.

6

0 1 2 3 4 5 6 7 8 9 10 11 12 13 14 15 16 17 18 19 20

When you jump back 6 from 20, you land on __14__.

▷ 20 − 6 = __14__

Understand: Use a number line with 2-digit numbers

Use a number line to find 12 + 16.

Remember!
You can add numbers in any order.

Start with the greater addend, 16.
Break the other addend into tens and ones. 12 = 10 + 2
First add the 10. Start at 16 and jump forward 10.

10

0 1 2 3 4 5 6 7 8 9 10 11 12 13 14 15 16 17 18 19 20 21 22 23 24 25 26 27 28 29 30

When you jump forward 10 from 16, you land on 26.

Now add the 2. Start at 26 and jump forward 2.

10   2

0 1 2 3 4 5 6 7 8 9 10 11 12 13 14 15 16 17 18 19 20 21 22 23 24 25 26 27 28 29 30

When you jump forward 2 from 26, you land on 28.

▷ 12 + 16 = 28

Unit 3 ■ Focus on Measurement and Data **195**

Support English Language Learners

The terms *jump forward* and *jump back* can be confusing to English language learners because these terms are not usually used to describe 2-dimensional representations. Explain that on the number line, *forward* means moving to the right toward greater numbers, while *back* means moving to the left toward lesser numbers.

Understand: Use a number line to subtract

■ Ask children why 20 is the starting point for this problem. They should remember to always subtract the lesser number from the greater number.

■ Have children count back aloud from 20. Be sure that the first number they say as they count back is 19, and not 20.

■ One big jump of 6 appears on this number line. Ask children to talk about how they could instead make 6 jumps of 1.

■ Ask children to compare this problem to the problem on page 194. Children should understand that the previous problem shows jumping forward to add. This problem shows jumping back to subtract.

Understand: Use a number line with 2-digit numbers

■ Ask children to identify ways this problem and number line are alike and different from the problem above and the problem on page 194.

■ Remind children that while the order of the addends does not matter, starting with the greater addend means having to make fewer jumps.

■ Once children have broken the lesser addend into tens and ones, have them use their mental math skills to add 10. Ask them how they can know the sum of 16 + 10 without making ten jumps of 1.

■ After children have finished the problem, ask them how the addend 12 is represented on the number line. You may wish to have them write 10 + 2 = 12.

Guided Instruction

Connect: What you know about number lines Use this page to help children extend their understanding of how to use a number line to subtract.

■ Be sure children know that they need to move back, or to the left, on the number line in order to subtract.

■ Ask why 26 is where the first jump starts for this problem and whether it would work to use 18 as the starting point.

■ Encourage children to determine where the first jump will land without making individual jumps of 1. They should be able to use mental math skills and their understanding of subtracting 10 to determine the landing point.

■ For Step 2, ask why 8 is broken into 6 and 2. Have children look at the number line and point out that subtracting 6 from 16 results in 10. Remind children that using mental math to determine this is a way to make solving more efficient.

■ Once Step 2 has been completed, have children summarize the action by describing how 18 is represented on the number line.

Guided Instruction

Connect: What you know about number lines

> Marco has 26 stamps. He gives 18 away.
> How many stamps does he have left?
> Use a number line to subtract 18 from 26.

Step 1

Start at 26 on the number line.

Break 18 into tens and ones. $18 = 10 + \underline{8}$

First subtract 10. Jump back 10 from 26.

Land on 16.

Step 2

Now subtract 8. Break 8 into 6 and 2.

Jump back 6 from 16. Land on $\underline{10}$.

Jump back 2 from 10. Land on $\underline{8}$.

$26 - 18 = \underline{8}$

▷ Marco has $\underline{8}$ stamps left.

Math-to-Math Connection

Using a Ruler Point out that a ruler is a lot like a number-line diagram. Distribute large sheets of paper and 30-cm rulers to pairs. Explain that children will draw a number-line diagram marked in centimeters. The first partner should hold the ruler in place while the other partner draws a 30-cm line with an arrowhead at each end. That partner also makes 1-cm marks from left to right along the line. The first partner can now write the numbers 0 to 30 below the marks.

Encourage pairs to write an addition and a subtraction equation. Each equation should use three numbers from 0 to 30. Have pairs use one color to mark the jumps that show how to solve their addition equation and another color to show the jumps for their subtraction equation.

Lesson 22

Guided Practice

I. Maria has 42 beads. Her sister gives her 16 more beads. How many beads does Maria have now?

Use a number line.

Step 1

Start at ___42___ on the number line.

Break 16 into tens and ones. $16 = 10 + $ ___6___

To add 10, jump forward ___10___ from ___42___.

Step 2

To add 6, jump forward ___6___ from ___52___.

Land on ___58___.

$42 + 16 = $ ___58___

Maria has ___58___ beads.

☺☺ Think·Pair·Share

MP3 **2.** What if Maria's sister gave her 25 beads instead of 16 beads? How would you use the number line to find $42 + 25$?

Answers may vary. Possible answer: From 42, jump forward 10 to 52, then jump forward 10 more to 62. Finally, from 62, jump forward 5 to 67. So, $42 + 25 = 67$.

Mathematical Practices

Mathematical Practice Standards underline the teaching and understanding of all concepts and skills presented. The emphasis of specific practices is noted throughout the guided and independent practice of this lesson.

MP3	**Construct viable arguments and critique the reasoning of others.**

Item 2: Children build on their understanding of the previous problem to determine a new solution, and then compare the new solution to the previous one.

Observational Assessment

Use page 197 to assess children's understanding of how to add and subtract using a number line. Take note of those children whose answers are always off by 1, as this would indicate that they are probably using the number line incorrectly.

☺☺ Think·Pair·Share

Peer Collaboration Ask pairs to share their methods after determining their answer. While they work, ask children questions such as:

• *How is this problem different from the first problem?*

• *How did you use the number line to solve this problem?*

• *Is there another way you could solve this problem?*

To summarize, point out that when children use a number line to add or subtract, they must first decide how to break the lesser addend to make the problem easier to solve.

Return to the Essential Question

Reread the Lesson 22 Essential Question on page 194: *How do you use a number line to add and subtract?*

Tell children to think about what they learned in this lesson to answer this question.

(Possible response: To add, I start with the greater number and jump forward, or to the right. To subtract, I start with the greater number and jump back, or to the left. In both cases, I can break the lesser number into its tens and ones to make adding or subtracting easier.)

Concept Application

Children may work independently on these pages in the classroom or at home. They may refer to the first four pages of the lesson to revisit the instruction or to see a worked-out example.

Common Errors and **Teaching Tips** may help you support learning either in the classroom or as a follow-up for work done at home.

Common Errors

Items 1–3

Check that children are counting correctly along the number line. Remind them that they should start counting after the first jump is made, not at the starting point. If children are having trouble, have them draw and label individual jumps of 1.

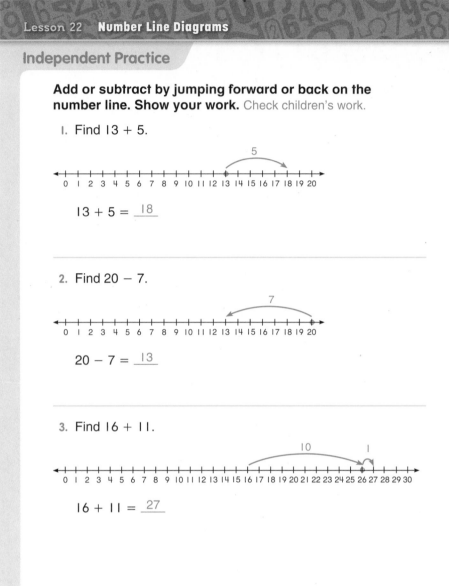

Add or subtract by jumping forward or back on the number line. Show your work. Check children's work.

1. Find 13 + 5.

13 + 5 = __18__

2. Find 20 − 7.

20 − 7 = __13__

3. Find 16 + 11.

16 + 11 = __27__

Talking About Math

Compare Different Methods Give children a subtraction problem and ask them to solve it by breaking the lesser number in two different ways. For example, you might give the problem 25 − 16. Children may solve this by subtracting 25 − 10 − 6. They may also solve by subtracting 25 − 10 − 5 − 1. Record two (or more) ways of solving on the board and invite discussion about them. Provide questions such as: *Which way of solving was faster? Did both ways give you the same answer? Which way do you like better? Why?* Repeat the activity for other problems.

Independent Practice

4. Find 37 − 13. Show how you use the number line to find the answer.

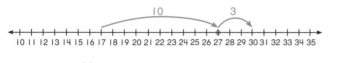

3   10
◄─┼─►
20 21 22 23 24 25 26 27 28 29 30 31 32 33 34 35 36 37 38 39 40

37 − 13 = __24__

5. Find 17 + 13. Show how you use the number line to find the answer.

10   3
◄─┼─►
10 11 12 13 14 15 16 17 18 19 20 21 22 23 24 25 26 27 28 29 30 31 32 33 34 35

17 + 13 = __30__

6. Find 24 − 12. Show how you use the number line to find the answer.

2   10
◄─┼─►
0 1 2 3 4 5 6 7 8 9 10 11 12 13 14 15 16 17 18 19 20 21 22 23 24 25

24 − 12 = __12__

Teaching Tips

Items 4-6
Remind children to break the lesser number in each subtraction problem and the smaller addend in the addition problem into tens and ones. Consider having children write the way they break up the number next to each problem. For example, for problem 6, they would write 13 = 10 + 3.

Digital Connection

Interactive Number Line Find an interactive number line on the Internet. Provide children with practice problems and allow them to use the interactive number line to solve them. Then have them write and solve equations for the practice problems on paper.

Independent Practice

Teaching Tips

Items 7–9

Encourage children to underline important information in the problem before using the number line. Tell them to then write and solve an equation for each problem.

Independent Practice

Add or subtract using a number line to solve the problems. Check children's work.

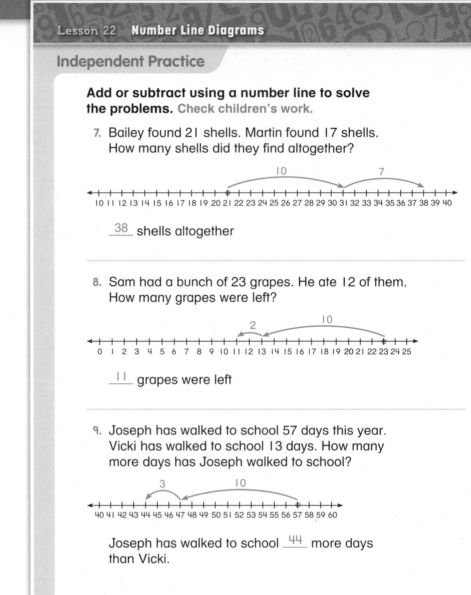

7. Bailey found 21 shells. Martin found 17 shells. How many shells did they find altogether?

   __38__ shells altogether

8. Sam had a bunch of 23 grapes. He ate 12 of them. How many grapes were left?

   __11__ grapes were left

9. Joseph has walked to school 57 days this year. Vicki has walked to school 13 days. How many more days has Joseph walked to school?

   Joseph has walked to school __44__ more days than Vicki.

Math-to-Science Connection

Increasing and Decreasing Temperatures Point to or display a thermometer. Tell children that thermometers are used to measure how warm or how cold it is. Explain that the thermometer is like an up-and-down number line. It is marked in *degrees,* not in inches or centimeters. Each mark on a thermometer stands for 1 degree.

Explain that changes in temperature can be measured on a thermometer. Provide scenarios such as: *In the morning, the temperature was 65°. By evening, the temperature had gone down by 22°. What was the temperature in the evening?* Ask children to write their answer in a sentence related to the problem.

MP1 10. A school bus picked up 13 children at the first stop.
At the second stop, 12 more children got on the bus.
At the third stop, 14 more children got on the bus.
Then how many children in all were on the bus?

Use the number lines to find the answer.

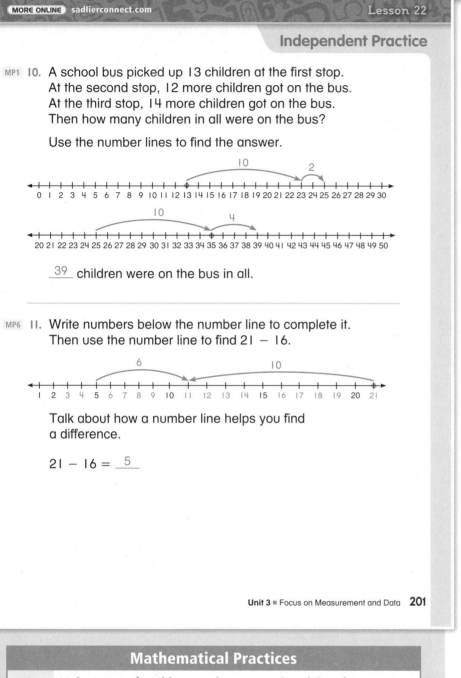

__39__ children were on the bus in all.

MP6 11. Write numbers below the number line to complete it.
Then use the number line to find $21 - 16$.

Talk about how a number line helps you find
a difference.

$21 - 16 = $ __5__

Independent Practice

Common Errors
Item 11
Some children may have trouble writing
numbers small enough to clearly label
this number line. You may want to
enlarge the number line on a copier
machine and then distribute copies so
that children have enough space to write
the numbers below the marks.

Teaching Tips
Item 10
Check that children identify this as a
two-step problem. They should not
try to add all three numbers at once.
Encourage them to jump along the first
number line to find 13 + 12, and then
build off that using the second number
line to find the total sum. Ask children
how using two number lines together
is different from using just one number
line to solve a problem.

Mathematical Practices

MP1	Make sense of problems and persevere in solving them.

Item 10: Children identify a two-step problem and determine a pathway
to the solution prior to solving. They also use number lines to justify
their answer.

MP6	Attend to precision.

Item 11: Children label a number line and then use it to determine the
solution to the problem.

Common Core Focus:

2.MD.7 Tell and write time from analog and digital clocks to the nearest five minutes, using A.M. and P.M.

OBJECTIVE

Read analog and digital clocks to the nearest five minutes.

ESSENTIAL QUESTION

Read the Essential Question aloud to the class. In Grade 1, children learned to tell time to the hour and half hour. In this lesson, they will extend this skill to tell time to the nearest five minutes.

PREREQUISITE SKILLS

Use Foundational Skills Handbook page 286, *Tell Time*, to review reading analog clocks to the nearest hour and half hour.

FLUENCY PRACTICE

Fluency practice is available at **sadlierconnect.com**.

Concept Development

Understand: Read time to the nearest five minutes

■ Have children point to the analog clock at the bottom of the presentation. Be sure that they can identify the hour hand and the minute hand. Explain that this clock is the same as the clock above it, but larger.

■ Encourage children to trace over the jumps that mark the 5-minute intervals around the outside of the clock. Have them use a pencil to point to each of the tiny marks they see on the clock face between the numbers 12 and 1.

■ Lead children to compare the way the time appears on the analog clocks and on the digital clock and explain how both kinds of clocks show the same time.

Essential Question:
How do you tell time to the nearest five minutes?
2.MD.7

Words to Know
hour
minute
midnight
noon
A.M.
P.M.

In this lesson you will learn how to tell time to the nearest five minutes.

Understand: Read time to the nearest five minutes

Renzo's class is on a trip to the zoo. The clock shows the time that the class gets to the zoo. What time does Renzo's class get to the zoo?

Look at the clock below. The short hand is the hour hand. The long hand is the minute hand.

The hour hand is between the 9 and the 10. This means that the time is past 9 o'clock, but not yet 10 o'clock. Look at the marks around the clock face. Each mark stands for one of the 60 minutes that make up 1 hour. There are 5 marks from each number to the next.

Start at 12. Skip count by 5s until you reach the minute hand. It is 20 minutes past 9 o'clock.
The time on the clock is 9:20.

▷ Renzo's class gets to the zoo at 9:20.

You can also show this time on a digital clock.

Words to Know

hour: There are 60 minutes in 1 hour.

minute: There are 60 minutes in 1 hour.

midnight: 12 A.M.

noon: 12 P.M.

A.M.: the time from midnight until noon

P.M.: the time from noon until midnight

Glossary can be found on pp. 293–304.

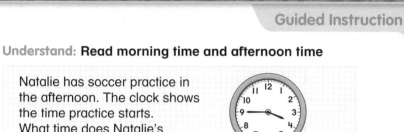

Understand: Read morning time and afternoon time

Natalie has soccer practice in the afternoon. The clock shows the time practice starts. What time does Natalie's soccer practice start?

Find the hour.
The hour hand is between 3 and 4. It is past 3 o'clock, but not yet 4 o'clock.

Find the minutes. Start at 12 on the clock. Skip count by 5s until you reach the minute hand.

The time on the clock is 3:45.

You can also show this time on a digital clock.

Midnight is 12 A.M. Noon is 12 P.M. The time from midnight to noon is A.M. time.
The time from noon until midnight is P.M. time.

Soccer practice is in the afternoon. The afternoon is between noon and midnight. Practice is during P.M. time.

▷ Natalie's soccer practice starts at 3:45 P.M.

Understand: Read morning time and afternoon time

■ Have children read the problem and identify the time that the clocks show.

■ Once children ave identified the time, give them sentences such as, *School starts at 8:00* and *Travis's bedtime is at 8:00.* Ask them how the two events can both happen at 8:00. Children should be able to explain that school starts at 8:00 in the morning while a bedtime is at 8:00 in the evening.

■ Have children list some words that mean *morning* and *evening.* They may give examples such as *daytime, nighttime, afternoon, early, late,* and *after dark.*

■ Once children have read the definitions of A.M. and P.M., have them go back to the problem and identify the word that tells when soccer practice takes place. They should explain that *afternoon* relates to P.M.

■ Remind children of your previous example about when school starts and Travis's bedtime. Have them identify each time as A.M. or P.M.

Support English Language Learners

The notion of passing time can be confusing to a child who comes from another culture because different cultures tell time in different ways. Most people in the United States use a 12-hour clock. Other countries run on a 24-hour clock. Still others have a different understanding of when the day begins and ends. English language learners may need to be taught, for example, that our day starts at midnight and all the times between midnight and noon are A.M. times. The times from 12:00 noon to just before 12:00 midnight are P.M. times. Use time lines, illustrations, books, and online activities to help strengthen children's basic understanding of time before asking them to learn how to tell time.

Guided Instruction

Connect: What you know about telling time Use this page to help children extend their understanding of reading analog clocks to the nearest five minutes.

■ After children read the problem, lead them to talk about the clock. Ask guiding questions to get them to describe the positions of the hour hand and the minute hand.

■ Remind children that each small mark between the numbers on the clock stands for a minute. Explain that it takes 1 minute for the minute hand to move from one small mark to the next.

■ Have children turn back to page 203 and look again at the 5-minute jumps around the outside of the clock. Ask them to draw similar jumps around the outside of the clock in this presentation from the 12 to the 6. Then have them label the jumps to help them skip-count by 5s.

■ Have children reread the problem and identify the key words that help them identify whether the time is A.M. or P.M.

Guided Instruction

Connect: What you know about telling time

The clock shows when Ethan eats breakfast.
What time does Ethan eat breakfast?

Step 1

Find the hour.

The hour hand is between __7__ and __8__.

It is past __7__ o'clock.

Step 2

Find the minutes. Start at 12. Skip count by 5s until you reach the minute hand.

5, 10, __15__, __20__, __25__, __30__

It is __30__ minutes past 7 o'clock.

The time is __7:30__.

Step 3

Decide if the time is A.M. or P.M.
Do you think Ethan eats breakfast in the morning

or in the evening? __morning__

Is the time A.M. or P.M.? __A.M.__

▷ Ethan eats breakfast at __7:30 A.M.__

204 Unit 3 ■ Focus on Measurement and Data

Math-to-Literature Connection

Morning or Afternoon Find a book that tells a story of activities that occur during one day. As you read the story, ask children to say if the activity occurred during the A.M. or P.M.

Challenge children to make a list of activities that typically occur during A.M. hours and a list of activities that typically occur during P.M. hours. Display the lists for the children's reference.

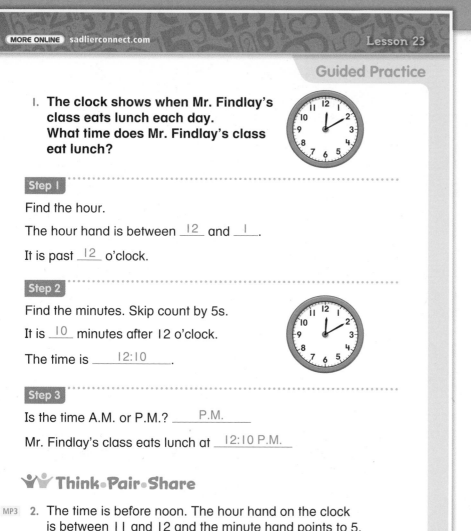

MORE ONLINE sadlierconnect.com

Lesson 23

Guided Practice

I. The clock shows when Mr. Findlay's class eats lunch each day. What time does Mr. Findlay's class eat lunch?

Step 1

Find the hour.

The hour hand is between __12__ and __1__.

It is past __12__ o'clock.

Step 2

Find the minutes. Skip count by 5s.

It is __10__ minutes after 12 o'clock.

The time is __12:10__.

Step 3

Is the time A.M. or P.M.? __P.M.__

Mr. Findlay's class eats lunch at __12:10 P.M.__

☺ Think·Pair·Share

2. The time is before noon. The hour hand on the clock is between 11 and 12 and the minute hand points to 5. What time is it? Talk about how you know the time.

11:25 A.M.; Answers may vary. Possible answer: The hour must be 11 since it comes before 12 on the clock. Counting by 5s, the number of minutes is 25. The time is before lunch so the time is 11:25 A.M.

Unit 3 ▪ Focus on Measurement and Data **205**

Mathematical Practices

Mathematical Practice Standards underline the teaching and understanding of all concepts and skills presented. The emphasis of specific practices is noted throughout the guided and independent practice of this lesson.

MP3	**Construct viable arguments and critique the reasoning of others.**

Item 2: Children use given information to determine the time. They must determine and justify their answer using words instead of an image.

Observational Assessment

Use page 205 to assess children's understanding of how to tell time to the nearest 5 minutes and how to write the time. Note those children who have trouble determining the 5-minute intervals. Have them count by 5s around the clock and write each 5-minute interval as they come to it.

☺ Think·Pair·Share

Peer Collaboration Have pairs share their work. Ask each pair of children questions such as:

• *Is the time A.M. or P.M.?*

• *Suppose the hour hand was pointing to the 11 and the minute hand was pointing to the 12. Then what time would it be?*

Summarize by telling children to decide on the hour first and then skip-count to find the minutes. Have them then write whether the time is A.M. or P.M.

Return to the Essential Question

Reread the Lesson 23 Essential Question on page 202: *How do you tell time to the nearest five minutes?*

Tell children to think about what they learned in this lesson to answer this question.

(Possible response: On an analog clock, I first look at the hour hand. If it is between two numbers, I look at the minute hand. If the minute hand is pointing to a number, I skip-count by 5s from 12 to that number. I name the time as the hour and that number of minutes past the hour. To tell time on a digital clock, I just read the hour and the number of minutes past it.)

Independent Practice

Concept Application

Children may work independently on these pages in the classroom or at home. They may refer to the first four pages of the lesson to revisit the instruction or to see a worked-out example.

Common Errors and **Teaching Tips** may help you support learning either in the classroom or as a follow-up for work done at home.

Common Errors

Items 1–6

Some children may read only the first line in the directions. Point out that they need to include A.M. or P.M. with each time.

Teaching Tips

Items 1–6

Encourage children to underline the word in each problem that tells them whether the time is A.M. or P.M.

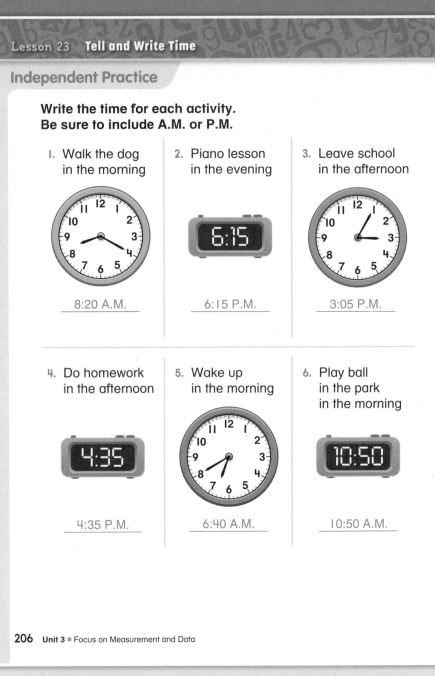

Independent Practice

**Write the time for each activity.
Be sure to include A.M. or P.M.**

1. Walk the dog in the morning

8:20 A.M.

2. Piano lesson in the evening

6:15

6:15 P.M.

3. Leave school in the afternoon

3:05 P.M.

4. Do homework in the afternoon

4:35

4:35 P.M.

5. Wake up in the morning

6:40 A.M.

6. Play ball in the park in the morning

10:50

10:50 A.M.

Talking About Math

Describing Your Day Have pairs take turns working with a classroom demonstration clock. One partner moves the clock hands so that the minute hand is pointing exactly to a number. The other partner names the time, decides whether it is A.M. or P.M., and says what he or she might be doing at that time. Partners exchange roles and the activity repeats.

MORE ONLINE sadlierconnect.com

Draw the minute hand on the clock face to show the time on the clock above.

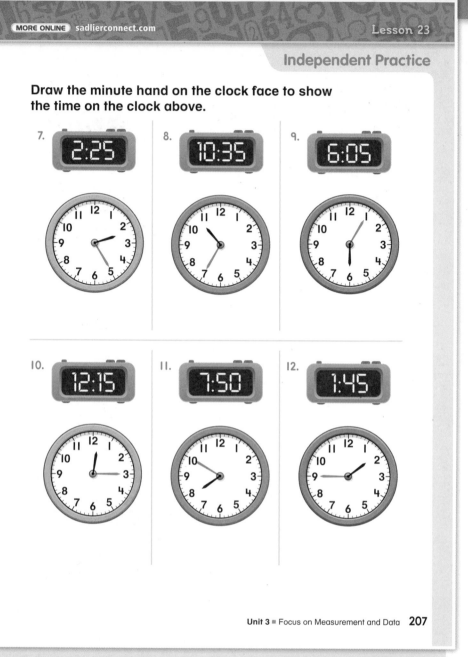

7. 2:25

8. 10:35

9. 6:05

10. 12:15

11. 7:50

12. 1:45

Unit 3 ■ Focus on Measurement and Data **207**

Teaching Tips

Items 7–12

Remind children that they must skip-count by 5s from 12 to determine the location of the minute hand. Have them write the intervals of 5 around the outside of the clock, if necessary, to help them skip-count.

Digital Connection

Real-World Clocks Take digital pictures of clocks and watches from around the neighborhood when the minute hands are pointing exactly to a number. Share these pictures with the class as a slide-show presentation. Say that all the clocks and watches are showing P.M. times. Have children identify each time to the nearest 5 minutes and then name an activity that they would like to be able to do at that time.

Teaching Tips

Items 13-16

Encourage children to underline the words that identify whether each time is A.M. or P.M., as a way to justify their answers.

Independent Practice

Write each time. Be sure to include A.M. or P.M.

13. Lily takes her dog to the park every Saturday morning. What time do they go to the park?

   8:55 A.M.

14. Owen has a baseball game on Thursday evening. What time is Owen's game?

   6:20 P.M.

15. Xavier has a guitar lesson after school. What time is his guitar lesson?

   4:30 P.M.

16. Ms. Jackson's plane lands at the airport early in the morning. What time does her plane land?

   12:40 A.M.

Math-to-School Connection

Telling Time Throughout the Day Mention that everyone has to know the time throughout the day, so children need to be able to tell the time on any clock or watch. Point out that clocks are in almost every room in school and that the school-day schedule is based on time.

Provide children with a schedule of their school day. If necessary, round the actual times to the nearest 5 minutes. Include each subject, lunchtime, recess, and any special classes or assemblies. Provide children with clock faces. Have them draw the hands on the clock to represent each start time of the school-day schedule.

Independent Practice

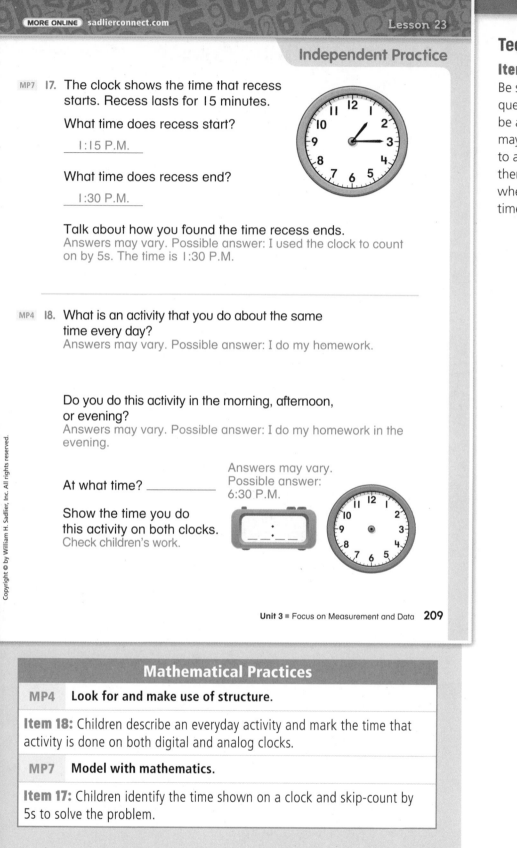

MP7 **17.** The clock shows the time that recess starts. Recess lasts for 15 minutes.

What time does recess start?

__1:15 P.M.__

What time does recess end?

__1:30 P.M.__

Talk about how you found the time recess ends.
Answers may vary. Possible answer: I used the clock to count on by 5s. The time is 1:30 P.M.

MP4 **18.** What is an activity that you do about the same time every day?
Answers may vary. Possible answer: I do my homework.

Do you do this activity in the morning, afternoon, or evening?
Answers may vary. Possible answer: I do my homework in the evening.

At what time? _____
Answers may vary. Possible answer: 6:30 P.M.

Show the time you do this activity on both clocks.
Check children's work.

Unit 3 ■ Focus on Measurement and Data **209**

Teaching Tips

Item 17

Be sure children understand what this question is asking. Most children should be able to answer the first part, but may get confused when attempting to answer the second part. Encourage them to draw a second clock that shows when recess ends and then read the time on that clock.

Mathematical Practices

MP4	**Look for and make use of structure.**

Item 18: Children describe an everyday activity and mark the time that activity is done on both digital and analog clocks.

MP7	**Model with mathematics.**

Item 17: Children identify the time shown on a clock and skip-count by 5s to solve the problem.

Common Core Focus:

2.MD.8 Solve word problems involving dollar bills, quarters, dimes, nickels, and pennies, using $ and ¢ symbols appropriately.

OBJECTIVE

Solve problems involving dollar bills, quarters, dimes, nickels, and pennies.

ESSENTIAL QUESTION

Read the Essential Question aloud. Have children discuss their experiences handling money.

FLUENCY PRACTICE

Fluency practice is available at **sadlierconnect.com**.

Concept Development

Understand: Count on to find the total value of a group of coins

■ Many children are likely to have had experiences handling money. Ask questions to gauge how much children already know about coin and bill values and to identify any misconceptions that they may have before beginning the lesson.

■ Have children examine play money coins. Ask them to identify each coin and tell how much it is worth. Discuss the use and meaning of the cent symbol (¢).

■ Have children write the amount each coin is worth on the coins pictured in the problem.

■ Point out that the answer is determined by grouping like coins, first the dimes and then the pennies. Tell children that this is a better way to solve than counting coins in a mixed-up order.

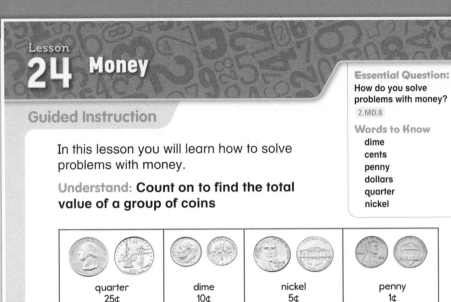

Lesson 24 Money

Guided Instruction

Essential Question:
How do you solve problems with money?
2.MD.8

Words to Know
dime
cents
penny
dollars
quarter
nickel

In this lesson you will learn how to solve problems with money.

Understand: Count on to find the total value of a group of coins

quarter 25¢	dime 10¢	nickel 5¢	penny 1¢

Rafa has these coins. How many cents does Rafa have?

A dime is worth 10 cents. Rafa has 2 dimes.

Skip-count by 10s to find how many cents 2 dimes are worth.

   10¢, 20¢

A penny is worth 1 cent. Count on from 20 to find how many cents Rafa has.

   10¢, 20¢, **21¢, 22¢, 23¢**

▷ Rafa has 23 cents.

210 Unit 3 ■ Focus on Measurement and Data

Words to Know

dime: a coin worth 10 cents, or 10¢

cent: a unit used for money

penny: a coin worth 1 cent, or 1¢

dollar: a dollar is worth 100 cents, or $1

quarter: a coin worth 25 cents, or 25¢

nickel: a coin worth 5 cents, or 5¢

Glossary can be found on pp. 293–304.

Guided Instruction

Understand: Find the value of a group of bills

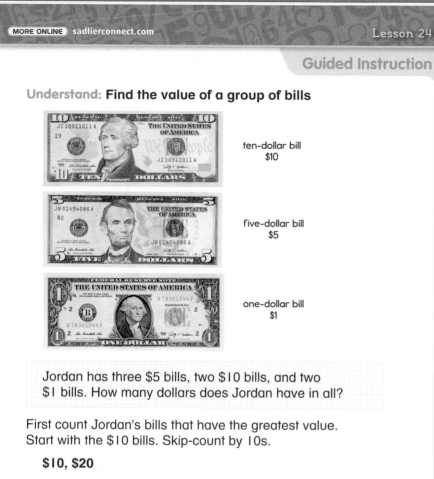

ten-dollar bill
$10

five-dollar bill
$5

one-dollar bill
$1

> Jordan has three $5 bills, two $10 bills, and two
> $1 bills. How many dollars does Jordan have in all?

First count Jordan's bills that have the greatest value.
Start with the $10 bills. Skip-count by 10s.

$10, $20

Then count the $5 bills. Start at 20 and skip-count by 5s.

$20, **$25, $30, $35**

Count on by 1s to find how many dollars Jordan has in all.

$35, **$36, $37**

▷ Jordan has $37 in all.

Understand: Find the value of a group of bills

■ Have children look carefully at the bills and discuss how they are alike and different.

■ You may wish to explain that some new bills look different from older ones of the same denomination. If possible, bring in an older $10 or $5 bill, or find pictures of older dollar bills, to show children how the look of the money has changed. Ask for ideas about why the bills might have been changed and how newer bills might be easier to use than older ones.

■ Read the word problem aloud and have children underline the information needed to solve it.

■ Encourage children to draw Jordan's bills and write the value on each bill.

■ Point out that solving begins by grouping the bills according to their values, from greatest to least. Explain that this is the best way to find total amounts of money.

Support English Language Learners

Explain that different countries use different money. Therefore, English language learners may not be familiar with American money. Allow children plenty of time to explore U.S. coins and bills. Remind them that the size of the coin does not affect the value. Point out, for example, that a dime is worth more than a penny and more than a nickel, even though it is smaller than both.

If possible, allow children to bring in coins and/or bills from their native country and talk about the value of each. This activity would be beneficial to everyone in the class.

Guided Instruction

Connect: **What you know about finding the value of groups of bills and coins** Use this page to help children extend their understanding of finding the value of a group of coins.

■ If an overhead projector and overhead coins are available, consider using them to demonstrate solving these problems.

■ For the first problem, have children draw Maria's coins and write each value on the coins.

■ Work through Steps 1 and 2 by emphasizing that the coins are grouped according to their values, from greatest to least. Have children point to the coins they drew to help them visualize the skip-counting.

■ For the last problem, have children draw Caleb's coins in order of their values; first the quarter, then the dimes, and then the nickels. Then encourage children to use their drawings to help them skip-count.

Guided Instruction

Connect: **What you know about finding the value of groups of bills and coins**

> Maria has a quarter, 3 dimes, and 2 nickels.
> How many cents does Maria have in all?

Step 1

Start with the coin that has the greatest value.
One quarter is worth 25 cents.
Each dime is worth 10 cents.

Start at 25 and skip-count by 10s for the dimes.

25, **35**, **45**, **55**

Step 2

A nickel is worth 5 cents.

Start at 55 and skip-count by 5s to find how many cents Maria has in all.

55, **60**, **65**

▷ Maria has __65__ cents in all.

Caleb has 1 quarter, 2 dimes, and 4 nickels.

Compare Caleb's money to Maria's money.
Does Caleb have more money, less money, or the same amount of money that Maria has?

the same amount of money

212 Unit 3 ■ Focus on Measurement and Data

Math-to-Business Connection

Selling Lemonade Ask the class to suggest ways that children can earn money. Suggestions may include services, such as walking a neighbor's dog or selling lemonade. Provide a scenario like the following. _Imogen set up a lemonade stand in her front yard. People paid 30¢ for a cup of lemonade. That day, Imogen earned 1 quarter, 5 dimes, and 3 nickels. How much money did she earn in all? How many people bought a cup of lemonade that day?_

Have children work in pairs to solve the problem. Encourage them to draw the coins in order of their values, from greatest to least, and to label each coin with its value. Then children should show how to skip-count to solve the problem.

Guided Practice

1. **Jamal has 2 quarters, 2 dimes, and 2 nickels. How much money does Jamal have?**

Step 1

Start with the quarters. One quarter is worth 25¢.
Find how much 2 quarters are worth.

25¢ + 25¢ = ■

$$\begin{array}{r} \overset{1}{2}5¢ \\ +25 \\ \hline 50¢ \end{array}$$

Step 2

Count on from 50¢.
Skip-count by 10s for the dimes.

50¢, 60¢, 70¢

Now skip-count by 5s for the nickels.

70¢, 75¢, 80¢

Jamal has 80¢.

Think•Pair•Share

MP2 2. Find different numbers of coins that make the same amount of money that Jamal has. Use at least 1 quarter, 1 dime, and 1 nickel.

Answers may vary. Possible answer: 1 quarter, 5 dimes, 1 nickel.

Mathematical Practices

Mathematical Practice Standards underline the teaching and understanding of all concepts and skills presented. The emphasis of specific practices is noted throughout the guided and independent practice of this lesson.

MP2	**Reason abstractly and quantitatively.**

Item 2: Children exhibit their understanding of coin values to identify coin combinations that equal a given amount.

Observational Assessment

Use page 213 to assess children's understanding of finding the value of groups of coins. Note those children who are struggling to remember the values of coins or who are having trouble skip-counting.

Think•Pair•Share

Peer Collaboration Ask pairs to share their work after determining their answer. Ask questions such as:

- *Which coin did you start with? How did you decide?*
- *How did you know how many coins to use?*

To summarize, remind children to group the coins in an amount according to their values. Children should skip-count starting with the coin(s) of greatest value and ending with the coins of least value.

Return to the Essential Question

Reread the Lesson 24 Essential Question on page 210: *How do you solve problems with money?*

Tell children to think about what they learned in this lesson to answer this question.

(Possible response: I first group the coins according to value. Starting with the greatest value, I skip-count until I count all the coins. I write the ¢ symbol with my answer. When the problem involves bills, I group the bills according to value. Starting with the greatest value, I skip-count until I count all the bills. I write the $ symbol with my answer.)

Concept Application

Children may work independently on these pages in the classroom or at home. They may refer to the first four pages of the lesson to revisit the instruction or to see a worked-out example.

Common Errors and **Teaching Tips** may help you support learning either in the classroom or as a follow-up for work done at home.

Teaching Tips

Items 1-4

Tell children to write the value on each pictured coin. Also encourage them to cross out each coin as they count it to keep them from recounting the same coin.

Items 5-6

Encourage children to write out their skip-counting in order to be sure they included all the bills.

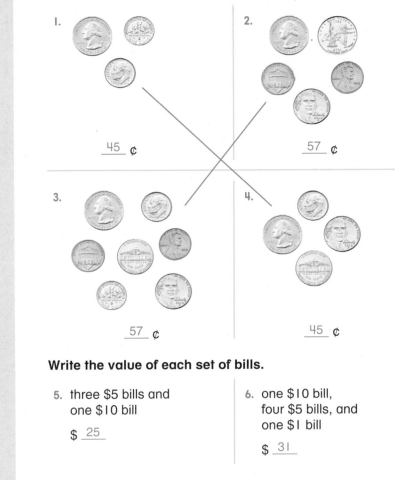

Lesson 24 **Money**

Independent Practice

Write the value of each group of coins.
Then draw lines to match groups with the same value.

1. <u>45</u> ¢

2. <u>57</u> ¢

3. <u>57</u> ¢

4. <u>45</u> ¢

Write the value of each set of bills.

5. three $5 bills and one $10 bill

$ <u>25</u>

6. one $10 bill, four $5 bills, and one $1 bill

$ <u>31</u>

214   Unit 3 ■ Focus on Measurement and Data

Talking About Math

Counting Coins Have children work in pairs with a set of play coins and dollar bills. Give a word problem, such as: *Liam has 2 quarters, 3 dimes, and 2 nickels. He wants to buy a cup of soup that costs 89¢. Does Liam have enough money to buy the cup of soup?*

Have children take play coins to show Liam's money and then group the coins of each kind, from those of greatest value to those of least value. Remind children to skip-count to decide if this is enough money to buy the cup of soup. Repeat the activity for other money-related scenarios.

MORE ONLINE sadlierconnect.com

Lesson 24

Independent Practice

Teaching Tips

Items 7–11
As children read the problem, have them underline the money amounts.

Item 11
To help children envision the money amounts that Burke and Marta each have, tell them to draw Burke's coins in the order in which they are listed. Then have them draw Marta's coins below Burke's.

Find the amount of money.
Write $ for dollars and ¢ for cents.

7. Vicki has saved $24. Her father gives her $7 more. How many dollars does Vicki have now?

   $31

8. Fred has 54¢. He buys a pencil for 15¢. How many cents does Fred have now?

   39¢

9. Mr. Phillips wants to buy a radio for $42. He has two $10 bills and one $5 bill. How many more dollars does Mr. Phillips need to buy the radio?

   $17

10. Tatiana has 37¢. She gives 1 dime and 1 nickel to her friend. How many cents does Tatiana have now?

   22¢

11. Burke has 3 dimes, 4 nickels, and 3 pennies. Marta has 2 quarters, 1 nickel, and 3 pennies.

   Who has more money? How much more? Fill in the blanks.

   __Marta__ has _5¢_ more than __Burke__.

Digital Connection

Counting Money Game Use a search engine to find an online game for children's use that involves counting money. Have children work independently or in pairs to answer the questions. You can also have children write or draw the money for each problem before solving the problem on the computer.

Independent Practice

Teaching Tips

Items 12–13

Remind children that, to find a money amount, they should start with the bills or coins with the greatest value and skip-count through those with the least value until all bills and coins are counted.

Item 14

Encourage children to draw Quinn's bills and then Carla's bills. Have them also label each bill and use it to show how they skip-counted to find their answer.

Independent Practice

12. Mrs. Kim has two $10 bills, three $5 bills, and two $1 bills. Find how many dollars Mrs. Kim has.

    Mrs. Kim has __37__ dollars.

    Show a different way to make the same amount of money as Mrs. Kim has using $10 bills, $5 bills, and $1 bills.

    Answers may vary. Possible answer: three $10 bills, one $5 bill, two $1 bills

---

13. Brian has 1 quarter, 2 dimes, a nickel, and 3 pennies. How many cents does Brian have?

    Brian has __53¢__.

    Show how to make the same amount of money as Brian has using only dimes, nickels, and pennies.

    Answers may vary. Possible answer: 4 dimes, 2 nickels, 3 pennies

---

14. Quinn has a $10 bill, three $5 bills, and seven $1 bills. Carla has two $10 bills, three $5 bills, and two $1 bills.

    Who has more money? How much more? Fill in the blanks.

    ___Carla___ has __$5__ more than ___Quinn___.

Math-to-Shopping Connection

Counting Change Explain that when you buy something, you may pay for it with money that has the same value as the price. If you do not have the exact amount of money, you may pay with bills or coins that have a greater value than the price. When you do this, you get back some money, called *change.*

Provide scenarios that involve determining an amount received in change, such as: *After Eric paid for a new shirt, he received 2 quarters, 2 dimes, and 1 nickel in change. He wanted to use the change to buy a candy bar for 75¢. Did Eric get enough change to pay for the candy bar?* Have children work in pairs to solve the problem. Ask them to write their answer in a sentence that tells about the problem.

MORE ONLINE sadlierconnect.com

Independent Practice

MP3 **15.** James has some quarters, dimes, and nickels worth 85¢. He spends 25¢ for an eraser.

What is the least number of coins that James could have left?

___3___ coins

What are the coins that he has left? _2 quarters and 1 dime_

Tell how you know this is the least number of coins.

Answers may vary. Possible answer: I subtracted 25 from 85 to find how many cents James has left. He has 60¢. Quarters are worth the most so I started with them. Two quarters make 50¢. A dime makes 60¢ in all. I know these make up the least number of coins since they have the greatest values I can use.

MP6 **16.** Harper has two $10 bills, one $5 bill, and two $1 bills to spend on toys.

$13 $17 $11 $14

Circle the two toys she can buy using all of her money.

Tell how you chose the toys.

Answers may vary. Possible answer: I counted on to find out how much money Harper has. She has $27. Then I found two toys with prices that add up to $27.

Unit 3 ■ Focus on Measurement and Data **217**

Common Errors

Item 16

Children may think that Harper may buy just one toy. Clarify the directions so they understand that Harper must use all her money to buy two toys.

Teaching Tips

Item 15

Be sure children understand that more than one step is needed to solve this problem. Have a volunteer read the problem aloud and explain each step. Point out that, to find the least number of coins left, children should start with the coins of greatest value.

Mathematical Practices	
MP3	**Construct viable arguments and critique the reasoning of others.**
Item 15: Children use given information to make a conjecture and then further develop that conjecture to justify their answer.	
MP6	**Attend to precision.**
Item 16: Children identify a total amount of money and then analyze the prices of objects to determine which two can be bought with that amount.	

Common Core Focus:

2.MD.9 Generate measurement data by measuring lengths of several objects to the nearest whole unit, or by making repeated measurements of the same object. Show the measurements by making a line plot, where the horizontal scale is marked off in whole-number units.

OBJECTIVE
Make and use line plots.

ESSENTIAL QUESTION

Read the Essential Question aloud. In this lesson, children will use length measurements to make line plots and interpret the graphed data. Have children share what they already know about measuring and comparing lengths.

PREREQUISITE SKILLS

Use Foundational Skills Handbook page 287, *Tables,* to review how to read and analyze data in a table.

FLUENCY PRACTICE

Fluency practice is available at **sadlierconnect.com**.

Concept Development

Understand: Make a line plot

■ Lead a discussion about what the data in the table mean.

■ Ask children what other numbers could be listed along the number line in the line plot. Some children may suggest that, like 4 for which there are no data, the number 9 could be listed.

■ Discuss with children what each X above a number stands for. Lead the class in checking to make sure that the correct number of Xs appear above each number.

Lesson
25 Line Plots

Guided Instruction

Essential Question:
How do you make and read a line plot?
2.MD.9

Words to Know
line plot
data

In this lesson you will learn how to make and read a line plot that shows data.

Understand: Make a line plot

The children in Ms. Clarkson's class are growing tomato plants. They measured the height of each plant on Monday. They recorded their findings in this table.

Heights of Tomato Plants	
Height (in inches)	Number of Plants
5	3
6	2
7	4
8	3

Then the children made a line plot of the data in the table.

The children started the line plot by drawing a number line. They labeled it by writing the heights of the plants. They gave their line plot a title.

Then the children drew an X above the labels for the height of each plant. They drew three Xs above 5, two Xs above 6, four Xs above 7, and three Xs above 8.

▷ Here is their completed line plot.

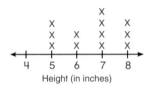

Heights of Tomato Plants

```
                    X
        X           X       X
        X   X       X       X
        X   X       X       X
    ←---+---+---+---+---+--→
        4   5   6   7   8
          Height (in inches)
```

Words to Know

line plot: a graph that uses a number line and Xs to show data

data: information sometimes shown in a table or graph

Example: The **data** are shown in this **line plot.**

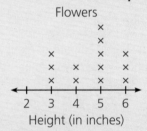

Flowers

```
                    ×
                    ×
        ×           ×   ×
        ×   ×       ×   ×
        ×   ×       ×   ×
    ←--+---+---+---+---+--→
       2   3   4   5   6
         Height (in inches)
```

Glossary can be found on pp. 293–304.

MORE ONLINE sadlierconnect.com

Guided Instruction

Understand: Use a line plot

The tally marks show the lengths of beetles in Jay's collection.

Make a line plot to show these data.

Jay's Beetle Collection	
Length (in centimeters)	Number of Beetles
1	IIII
2	IIII I
3	III
4	I
5	II
8	I

Here is the line plot.

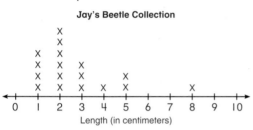

Jay's Beetle Collection

Length (in centimeters)

Use the line plot to answer this question.

How many beetles are more than 2 centimeters long?

Start at 3 on the line plot. Count the number of Xs above 3, 4, 5, and 8.

There are 7 Xs in all.

▷ Jay has __7__ beetles that are more than 2 centimeters long.

Understand: Use a line plot

■ Discuss the use of tally marks in a table. Help children see how making tally marks can help them easily keep track of data.

■ Be sure children understand that each of Jay's tally marks stands for one beetle in his collection. Have them point to the row in the table that shows how many beetles are 2 centimeters long. Explain that the mark that crosses the group of 4 tally marks means that the whole group represents 5.

■ Have children study and describe what they see on the line plot. Ask why some numbers, such as 6 and 7, do not have Xs above them. Make sure children understand why 6 and 7 need to appear along the line even though they do not have Xs.

Support English Language Learners

English language learners will likely be familiar with the word *line*. However, they may not know the word *plot* as used in this lesson. Now say that a *line plot* shows data. Explain that *data* means information.

Have children point to the number line that forms the base of a line plot. Tell them that the marks above the number line—in this case, Xs—are used to show the data. Explain that children will count different kinds of data that appear in line plots.

Connect: **What you know about making and using a line plot** Use this page to help children strengthen their understanding of making and using line plots.

■ Have a volunteer read the problem aloud. Make sure children understand the question they need to answer. Ask them what the word *or* means in the question.

■ Have children explain what the number line shows. Point out that the number line forms a *scale*. Help children see that the scale is labeled in feet and that each number stands for how many feet tall a tree might be.

■ Discuss with children why they need to find the 5-feet mark along the scale. If necessary, refer them back to the question they need to answer.

■ Review with children what the numbers they are adding stand for. You may wish to have them count the Xs that are above the numbers 5, 6, and 7 to check their answer.

Connect: What you know about making and using a line plot

Volunteers helped plant trees at a new park.

This line plot shows the heights of the trees they planted.

Trees Planted

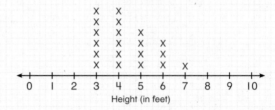

Height (in feet)

How many trees did they plant that were 5 feet tall or taller?

A number line forms a scale at the bottom of the line plot. The scale shows the height of the trees in feet. It is marked from 0 feet to 10 feet.

Find 5 feet along the scale of the line plot. Count the number of Xs above 5 feet. There are 4 Xs above 5 feet.

Count the number of Xs above 6 feet.

There are __3__ Xs above 6 feet.

Count the number of Xs above 7 feet. There is __1__ X above 7 feet. Add to find how many in all.

4 + 3 + 1 = __8__

▷ The volunteers planted __8__ trees that were 5 feet tall or taller.

Math-to-Social Studies Connection

How Many Wheels? Share this scenario with the class: *A unicycle has 1 wheel, a bicycle has 2 wheels, and a tricycle has 3 wheels. In the Fourth of July parade, 5 members of a club rode unicycles, 6 members rode bicycles, and 4 members rode tricycles.*

Help the class build a line plot on the board to show the bicycle data. Begin with a scale that shows the numbers of wheels. Call up volunteers to mark the numbers along the scale. Then call on others to draw Xs to show how many club members rode unicycles, bicycles, and tricycles in the parade. After children agree that the line plot represents the data in the problem, have them suggest a title for the line plot.

1. There were 12 cars parked in a parking lot.
Five of the cars were 3 meters long, 7 cars were
4 meters long, and 4 cars were 5 meters long.

Make a line plot to show these data.
Draw Xs to complete the line plot.
Remember to give the line plot a title.

Title: Length of Parked Cars

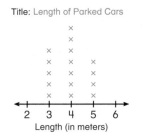

Length (in meters)

Think•Pair•Share

MP1 2. Use the data in your line plot above to answer
this question. One of the cars 5 meters long leaves
the parking lot. Then 3 of the cars 4 meters long
leave the parking lot. What length are most of the
cars then?

___3___ meters

Unit 3 ▪ Focus on Measurement and Data **221**

Mathematical Practices

Mathematical Practice Standards underline the teaching and
understanding of all concepts and skills presented. The emphasis of
specific practices is noted throughout the guided and independent practice
of this lesson.

MP1	Make sense of problems and persevere in solving them.

Item 2: Children make sense of changing data and answer questions
based on the changes.

Observational Assessment

Use page 221 to assess children's
understanding of how to use data
to make a line plot. You may wish to
review how to decide which numbers
to write along the scale. Discuss with
children that a title is needed to help
people understand the line plot.

Think•Pair•Share

Peer Collaboration Ask pairs to share
how they found the length of most of
the cars after some cars leave:

• *How could you show on your line plot
that a car left the parking lot? What
did you do?*

• *How did this change the line plot?
What length are most of the cars
after some cars left?*

To summarize, point out that data can
change and changes can be made to a
line plot to show what happened.

Return to the Essential Question

Reread the Lesson 25 Essential Question
on page 218: *How do you make and
read a line plot?*

Tell children to think about what they
learned in this lesson to answer
this question.

(Possible response: I know that I need to
make a scale so I can show the data in
the problem. I need to label the scale. I
need to draw Xs above the numbers to
show the data. Then, I need to write a
title for my line plot.)

Concept Application

Children may work independently on these pages in the classroom or at home. They may refer to the first four pages of the lesson to revisit the instruction or to see a worked-out example.

Common Errors and **Teaching Tips** may help you support learning either in the classroom or as a follow-up for work done at home.

Common Errors

Items 6-7

In problem 6, some children might not understand that they should be looking for the children that are taller than 48 inches. They may also make the mistake of including those children that are exactly 48 inches tall. Children may make similar mistakes for problem 7.

Teaching Tips

Item 5

Problem 5 provides an excellent example of the mathematical use of the word *or*. Discuss what *or* means in this problem. Children should understand that it means to find those that are 50 inches tall and also those that are 51 inches tall.

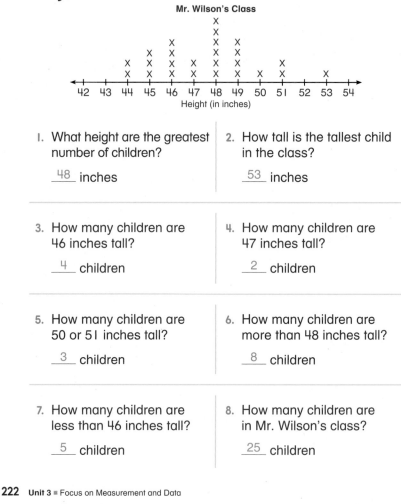

Lesson 25 **Line Plots**

Independent Practice

The line plot shows the heights of the children in Mr. Wilson's class. Use the line plot to answer the questions.

Mr. Wilson's Class

1. What height are the greatest number of children?

   _48_ inches

2. How tall is the tallest child in the class?

   _53_ inches

3. How many children are 46 inches tall?

   _4_ children

4. How many children are 47 inches tall?

   _2_ children

5. How many children are 50 or 51 inches tall?

   _3_ children

6. How many children are more than 48 inches tall?

   _8_ children

7. How many children are less than 46 inches tall?

   _5_ children

8. How many children are in Mr. Wilson's class?

   _25_ children

222 Unit 3 ■ Focus on Measurement and Data

Talking About Math

Collaborative Conversations Have children work in pairs to study the line plot. Tell them to discuss what the scale shows. Explain that there is more information in this line plot than the problems on the page show. Then, to help them see how much information the line plot shows, have children make up other problems that they can solve using this line plot. Have pairs share some of their problems.

Lesson 25

Independent Practice

9. James measured the length of each nail in his toolbox. He made a table to show his data. Use the number line to make a line plot of the data.

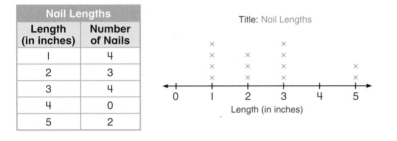

Nail Lengths	
Length (in inches)	Number of Nails
1	4
2	3
3	4
4	0
5	2

Title: Nail Lengths

10. Emily estimated the lengths of the sharks at Ocean World. She made this line plot to show her data. Complete the table to match the data in the line plot.

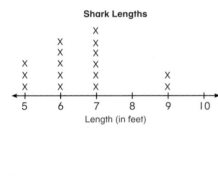

Shark Lengths

Length (in feet)

Shark Lengths	
Length (in feet)	Number of Sharks
5	3
6	5
7	6
8	0
9	2
10	0

Teaching Tips

Item 9
Discuss with children why it is important to include the number 4 along the scale even though there were no nails that were exactly 4 inches long.

Item 10
Consider asking children whether they prefer to look at the information in the line plot or in the table. Have them explain their reasons.

Digital Connection

Interactive Whiteboard Research an online number-cube toss that children can use to generate data to plot on a line plot. Outline a 2-column tally chart on the whiteboard. Have a volunteer draw tallies to record the numbers tossed. After recording 20 randomly tossed numbers, have another volunteer set up a line plot by drawing a number line on the whiteboard and marking the scale. Call on several more children to draw Xs above the numbers on the scale. Finally, have someone write a title for the line plot. If time permits, have children record more data as they continue the online number-cube toss. As data are recorded, ask questions such as: *Which number was tossed most often? How many more times was 5 tossed than 3? How many times was 1 or 2 tossed?*

Independent Practice

Common Errors

Item 11

Children may mistakenly record the first entry in the table, 2, above the "1" if they have marked "1" as the first number along the scale. Point out that the table does not list 1-inch-long trucks and that the first truck length listed is for trucks that are 2 inches long.

Item 12

Some children might draw too few or too many Xs for a number. Have these children count the Xs and compare the number of Xs with the numbers in the problem.

Teaching Tips

Item 12

Encourage children to make a tally chart of the data before starting to make their line plot.

Independent Practice

11. The table shows the lengths of some toy trucks. Make a line plot to show the data.

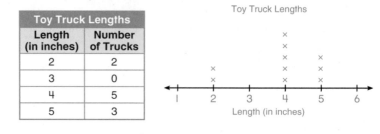

Toy Truck Lengths	
Length (in inches)	Number of Trucks
2	2
3	0
4	5
5	3

MP1 12. The lengths of some snakes in a pet store are 12, 15, 18, 12, 14, 15, 12, 14, 13, and 15 inches. Make a line plot of these data.

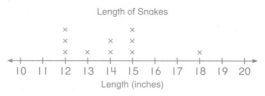

Talk about how you used the numbers to make your line plot.

Answers may vary. Possible answer: I drew a number line from 10 to 20. Then I drew an X above each of the numbers listed in the sentence.

Mathematical Practices
MP1 **Make sense of problems and persevere in solving them.**
Item 12: Children make sense of disorganized data by showing them in a line plot.

Lesson 25

Independent Practice

MP5 13. Janice measured the length of some crayons to the nearest centimeter (cm). She recorded the lengths in a tally chart.

Crayon Lengths	
Length (in cm)	Number of crayons
5				
6	⊬⊬	
7	⊬⊬	
8				
9			

Use a centimeter ruler to measure the two crayons below. Draw a tally mark in Janice's table to show each length.

Then use the data from the table to make a line plot.

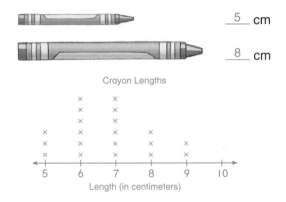

_5_ cm

_8_ cm

Crayon Lengths

Line plots may vary. Check children's work.

Talk about how your line plot helps to show the crayon data.

Answers may vary. Possible answer: It makes it easy to compare the lengths of the crayons.

Unit 3 ■ Focus on Measurement and Data **225**

Common Errors
Item 13
Some children may think that because one crayon is thinner than the other, the lengths will be different. Remind them that the length is from one end of the crayon to the point at the other end.

Teaching Tips
Item 13
Point out that the crayons are listed in the table according to length from shortest to longest. Ask children how this can help them decide how to mark the line-plot scale.

Remind children to try to draw all their Xs the same size. Tell them also to try to draw the Xs in straight columns so that the line plot is easy to read.

After children have made their line plots, consider having them compare this process with the process of making the line plot for problem 12, for which the data were not listed in order.

Mathematical Practices	
MP5	**Use appropriate tools strategically.**

Item 13: Children use a centimeter ruler to measure correctly.

Common Core Focus:

2.MD.10 Draw a picture graph and a bar graph (with single-unit scale) to represent a data set with up to four categories. Solve simple put-together, take-apart, and compare problems using information presented in a bar graph.

OBJECTIVE

Make and read picture graphs and solve problems using them.

ESSENTIAL QUESTION

After reading the Essential Question aloud to the class, explain that in this lesson, children will use picture graphs to show data, just as they showed data with line plots in the last lesson.

FLUENCY PRACTICE

Fluency practice is available at **sadlierconnect.com**.

Concept Development

Understand: Read a picture graph

■ Ask children to look at the picture graph and point to the title as you read it aloud. Lead a discussion about what children think the graph is showing. Confirm that looking at the names and the pictures of apples can help them tell what the graph is about.

■ Draw attention to the key below the graph and discuss how to read it. Explain that the key for a graph is like a key for a door. The key "unlocks," or explains, data about the graph much like a door key unlocks a door.

■ After children find how many apples Tara picked, ask them other questions about the graph before moving onto the next presentation.

Lesson
26 Picture Graphs

Essential Question:
How do you read and make a picture graph?
2.MD.10

Words to Know
picture graph
data
key

Guided Instruction

In this lesson you will learn how to read and make picture graphs.

Understand: Read a picture graph

A picture graph uses pictures to show data. A key tells what each picture stands for. This picture graph shows the number of apples some children picked.

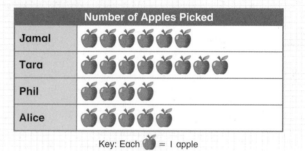

Number of Apples Picked	
Jamal	🍎🍎🍎🍎🍎🍎
Tara	🍎🍎🍎🍎🍎🍎🍎🍎
Phil	🍎🍎🍎🍎
Alice	🍎🍎🍎🍎🍎

Key: Each 🍎 = 1 apple

How many apples did Tara pick?

Look at the graph. Find the row for Tara. There are 8 🍎 in the row for Tara.

Look at the key below the picture graph.

The key tells you that each 🍎 stands for 1 apple.

▷ Tara picked 8 apples.

Words to Know

picture graph: A display of data, or information, that uses symbols or pictures.

Books Read	
June	☐☐☐☐
July	☐☐☐☐☐☐
August	☐☐☐☐☐

Key: Each ☐ = 1 Book

data: information sometimes shown in a table or graph

key: the part of a picture graph that shows what each picture means

Glossary can be found on pp. 293–304.

Understand: Make a picture graph

The table shows the number of rainy days in March, April, May, and June.

Make a picture graph to show these data.

Rainy Days	
Month	**Number of Rainy Days**
March	4
April	6
May	5
June	3

Write a title at the top of the graph.
Make a row for each month.
Use a symbol to stand for a rainy day.

Write a key for your picture graph to show that each 🌂 stands for 1 rainy day.

Rainy Days
March	
April	
May	
June	

Key: Each 🌂 = 1 rainy day

Fill in the picture graph.
Use 4 🌂 for the rainy days in March. Use 6 for April. Use 5 🌂 for May, and use 3 🌂 for June.

▷ This picture graph shows the data.

Rainy Days
March	🌂🌂🌂🌂
April	🌂🌂🌂🌂🌂🌂
May	🌂🌂🌂🌂🌂
June	🌂🌂🌂

Key: Each 🌂 = 1 rainy day

Unit 3 ■ Focus on Measurement and Data **227**

Understand: Make a picture graph

■ In this presentation, children will use data from a table to make a picture graph. Guide them to understand how to decide on a title, labels, and the symbol for a key.

■ Children should see that the picture graph repeats the information in the table. Lead a discussion about why it is important to show the symbols for the number of rainy days in different rows.

■ Finally, ask children why they think an umbrella was used for the key. Make sure they understand that any other symbol could have been used to represent 1 rainy day.

Support English Language Learners

Children are likely to know that the word *key* means a metal object used to open a door or start a car. Write the word *key* on the board and have children talk about what the word means to them.

Explain that the *key* below a picture graph tells what each picture stands for. Point out that it is important to read the key in order to understand the graph. On the board, write a few examples of how to read a key for a picture graph. For example, write *Key: Each ♥ = 1 vote.* Then read the key aloud and have children repeat it after you.

Guided Instruction

Connect: Use data from a picture graph to solve problems Use this page to strengthen children's understanding of how to interpret data from a picture graph and use it to solve a problem.

■ Have children explain what the picture graph tells them. Then ask a volunteer to explain how to use the key to find the number of tickets sold on any particular day.

■ Ask children to explain what they need to do in order to answer the question. They should explain the need to count to find the total number of tickets sold on Monday and Tuesday.

■ Encourage children to explain what the numbers 4 and 6 represent in Step 3. They should understand that these are the numbers of tickets Sylvia sold on Monday and on Tuesday.

Guided Instruction

Connect: Use data from a picture graph to solve problems

The picture graph shows the number of tickets to the school fair that Sylvia sold on four different days.

Tickets Sylvia Sold	
Monday	🎫 🎫 🎫 🎫
Tuesday	🎫 🎫 🎫 🎫 🎫 🎫
Wednesday	🎫 🎫
Thursday	🎫 🎫 🎫

Key: Each 🎫 = 1 ticket

How many tickets did Sylvia sell in all on Monday and Tuesday?

Step 1

Find the number of tickets Sylvia sold on Monday. The key shows that each 🎫 stands for 1 ticket. Count the number of tickets she sold on Monday. Sylvia sold 4 tickets on Monday.

Step 2

Find the tickets Sylvia sold on Tuesday. Count them.

Sylvia sold __6__ tickets on Tuesday.

Step 3

Write and solve an addition equation to show how many tickets Sylvia sold in all on the two days.

$4 + 6 =$ __10__

▷ Sylvia sold __10__ tickets in all on Monday and Tuesday.

228 Unit 3 ■ Focus on Measurement and Data

Math-to-Math Connection

Statistics Using and interpreting data analysis is a valuable skill that will benefit children throughout their mathematical careers. Children learned how to read and make line plots in Lesson 25. In Lesson 27, they will learn to create, read, and interpret bar graphs. In the future, children will work with other graphic representations such as circle graphs, histograms, and stem-and-leaf plots.

Use a computer search engine to find some simply-drawn graphs that show statistical data. Display these and explain how each graph helps to make the data it shows easy to understand.

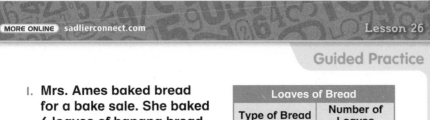

I. **Mrs. Ames baked bread for a bake sale. She baked 6 loaves of banana bread, 3 loaves of pumpkin bread, and 4 loaves of corn bread. Write these data in the table.**

Use the table to make a picture graph.

Loaves of Bread	
Type of Bread	**Number of Loaves**
Banana	6
Pumpkin	3
Corn	4

The title of this picture graph is Loaves of Bread. The rows are labeled with types of bread.

Loaves of Bread	
Banana Bread	🍞 🍞 🍞 🍞 🍞 🍞
Pumpkin Bread	▬ ▬ ▬
Corn Bread	▬ ▬ ▬ ▬

Key: Each 🍞 = I loaf of bread

The key tells you that each 🍞 stands for I loaf of bread.

Draw bread symbols to show the numbers of loaves of pumpkin bread and corn bread.

👑 Think·Pair·Share

MP2 2. Write a question that can be answered using the data in the Loaves of Bread picture graph.

Answers may vary. Possible answer: How many more loaves of banana bread than corn bread did Mrs. Ames bake? 2 more

Observational Assessment

Use page 229 to assess children's understanding of how to make a picture graph. Take note of those children who have trouble putting the information into the table correctly. Then check whether children draw the correct number of loaves in the picture graph.

👑 Think·Pair·Share

Peer Collaboration Ask pairs to share their work by reading the question they wrote. Then ask them how to solve the problem using the data in the picture graph. Ask each pair questions such as:

• *What data does the picture graph tell you? How do you know this?*

• *What problem can you make from the data? Explain how to use the data in the graph to solve the problem.*

Return to the Essential Question

Reread the Lesson 26 Essential Question on page 226: *How do you read and make a picture graph?*

Tell children to think about what they learned in this lesson to answer this question.

(Possible response: I can use data from a table or a problem to represent in a picture graph. I first need to write a title, then a row for each item with labels, and a key that tells what each picture stands for. Finally, I need to draw the correct number of pictures in each row. When I read a picture graph I need to look at the title, the rows, the key, and the pictures to understand the data in the graph.)

Mathematical Practices

Mathematical Practice Standards underline the teaching and understanding of all concepts and skills presented. The emphasis of specific practices is noted throughout the guided and independent practice of this lesson.

MP2	**Reason abstractly and quantitatively.**

Item 2: Children write a word problem based on a completed picture graph.

Independent Practice

Concept Application

Children may work independently on these pages in the classroom or at home. They may refer to the first four pages of the lesson to revisit the instruction or to see a worked-out example.

Common Errors and **Teaching Tips** may help you support children's learning either in the classroom or as a follow-up for work done at home.

Common Errors

Items 5–6

Children may not read the problem carefully and, instead of finding a difference, may find a total number of thunderstorms for the two months. Help children see that the questions ask them to compare the numbers of thunderstorms for the two months.

Teaching Tips

Items 4–6

Help children understand that they need to write and solve an equation using the information from the picture graph.

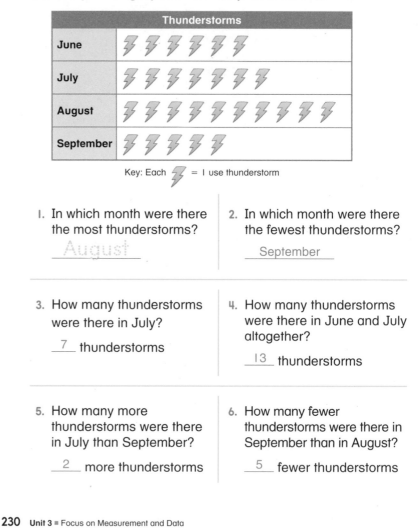

Independent Practice

Use the picture graph to answer problems 1–6.

Thunderstorms	
June	⚡⚡⚡⚡⚡
July	⚡⚡⚡⚡⚡⚡
August	⚡⚡⚡⚡⚡⚡⚡⚡
September	⚡⚡⚡⚡⚡

Key: Each ⚡ = 1 use thunderstorm

1. In which month were there the most thunderstorms?

   August

2. In which month were there the fewest thunderstorms?

   September

3. How many thunderstorms were there in July?

   _7_ thunderstorms

4. How many thunderstorms were there in June and July altogether?

   _13_ thunderstorms

5. How many more thunderstorms were there in July than September?

   _2_ more thunderstorms

6. How many fewer thunderstorms were there in September than in August?

   _5_ fewer thunderstorms

Talking About Math

Collaborative Conversations Have pairs of children look at the Thunderstorms picture graph and decide how to make another picture graph that shows a different kind of weather. Have them share their ideas with the class. Turn one pairs' idea into a class project to extend over a period of time. For example, the class might record how many sunny days there are during the next four weeks. Discuss how to record the weather in a table.

When all the data have been collected, have pairs use the table to make the picture graph. Tell them to be sure to include a title, labels for each row, and a key. Display the completed picture graphs. Although the graphs should all show the same data, encourage children to compare them and point out any differences.

Lesson 26

Independent Practice

7. The table shows how many books some children read in a week. Use the data in the table to complete the picture graph.

Books Read	
Name	Number of Books
Jared	2
Deena	6
Marco	5
Tony	3

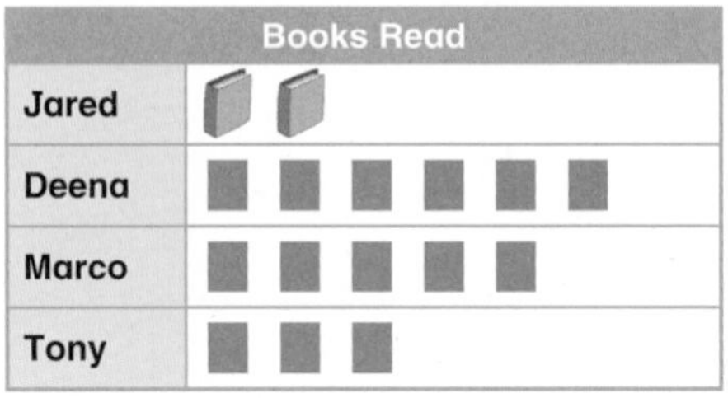

Books Read	
Jared	📖 📖
Deena	▪ ▪ ▪ ▪ ▪
Marco	▪ ▪ ▪ ▪
Tony	▪ ▪ ▪

Key: Each 📖 = 1 book

8. The picture graph shows how many flowers some children picked. Use the data in the picture graph to complete the table.

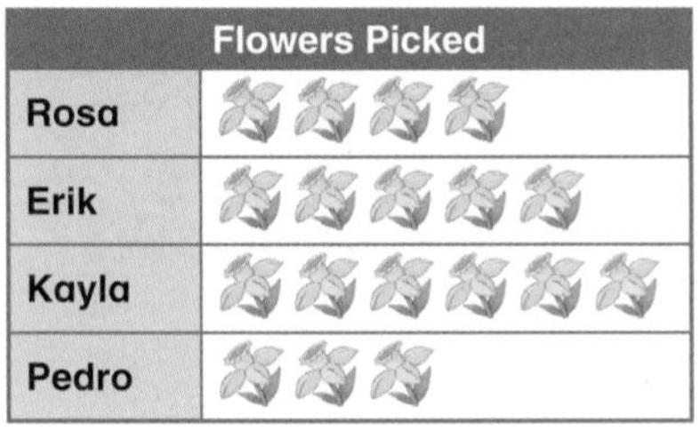

Flowers Picked	
Rosa	🌸 🌸 🌸 🌸
Erik	🌸 🌸 🌸 🌸 🌸
Kayla	🌸 🌸 🌸 🌸 🌸 🌸
Pedro	🌸 🌸 🌸

Key: Each 🌸 = 1 flower

Flowers Picked	
Name	Number of Flowers
Rosa	4
Erik	5
Kayla	6
Pedro	3

Teaching Tips

Item 7

Remind children to look at the key before they start to work on the picture graph. Make sure they understand that each symbol stands for 1 book. You may wish to have children find the row in the table with Jared's name to help them understand why 2 book symbols appear next to *Jared* in the graph.

Item 8

This is the first time in this lesson that children will record data from a picture graph in a table. Discuss with children how they will label the rows and where they will find the data for the numbers of flowers.

Digital Connection

Digital Whiteboard Have children use the digital whiteboard to create a picture graph that tells something about them. For example, children may want to make a graph that shows the color of the shoes the class is wearing one day. Have children call out the colors of their shoes and set up the graph with a row for each color. Then allow each child to come to the board and draw a shoe in the row for his or her color. Alternatively, children may want to make a picture graph that shows how many of their names begin with different letters of the alphabet. For this, set up the graph with a row for each letter. Have children come up and draw stick figures in the rows with the letter of their names. Discuss the completed graph with the class asking volunteers to describe the data.

Independent Practice

Common Errors

Item 12

Some children may have difficulty comparing the numbers of fish caught by Lauren and Ellie since the rows for their data are not next to each other. Show children how to hold a straightedge vertically at the right of the tally marks to help them find the correct answer.

Teaching Tips

Item 9

Discuss the importance of drawing symbols to show the correct numbers of fish caught. However, some children may struggle to copy the fish symbol that appears in the key. Explain that they may make up a simpler symbol of their own as long as they draw the correct numbers of their symbol in the picture graph.

Independent Practice

9. The tally chart shows how many fish some friends caught.

Fish Caught	
Name	**Number of Fish Caught**
Angel	ЖЖ ЖЖ
Lauren	ЖЖ I
Parker	IIII
Ellie	ЖЖ II

Complete the picture graph to show the data in the chart.

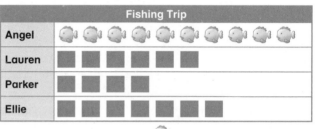

Key: Each 🐟 = I fish

Use the picture graph to answer problems 10–12.

10. Who caught the most fish?

    _____Angel_____

11. Who caught the fewest fish?

    _____Parker_____

12. Who caught more fish, Lauren or Ellie? How many more?

    _____Ellie_____ caught __I__ more fish than _____Lauren_____.

Math-to-Science Connection

Weather Explain that a weather forecast tells what the weather will likely be in days to come. Use the Internet to find the forecast in your area for the next 10 days. Discuss with the class how to make a picture graph to represent these data. Invite volunteers to the board to draw and label the rows to set up the picture graph. Then, with children's assistance, complete the picture graph. Have children summarize the graphed data by telling how many days are forecast to be sunny, rainy, cloudy, and so on.

Lesson 26

Independent Practice

MP2 **13.** George asked his friends to vote for their favorite color. Here are the data he collected.

red	green	blue	yellow
yellow	red	green	red
red	blue	red	blue

Complete the table to find how many votes there were for each color.

Color	Number of Votes
red	5
green	2
blue	3
yellow	2

Make a picture graph to show the data in the table.

Let 🙂 stand for 1 vote. Give your picture graph a title.

Title: _____ Favorite Colors _____

Color	Number of Votes
red	🙂 🙂 🙂 🙂 🙂
green	🙂 🙂
blue	🙂 🙂 🙂
yellow	🙂 🙂

Key: Each 🙂 = 1 vote

Unit 3 ■ Focus on Measurement and Data **233**

Common Errors

Item 13

Children may count some votes more than once, or they may not count all the votes. Encourage them to cross out each vote as they count it, to keep from counting it again.

Teaching Tips

Item 13

If children are spending too much time drawing the symbols, make sure they understand that they may draw simpler symbols, as long as their symbols are all alike. Also, review the importance of lining up the symbols in the graph so they can be counted easily.

Mathematical Practices

MP2	**Reason abstractly and quantitatively.**

Item 13: Children use information from a word problem to complete a table, and then a picture graph, representing colors with objects.

Common Core Focus:

2.MD.10 Draw a picture graph and a bar graph (with single-unit scale) to represent a data set with up to four categories. Solve simple put-together, take-apart, and compare problems using information presented in a bar graph.

OBJECTIVE
Interpret and create bar graphs.

ESSENTIAL QUESTION

Read the Essential Question aloud and ask children to talk about the kinds of graphs they know about. Point out that they have already worked with line plots and picture graphs, and that in this lesson, they will learn about bar graphs.

FLUENCY PRACTICE

Fluency practice is available at **sadlierconnect.com**.

Concept Development

Understand: Read a bar graph

■ This presentation extends children's knowledge of representing data in graphs by having them read a bar graph. Direct children to look at the graph and explain why they think it is called a bar graph. Say that the bars in this graph go up and down, but the bars in other graphs can go across, from left to right.

■ Explain that *scale* refers to the numbers on the side of the graph. These numbers show the value of each of the bars.

■ Ask children to identify the title, the labels, the months, the scale, and the bars. Explain that all these together help us to understand the data in the bar graph.

■ Ask children to point to the bar that represents May and determine the number of games won. Instruct them to move their fingers to the top of the bar and then left along the line until they reach the 4.

Lesson

27 Bar Graphs

Guided Instruction

Essential Question:
How do you read and make a bar graph?
2.MD.10

Words to Know
bar graph

In this lesson you will learn how to read and make bar graphs.

Understand: Read a bar graph

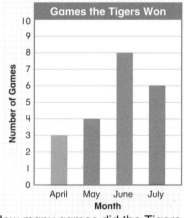

A bar graph uses bars to represent data. This bar graph shows how many games a soccer team won from April to July.

How many games did the Tigers win in May?

The scale on the left side of the graph goes from 0 to 10.

Find the bar for May. Look at the top of the bar.

Read the number on the scale that lines up with the top of the bar.

▷ The Tigers won 4 games in May.

Words to Know

bar graph: a graph that uses bars to show data

scale: On a bar graph, it tells how many are represented by the length of a bar.

Example:

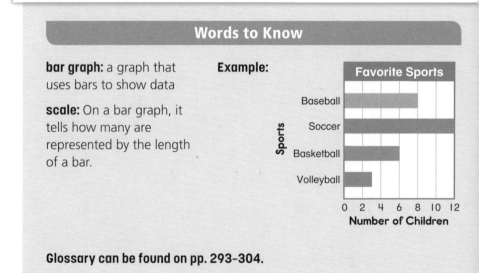

Glossary can be found on pp. 293–304.

Understand: Make a bar graph

The table shows how many flowers four children picked.

Flowers Picked	
Name	**Number of Flowers**
Joey	6
Zoe	8
Anna	5
Pat	9

Make a bar graph to show these data.

The title of this bar graph is Flowers Picked.
The scale on the left side of the graph goes from 0 to 10.
The columns are labeled with the names of the children.
The bars show the number of flowers each child picked.

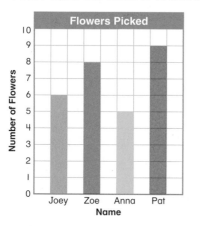

⇨ This bar graph shows the data from the table.

Understand: Make a bar graph

■ Ask children to explain what the table shows. Point out that the bar graph below shows the same data that are in this table.

■ Have children tell why there are more numbers on the bar graph scale than are needed to show the data in the table. Explain that the scales on all bar graphs start at 0. The highest number is either equal to, or a little greater than, the greatest value in the data.

Support English Language Learners

To help children understand the terminology used in this lesson, draw a simple bar graph on the board. Label three parts of the graph with the words *title, bar,* and *scale.* Have children practice saying these words aloud as you point to them. Then have children copy each of the words onto their Flowers Picked bar graph. Show them how to draw an arrow from each word to the corresponding part of the graph.

Connect: Use data from a bar graph to solve problems Use this page to strengthen children's abilities to solve problems using a bar graph.

■ Ask children to analyze the bar graph by identifying the kinds of pets and the number of each kind.

■ Have children talk about what they need to find to solve this problem. Encourage a discussion on how following the steps will help.

■ Make sure children understand how to find the number of birds and the number of dogs. Once children find the numbers of birds and dogs, discuss what operation they will use to solve the problem.

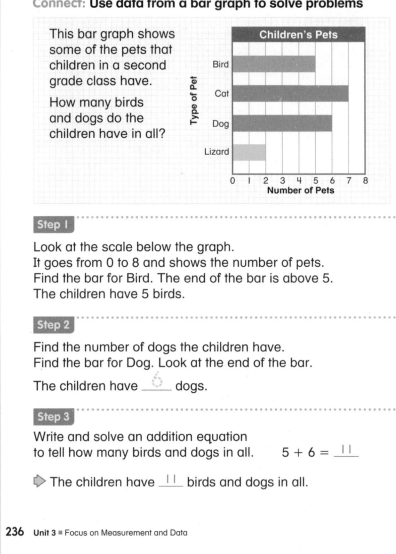

Connect: Use data from a bar graph to solve problems

This bar graph shows some of the pets that children in a second grade class have.

How many birds and dogs do the children have in all?

Children's Pets

Step 1

Look at the scale below the graph.
It goes from 0 to 8 and shows the number of pets.
Find the bar for Bird. The end of the bar is above 5.
The children have 5 birds.

Step 2

Find the number of dogs the children have.
Find the bar for Dog. Look at the end of the bar.

The children have ___6___ dogs.

Step 3

Write and solve an addition equation to tell how many birds and dogs in all.   5 + 6 = _11_

▷ The children have _11_ birds and dogs in all.

Math-to-Real World Connection

Bar Graphs in the News Explain to children that when reporters include data in their news stories, they often show them in bar graphs. Bar graphs make it easy for people who read the news in newspapers or online to understand data. Point out that the data could instead be written in words. But if words would take up too much space or be too hard to read, using a bar graph might be better. Usually, a news story appears with a bar graph. The story tells what the data mean and why they are important.

Lesson 27

Guided Practice

1. **Zelda picked tomatoes on four different days. She picked 5 tomatoes on Thursday, 9 tomatoes on Friday, 3 tomatoes on Saturday, and 7 tomatoes on Sunday. Write this data in the table.**

Tomatoes Picked	
Day	Number of Tomatoes Picked
Thursday	5
Friday	9
Saturday	3
Sunday	7

Use the table to make a bar graph.

The title of this bar graph is Tomatoes Zelda Picked.
The scale goes from 0 to 10.
It shows the Number of Tomatoes Picked.
The bottom of the bar graph is labeled with the Days.

Draw bars to show the data for Friday, Saturday, and Sunday.

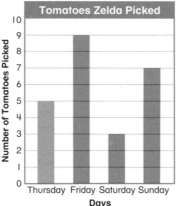

Tomatoes Zelda Picked

👑 Think•Pair•Share

MP2 2. Write a question that can be answered using the data in the Tomatoes Zelda Picked bar graph.
See Additional Answers.

Observational Assessment

Use page 237 to assess children's understanding of reading and making bar graphs. Children should be able to transfer data from the table to a bar graph. Then, they should be able to interpret the data and determine what information they can find out from the bar graph.

👑 Think•Pair•Share

Peer Collaboration Ask pairs to share their questions. Then, ask children to explain how to use the graph to answer the question. To help children write a question, ask:

- *What does the graph show?*

- *What does the graph tell you about the number of tomatoes Zelda picked on Friday?*

Return to the Essential Question

Reread the Lesson 27 Essential Question on page 234: *How do you read and make a bar graph?*

Tell children to think about what they learned in this lesson to answer this question.
(Possible response: I can look at the title to know what the graph is about. Then I can look at the bars to find out about the data. I can use the greatest number of data to determine the scale. The heights of bars help me answer questions about the data.)

Additional Answers

Item 2: Answers may vary. Possible answer: How many more tomatoes did Zelda pick on Friday than on Sunday?

Mathematical Practices

Mathematical Practice Standards underline the teaching and understanding of all concepts and skills presented. The emphasis of specific practices is noted throughout the guided and independent practice of this lesson.

MP2	Reason abstractly and quantitatively.

Item 2: Children write a question that can be answered using the data from a bar graph.

Concept Application

Children may work independently on these pages in the classroom or at home. They may refer to the first four pages of the lesson to revisit the instruction or to see a worked-out example.

Common Errors and **Teaching Tips** may help you support learning either in the classroom or as a follow-up for work done at home.

Teaching Tips

Item 2

Ask children how the words *how many more* help them decide whether to add or subtract.

Item 4

Have children compare the bars for Manny and Luis. Explain that they need to find the difference between the number of gold stars Manny earned and the number Luis earned.

Independent Practice

Use this bar graph to answer problems 1–5.

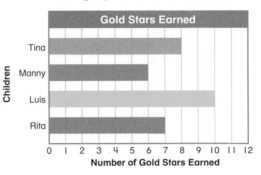

1. Who earned the fewest gold stars? __Manny__

2. How many more stars did Tina earn than Rita?

   __1__ more

3. How many gold stars did the four children earn in all?

   __31__ gold stars

4. How many fewer gold stars did Manny earn than Luis?

   __4__ fewer gold stars

5. Tina earned 2 more gold stars than her friend Sam.

   How many did Sam earn? __6__ gold stars

Talking About Math

Display a sheet or box of sticky-back gold stars and distribute one to each child. Brainstorm reasons for which Tina, Manny, Luis, and Rita could have earned their gold stars. Ask children to use the data in the graph to make up stories about earning each number of gold stars.

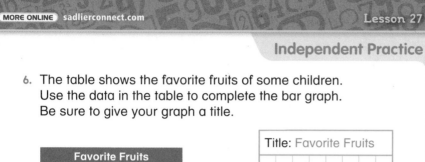

6. The table shows the favorite fruits of some children.
Use the data in the table to complete the bar graph.
Be sure to give your graph a title.

Favorite Fruits	
Type of Fruit	Number of Children
Apple	7
Mango	6
Orange	8
Peach	5

Title: Favorite Fruits

7. The bar graph shows the rainfall in Fox City from April
to July. Use the data in the bar graph to complete the table.

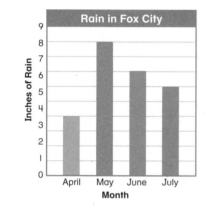

Rain in Fox City	
Month	Inches of Rain
April	3
May	8
June	6
July	5

Common Errors

Item 6

Some children may not leave space
between the bars they draw. Explain
that the bars in a bar graph should
not touch. Tell children to be sure to
leave space above and below each bar
they draw.

Digital Connection

Digital Whiteboard Write a survey question on the board; for example,
*Which of these sports is your favorite: basketball, baseball, football, or
soccer?* List the choices on the board and have children make a tally mark
next to the choice they like best. Then, have children use the whiteboard
tools to create a bar graph to display their data.

Teaching Tips

Item 8

Review how to make tally marks to record data. Encourage children to write the number represented by the tally marks for each row.

Independent Practice

8. The tally chart shows the number of books some students read.

Books Read	
Name	**Number of Books**
Teresa	ЖЖ IIII
Mark	ЖЖ II
Jacob	ЖЖ ЖЖ I
Flora	ЖЖ III

Complete the bar graph to match the data in the chart.

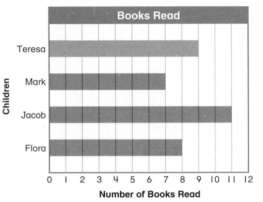

Use the bar graph to answer problems 9 and 10.

9. How many more books did Jacob read than Flora?

    __3__ more books

10. How many books did the four children read in all?

    35 books

Math-to-Math Connection

Data Analysis Help children understand why a bar graph can be used to help them quickly determine some answers about data. Show children a few bar graphs pulled from news reports. Guide them to determine which bar shows the greatest number and which bar shows the least number.

MORE ONLINE sadlierconnect.com

Independent Practice

MP6 **11.** Use the data in the tally chart to complete the bar graph.

Tickets Sold

Children	Tally
Sara	卌 卌
Joe	卌 III
Alma	卌 II
Chen	卌 III

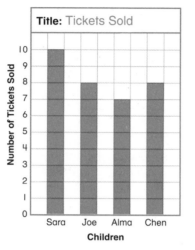

Title: Tickets Sold

MP7 **12.** Write a question that you could answer using the data in the bar graph above. Then answer your question.

Answers may vary. Possible answer: Which child sold the same number of tickets as Chen? Joe

Talk about how you used the bar graph to answer your question.

Answers may vary. Possible answer: I looked for a bar that was the same height as the bar for Chen.

Unit 3 ■ Focus on Measurement and Data **241**

Common Errors

Item 11

Children may be confused about where to start drawing each bar. Tell them to start at the bottom of the graph directly above the name of a child. From there, they should draw the bar upward until it reaches the line that shows the number of tickets that the child sold.

Mathematical Practices

MP6	**Attend to precision.**

Item 11: Children accurately represent data from a table in a bar graph.

MP7	**Look for and make use of structure.**

Item 12: Children use data in a bar graph to write a question and describe how to answer it.

The Common Core Review covers all the standards presented in the unit. Use it to assess your children's mastery of the unit's concepts and skills.

Depth of Knowledge

The depth of knowledge is a ranking of the content complexity of assessment items based on Webb's Depth of Knowledge (DOK) levels. The levels increase in complexity as shown below.

Level 1: Recall and Reproduction
Level 2: Basic Skills and Concepts
Level 3: Strategic Reasoning and Thinking
Level 4: Extended Thinking

Item	Standard	DOK
1	2.MD.1	1
2	2.MD.4	2
3	2.MD.6	2
4	2.MD.7	1
5	2.MD.9	2
6	2.MD.10	2
7	2.MD.2	3
8	2.MD.8	3
9	2.MD.2	3
10	2.MD.5	4

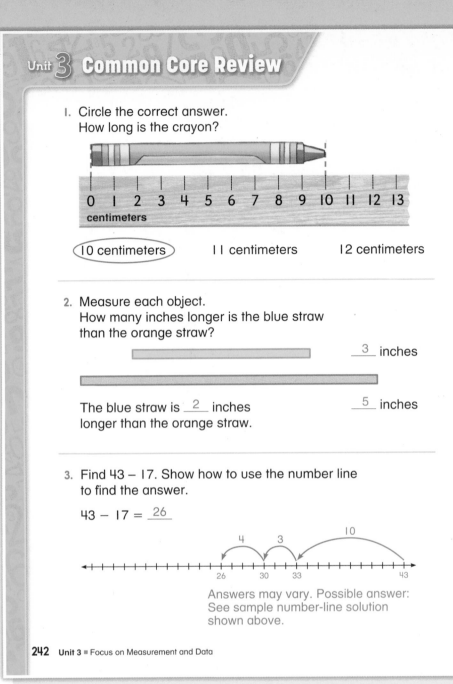

Unit 3 **Common Core Review**

1. Circle the correct answer.
   How long is the crayon?

   (10 centimeters)   11 centimeters   12 centimeters

2. Measure each object.
   How many inches longer is the blue straw than the orange straw?

   __3__ inches

   The blue straw is __2__ inches longer than the orange straw.

   __5__ inches

3. Find 43 – 17. Show how to use the number line to find the answer.

   43 – 17 = __26__

   Answers may vary. Possible answer: See sample number-line solution shown above.

Unit 3 Common Core Review

4. Write the time for the event. Be sure to include A.M. or P.M.

Piano lesson in the evening

6:40 P.M.

5. Jan used an inch ruler to measure the length of some tiles. She made a table to show her data. Use the number line to make a line plot of the data.

Tile Lengths	
Length (in inches)	Number of Tiles
1	0
2	4
3	3
4	4
5	0

Tile Lengths

```
X           X
X     X     X
X     X     X
X     X     X
+--+--+--+--+--+
1  2  3  4  5
```

Length (in inches)

6. The table shows some children's favorite colors. Use the data in the table to complete the bar graph.

Favorite Color	
Color	Number of Children
Red	4
Blue	6
Green	3
Yellow	2

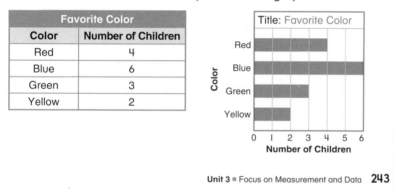

Title: Favorite Color

Color: Red, Blue, Green, Yellow

Number of Children

Unit 3 ■ Focus on Measurement and Data **243**

This chart correlates the Common Core Review items with the lessons in which the concepts and skills are presented.

Item	Lesson
1	17
2	20
3	22
4	23
5	25
6	27
7	18
8	24
9	18
10	21

Talking About Math

Direct children to respond to the Unit 3 Essential Question. (This can also be found on page 145.)

Essential Question:
How can you estimate and measure length?

Possible responses:
- Length can be measured with rulers, tape measures, and other tools.
- You can estimate and check length measurements with inches, feet, centimeters, and meters.

Unit Assessment

- Unit 3 Common Core Review, *pp. 242–244*
- Unit 3 Performance Task (ONLINE)

Additional Assessment Options

Optional Purchase:
- iProgress Monitor (ONLINE)
- Progress Monitor Student Benchmark Assessment Booklet

---

7. Do you need more inches or more yards to measure the length of a rug?

   You need more ___inches___.

8. Taylor has some quarters, dimes, and nickels worth 40¢.

   What is the least number of coins Taylor could have? __3__

   Name the coins. __I quarter__, __I dime__, __I nickel__

MP3 9. Use an inch ruler to measure the length of these scissors.

   Explain how the measure of the scissors would change if you used a centimeter ruler to measure. The scissors are 3 inches long. Answers may vary. Possible answer: I centimeter is a shorter unit of measure than I inch. It takes more centimeters to measure the same object. If I measure in centimeters it will measure more centimeters than if I measure in inches.

MP4 10. Niko measures the length of a toy truck and a toy tractor. The tractor is longer than the truck. One of the toys is 6 inches long. The sum of the lengths is 15 inches. Find the length of each toy. Show your work. Sample answer: I wrote the equation 6 + ▇ = 15. I used the related subtraction fact to find the missing measurement. 15 − ▇ = 6. The missing addend is 9. So one object is 6 inches long and the other is 9 inches long. Since the tractor is longer than the truck, the tractor must be 9 inches long and the truck must be 6 inches long.

	Mathematical Practices
MP3	**Construct viable arguments and critique the reasoning of others.**
Item 9: Children reason inductively to compare how measuring with different tools affects data.	
MP4	**Model with mathematics.**
Item 10: Children use data about two models to draw conclusions about the lengths of the models.	

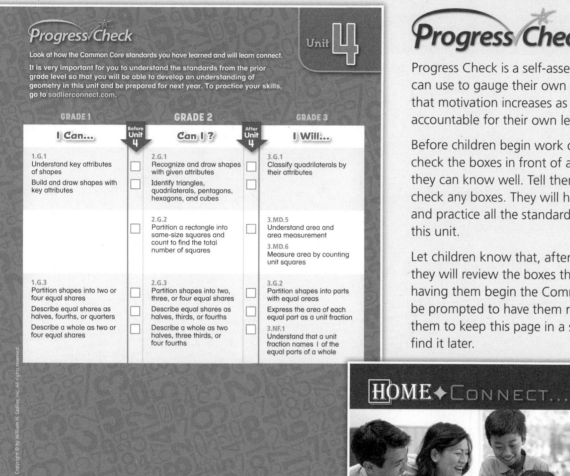

Progress Check

Look at how the Common Core standards you have learned and will learn connect.

It is very important for you to understand the standards from the prior grade level so that you will be able to develop an understanding of geometry in this unit and be prepared for next year. To practice your skills, go to sadlierconnect.com.

GRADE 1 I Can...	Before Unit 4	GRADE 2 Can I?	After Unit 4	GRADE 3 I Will...
1.G.1 Understand key attributes of shapes	☐	**2.G.1** Recognize and draw shapes with given attributes	☐	**3.G.1** Classify quadrilaterals by their attributes
Build and draw shapes with key attributes	☐	Identify triangles, quadrilaterals, pentagons, hexagons, and cubes	☐	
		2.G.2 Partition a rectangle into same-size squares and count to find the total number of squares	☐	**3.MD.5** Understand area and area measurement **3.MD.6** Measure area by counting unit squares
1.G.3 Partition shapes into two or four equal shares	☐	**2.G.3** Partition shapes into two, three, or four equal shares	☐	**3.G.2** Partition shapes into parts with equal areas
Describe equal shares as halves, fourths, or quarters	☐	Describe equal shares as halves, thirds, or fourths	☐	Express the area of each equal part as a unit fraction
Describe a whole as two or four equal shares	☐	Describe a whole as two halves, three thirds, or four fourths	☐	**3.NF.1** Understand that a unit fraction names 1 of the equal parts of a whole

Unit 4 ■ Focus on Geometry 2

Progress Check

Progress Check is a self-assessment tool that children can use to gauge their own progress. Research shows that motivation increases as children gradually become accountable for their own learning.

Before children begin work on Unit 4, have them check the boxes in front of any standards they think they can know well. Tell them it is okay if they cannot check any boxes. They will have a chance to learn and practice all the standards as they work through this unit.

Let children know that, after they complete Lesson 30, they will review the boxes they checked today. Before having them begin the Common Core Review, you will be prompted to have them revisit this page. Remind them to keep this page in a safe place where they can find it later.

HOME ◆ CONNECT...

The Home Connect feature keeps parents or other adult family members apprised of what their children are learning. The key learning objectives are listed, and some ideas for related activities and discussions are included.

Tell children that there is an activity connected to their classroom learning that they can do at home with their families.

Encourage children and their families to share their experiences using the ideas on the Home Connect page. Afterward, you may wish to invite children to share the work they did at home with the class.

HOME ◆ CONNECT...

I n second grade your child is learning to identify and draw closed, flat shapes. Your child is also identifying shapes by their numbers of sides and angles.

side ⟶ ☐ ⟵ angle

This table lists the flat shapes your child will learn to recognize and draw in this unit.

Shape	Number of sides	Number of angles
Triangle	3	3
Quadrilateral	4	4
Pentagon	5	5
Hexagon	6	6

In addition to these flat shapes, your child is learning about a solid shape called a **cube**. A cube has 6 faces. Each of the cube's faces is a square. A square is a special quadrilateral with 4 equal sides and 4 equal angles.

Activity: Ask your child to demonstrate how to partition shapes into 2, 3, and 4 equal shares. Use the terms *halves*, *thirds*, and *fourths*. Ask your child to explain how he or she knows the shares are equal.

246 Unit 4 ■ Focus on Geometry

In this unit, your child will:

- Identify and draw shapes.
- Partition rectangles into same-size squares.
- Make and identify two, three, and four equal shares.

NOTE: All of these learning goals for your child are based on the Grade 2 Common Core State Standards for Mathematics.

Ways to Help Your Child

In second grade and beyond, it is likely that your child will spend increasing amounts of time doing homework. Knowing the teacher's expectations for homework will allow you to help your child at home, and also gauge whether your child is spending too little or too much time completing assignments. Ask the teacher how much time he or she expects your child to spend on Math homework.

ONLINE
For more Home Connect activities, continue online at sadlierconnect.com

UNIT PLANNER

	Lesson	Standard(s)	Objective
28	Identify and Draw Shapes	2.G.1	Identify and draw shapes.
29	Partition Rectangles into Same-Size Squares	2.G.2	Use rows and columns to partition a rectangle into squares, and then find the total number of squares.
30	Equal Shares	2.G.3	Make and recognize equal shares of rectangles, circles, and squares.

Essential Question	Words to Know
How do you identify and draw shapes?	flat shape, sides, angles, triangle, quadrilateral, pentagon, hexagon, rectangle, square, solid shape, cube, face
How do you make same-size squares in rectangles?	
How do you make and recognize equal shares?	equal shares, fourth, quarter, third, half, halves

Unit Assessment

- Unit 4 Common Core Review, *pp. 272–274*
- Unit 4 Performance Task ONLINE

Additional Assessment Options

- Performance Task 2, *pp. 275–278*
  ALSO ONLINE

Optional Purchase:

- iProgress Monitor ONLINE
- Progress Monitor Student Benchmark Assessment Booklet

ONLINE Digital Resources

- Home Connect Activities
- Unit Performance Tasks
- Additional Practice
- Fluency Practice
- Teacher Resources
- iProgress Monitor (optional purchase)

Go to SadlierConnect.com to access your Digital Resources.

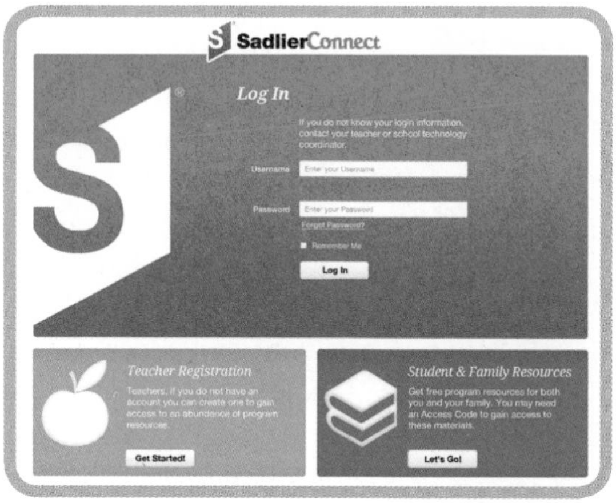

For more detailed instructions see page T3.

LEARNING PROGRESSIONS

This page provides more in-depth detail on the development of the standards across the grade levels. See also the unit Progress Check page in the Student Edition for a roadmap of the Learning Progressions.

Grade 1

- Students distinguish between attributes that define shapes (e.g., number of sides) and non-defining attributes (e.g., color, size, orientation). (1.G.1)
- Students partition shapes into two or four equal shares, describe the shares as *halves, fourths,* and *quarters,* and use the phrases *half of, fourth of,* and *quarter of.* They describe a whole as two halves, four fourths, or four quarters, and understand that partitioning the same shape into more equal shares creates smaller shares. (1.G.3)

Grade 2

- Students identify and draw shapes with specified attributes, such as a given number of angles or equal faces. (2.G.1)
- Students identify triangles, quadrilaterals, pentagons, hexagons, and cubes. (2.G.1)
- Students partition rectangles into rows and columns of same-size squares and count to find the total number of squares. (2.G.2)
- Students partition circles and rectangles into two, three, or four equal shares and describe the shares as halves, thirds, and fourths. They describe a whole as two halves, three thirds, or four fourths. (2.G.3)

Grade 3

- Students understand that shapes in different categories may share attributes and that the shared attributes may define a larger category. For example, rhombuses and rectangles have four sides, and having four sides defines the larger category of quadrilaterals. Students recognize rhombuses, rectangles, and squares as types of quadrilaterals, and can draw examples of quadrilaterals that do not belong to any of these subcategories. (3.G.1)
- Area is formally introduced as an attribute of two-dimensional figures. Students understand the concept of a unit square. (3.MD.5a, 3.MD.5b)
- Students measure area by counting unit squares (square cm, square m, square in., square ft, and improvised units). (3.MD.6)
- Students partition shapes into equally sized parts and express the area of each part as a unit fraction. (3.G.2)
- Students understand a fraction $1/b$ as being formed by 1 part of a whole that is partitioned into b equal parts; and they understand a fraction a/b as being formed by a parts that are each the size of $1/b$. (3.NF.1)

Focus on Geometry

Unit 4

Essential Question:
What are halves, thirds, and fourths?

Essential Question:
What are halves, thirds, and fourths?

As children become involved with the Essential Question they will identify shapes, partition rectangles into same-size squares, and break apart rectangles, squares, and circles to make equal shares.

Conversation Starters

Have children discuss the photograph. Ask question such as: *How many plates of food do you see? Why do you suppose some of the food has been cut? Describe some foods that you need to cut before you can eat them. Why do you need to cut them?*

Ask children to describe the ways that the food items are cut. *Which plates show two equal shares?* (bottom two plates) *If you ate one part of the bagel, how much of the whole bagel would that be?* (half) *Which plate shows 4 equal shares?* (top left) *What are four equal shares called?* (fourths, or quarters) Have children look at the whole sandwich and think about ways that it could be cut. *What is one way to cut the whole sandwich to make two equal shares that are* not *triangles?* (across or up and down) *Could you cut the whole sandwich into thirds? Explain why or why not.* (Answers may vary. It may be possible to cut the sandwich into thirds but doing that would be hard because the shares would include the edges and the food that sticks out.)

Draw circles and rectangles on the board. Have children take turns showing how the shapes could be cut to show 2, 3, or 4 equal shares.

Activity

Materials: pattern blocks or paper pattern-block facsimilies (triangles, squares, trapezoids, hexagons, and rhombi)

Explain to children that there are many ways to show 2, 3, or 4 equal shares of a whole. In this activity, they will put flat shapes together to show some of the ways. Have children work in small groups to explore ways to show halves, thirds, and fourths. Give each group a collection of pattern blocks. Assign each group *halves, thirds,* or *fourths* to show using the blocks. Possible halves arrangements include: 2 trapezoids make 1 hexagon; 2 squares make 1 rectangle. Possible thirds arrangements include: 3 rhombi make 1 hexagon; 3 triangles make 1 trapezoid. Possible fourths arrangements include: 4 triangles make 1 parallelogram; 4 squares make 1 rectangle or 1 larger square.

Guided Instruction

Common Core Focus:

2.G.1 Recognize and draw shapes having specified attributes, such as a given number of angles or a given number of equal faces. Identify triangles, quadrilaterals, pentagons, hexagons, and cubes.

OBJECTIVE
Identify and draw shapes.

ESSENTIAL QUESTION

Ask children to name shapes that they know. Then ask them to think about how they know the name of a shape. Read the Essential Question aloud, and explain that in this lesson children will learn ways to identify and draw shapes.

FLUENCY PRACTICE

Fluency practice is available at **sadlierconnect.com**.

Concept Development

Understand: Use sides and angles to identify a flat shape

■ In first grade, children learned to use defining attributes to identify basic flat shapes. In this lesson, children expand their understanding of defining attributes. They do this by identifying and drawing additional flat shapes according to the number of sides and angles of each.

■ Draw attention to the chart. Discuss how to pronounce the name of each shape. Ask children to read the names aloud with you to practice pronunciation.

■ Have children look for a pattern in the number of sides and the number of angles for the shapes. Children should conclude that a flat shape has an equal number of sides and angles.

■ To reinforce the difference between sides and angles, ask children to trace the sides of one shape with a finger. Then, ask them to point to each angle in that shape. Have them count the sides and angles as they trace or point.

248 Unit 4 ■ Focus on Geometry

Lesson **28** **Identify and Draw Shapes**

Essential Question:
How do you identify and draw shapes?
2.G.1

Words to Know
flat shape
sides
angles
triangle
quadrilateral
pentagon
hexagon
rectangle
square
solid shape
cube
face

Guided Instruction

In this lesson you will learn how to identify and draw shapes.

Understand: Use sides and angles to identify a flat shape

Adam drew this shape.
What shape did Adam draw?

You can identify a closed flat shape by its sides and its angles.

Shape		Number of Sides	Number of Angles
Triangle		3	3
Quadrilateral		4	4
Pentagon		5	5
Hexagon		6	6

Adam's shape has 5 sides and 5 angles.

▷ Adam drew a pentagon.

248 Unit 4 ■ Focus on Geometry

Words to Know

flat shape: a shape that has no gaps in its sides

sides: straight lines that outline a flat shape

angle: where two sides meet

triangle: flat shape with 3 sides and 3 angles

quadrilateral: flat shape with 4 sides and 4 angles

pentagon: flat shape with 5 sides and 5 angles

Glossary can be found on pp. 293–304.

Guided Instruction

Understand: Use sides and angles to identify special quadrilaterals

Jenna drew these special quadrilaterals.

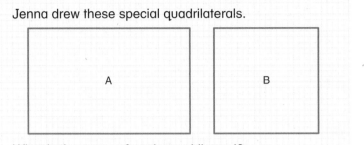

A   B

What is the name of each quadrilateral?

You can identify each quadrilateral by comparing its sides and angles.

Look at the shapes Jenna drew.

Quadrilateral A has opposite sides that are the same length.
It has 4 angles that are the same shape.
   Quadrilateral A is a rectangle.

In Quadrilateral B, all the sides are the same length.
It has 4 angles that are the same shape.
   Quadrilateral B is a square.

▷ The quadrilaterals Jenna drew are a ___rectangle___

and a ___square___.

Unit 4 ■ Focus on Geometry **249**

Concept Development

Understand: Use sides and angles to identify special quadrilaterals.

■ In this presentation, children differentiate between the attributes of two similar shapes. Ask children to describe the similarities and differences between the two shapes.

■ Explain that both shapes are called *quadrilaterals*. Encourage children to use their new vocabulary to tell you why the shapes are both quadrilaterals.

■ Help children identify opposite sides. Have them use a crayon of one color to trace over one pair of opposite sides and a crayon of another color to trace over the other pair of opposite sides. Then lead a discussion on why Quadrilaterals A and B are called "special quadrilaterals."

■ Children should understand that the shapes are called special because they each have four angles of the same shape and opposite sides of the same length. Also, the square is special because all its sides are the same length.

■ Ask children to describe how they can tell which sides are equal. Explain that they can use a ruler to measure the lengths of the sides. Those with equal measures are the same length.

Words to Know

hexagon: flat shape with 6 sides and 6 angles

rectangle: flat shape with 4 sides and 4 angles

square: flat shape with 4 equal sides and 4 angles

solid shape: a shape with three dimensions

cube: a solid shape with faces that are squares

face: one flat side of a cube

Glossary can be found on pp. 293–304.

Guided Instruction

Connect: What you know about identifying shapes Use this page to help children strengthen their understanding of identifying shapes.

■ This presentation helps children identify a cube by examining its faces. Discuss how children can determine whether a shape is flat or solid. Use pictures and objects in the room to assess this skill.

■ Guide children to understand that each face of the cube is a square. Discuss the attributes of a square.

■ Explain why we cannot see all the faces of the cube in the drawing and why some of the faces we can see do not look like squares.

■ Provide pairs with a die or a cubical block that they can examine and count the faces.

■ Review non-defining attributes with children by discussing the color of the square. Remind them that the shape is called a square because it has an equal number of sides and angles and because its sides are all the same length. Color has nothing to do with its being a square.

Guided Instruction

Connect: What you know about identifying shapes

Carlos has this block.

What is the shape of each face of the block?
What is another name for the block?

Step 1

The block is a solid shape called a cube.

Each side of the cube is called a face.

face →

Step 2

Each face of the cube is a flat shape

with __4__ sides and __4__ angles.

Look at one of the faces.

    Are all the sides the same length? __yes__

    Are all the angles the same shape? __yes__

Is the face a special quadrilateral? __yes__

What is the name of the quadrilateral? __square__

▷ Each face of Carlos' block is a __square__.

    Another name for the block is a __cube__.

Support English Language Learners

Help English language learners make the connection between the name of a shape and the number of its sides by explaining the prefixes of shape names.

Draw a four-column chart on the board. At the top of each column, write a prefix: *tri-, quad-, pent-,* and *hex-*. Under each prefix, write *3, 4, 5,* and *6.* Below these, write the name of the shape that uses the prefix—*triangle, quadrilateral, pentagon,* and *hexagon.* Circle the prefix in each shape name as you point out that it tells how many sides and angles that shape has.

Lesson 28

Guided Practice

**I. Riya drew these shapes.
What is the name of the shapes?**

Step 1

Count the number of sides of each shape.

Do the shapes have the same number of sides? _yes_

Count the number of angles of each shape.

Do the shapes have the same number of angles? _yes_

Step 2

Each shape has _6_ sides and _6_ angles.

What is the name of each shape? _hexagon_

The shapes Riya drew are _hexagons_.

Think·Pair·Share

MP2 **2.** Both shapes that Riya drew have the same name but they look different.

Draw another shape with the same name that looks different from Riya's shapes.

Check children's work.

Talk about how you know the shapes have the same name.

All the shapes have 6 sides and 6 angles so they are all hexagons.

Mathematical Practices

Mathematical Practice Standards underline the teaching and understanding of all concepts and skills presented. The emphasis of specific practices is noted throughout the guided and independent practice of this lesson.

MP2 **Reason abstractly and quantitatively.**

Item 2: Children find a different way to draw a specified shape and explain why it is that shape.

Observational Assessment

Use page 251 to assess children's understanding of identifying and drawing shapes. Be sure that children are able to distinguish between defining attributes and non-defining attributes, such as color. They also should be able to tell why a rectangle and a square are called special quadrilaterals.

Think·Pair·Share

Peer Collaboration Ask pairs to trace over each side of their hexagon in a different color. Then have them display what they drew. To encourage them to identify the defining attributes, ask:

• *How do you know that your shape is a hexagon?*

• *How many sides does your shape have? How many angles?*

To summarize, remind children that a closed, flat shape is named by its number of sides and angles.

Return to the Essential Question

Reread the Lesson 8 Essential Question on page 248: *How do you identify and draw shapes?*

Tell children to think about what they learned in this lesson to answer this question.

(Possible responses: I can count to find the number of sides and the number of angles a shape has. This will help me know the name of the shape.)

Concept Application

Children may work independently on these pages in the classroom or at home. They may refer to the first four pages of the lesson to revisit the instruction or to see a worked-out example.

Common Errors and **Teaching Tips** may help you support learning either in the classroom or as a follow-up for work done at home.

Teaching Tips

Items 1-12

If children count the number of sides incorrectly, have them mark each side as they count.

Remind children to pay special attention to each quadrilateral and think about whether it is a special quadrilateral.

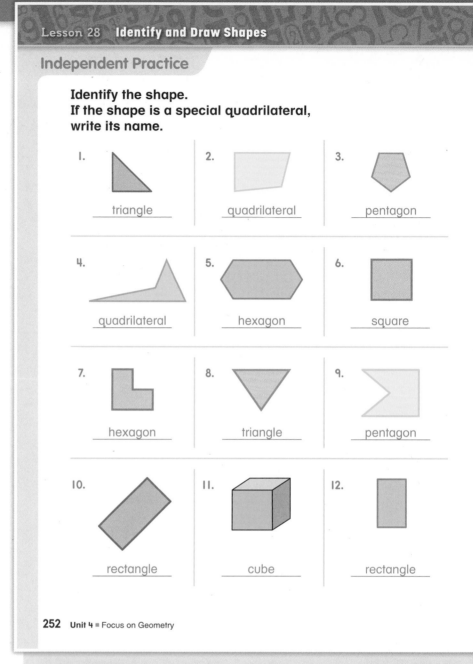

Lesson 28   **Identify and Draw Shapes**

Independent Practice

Identify the shape.
If the shape is a special quadrilateral,
write its name.

1. triangle

2. quadrilateral

3. pentagon

4. quadrilateral

5. hexagon

6. square

7. hexagon

8. triangle

9. pentagon

10. rectangle

11. cube

12. rectangle

Math-to-School Connection

Tiles Children are likely to have seen floor and wall tiles around the school. Explain that tiles are made in different shapes and sizes. Have them look around the classroom or elsewhere in the school for tiles of different shapes. Although most tiles that children find will probably be squares, suggest that they also look for tiles that are triangles, rectangles, and hexagons.

Lesson 28

Independent Practice

13. Draw a closed shape that has 5 sides. What is its name?

Check children's work.

___pentagon___

14. Draw a closed shape that has 3 angles. What is its name?

Check children's work.

___triangle___

15. Draw a closed shape that has 4 angles of the same shape and 4 sides of the same length. What is its name?

Check children's work.

___square___

16. Draw a closed shape that has two pairs of opposite sides of the same length. What is its name?

Check children's work.

___rectangle___

17. How many of the shapes you drew for problems 13–16 are quadrilaterals?

___2___ shapes are quadrilaterals.

Common Errors

Item 14

Children may draw a quadrilateral, pentagon, or hexagon and justify doing so by saying that each has 3 angles. Explain that they are being asked to draw a closed shape that has *exactly* 3 angles and no more.

Teaching Tips

Item 16

Remind children that a *pair* means 2 sides, so they will need to draw a figure with 4 sides. Guide them to conclude that the shape they need to draw is a quadrilateral. Then, if necessary, explain that opposite sides do not cross each other.

Digital Connection

Geometry Software Have children practice drawing and composing shapes using either geometry software or an online geometry program. Encourage them to draw the flat shapes that they have learned about in this lesson as well as the solid shape, the cube. Challenge them to draw each shape in more than one way.

Teaching Tips

Items 18 and 20

Ask children to tell how many sides a rectangle has. Then guide them to find the rectangles by having them identify shapes that have opposite sides of the same length.

Independent Practice

18. Circle all the rectangles.

19. Circle all the triangles.

20. Circle all the quadrilaterals.

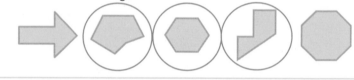

21. Circle all the hexagons.

22. Circle all the cubes.

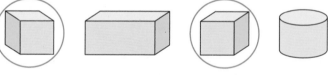

Talking About Math

Collaborative Conversations Ask children to talk about how they could use shapes to make pictures. Have them make their pictures and write a few sentences about the shapes they used. Then, have children display their work and point to each shape as they describe it.

Independent Practice

MP6 **23.** Is either one of these shapes a pentagon? __no__

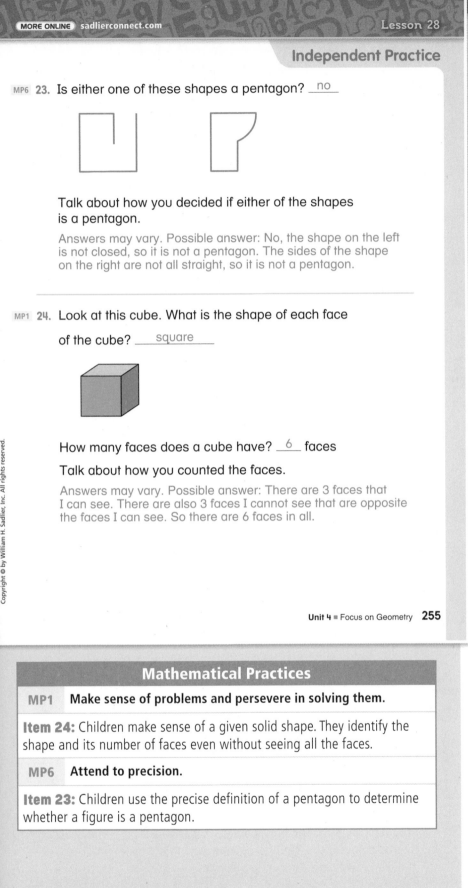

Talk about how you decided if either of the shapes is a pentagon.

Answers may vary. Possible answer: No, the shape on the left is not closed, so it is not a pentagon. The sides of the shape on the right are not all straight, so it is not a pentagon.

MP1 **24.** Look at this cube. What is the shape of each face

of the cube? __square__

How many faces does a cube have? __6__ faces

Talk about how you counted the faces.

Answers may vary. Possible answer: There are 3 faces that I can see. There are also 3 faces I cannot see that are opposite the faces I can see. So there are 6 faces in all.

Unit 4 ■ Focus on Geometry **255**

Common Errors

Item 24

Children may not count all of the faces on the cube. They may only count the faces that they can see, they may forget to count the bottom face, or they may say that a cube has four faces since there are four sides on a square. Supply children with cubical objects to handle so that they can approach the problem kinesthetically.

Mathematical Practices

MP1	Make sense of problems and persevere in solving them.

Item 24: Children make sense of a given solid shape. They identify the shape and its number of faces even without seeing all the faces.

MP6	Attend to precision.

Item 23: Children use the precise definition of a pentagon to determine whether a figure is a pentagon.

Common Core Focus:

2.G.2 Partition a rectangle into rows and columns of same-size squares and count to find the total number of them.

OBJECTIVE

Use rows and columns to partition a rectangle into squares, and then find the total number of squares.

ESSENTIAL QUESTION

Ask children to tell what they know about squares and rectangles. Then ask children how they might find out exactly how many squares would fit into a rectangle. If color tiles are available, distribute them to help children do their work

FLUENCY PRACTICE

Fluency practice is available at **sadlierconnect.com**.

Concept Development

Understand: Identify rows and columns in a rectangle made up of same-size squares

■ After having children read the problem, have them look closely at the diagram to identify the rectangle and the squares within it. Ask children to explain how they could tell that the garden is a rectangle and that each part inside it is a square.

■ Review the meaning of *row* and *column*. Children should understand that the rows and columns together form the rectangle.

■ Be sure that children understand that the rows and columns are made up of straight lines that form squares that are all equal in size.

Partition Rectangles into Same-Size Squares

Essential Question: How do you make same-size squares in rectangles? 2.G.2

Guided Instruction

In this lesson you will learn how to make same-size squares in rectangles.

Understand: Identify rows and columns in a rectangle made up of same-size squares

Mr. Rosa's garden is in the shape of a rectangle. He marks his garden in same-size squares. How many rows and columns of same-size squares are in his garden?

Remember!
A square is a quadrilateral with all 4 sides the same length and all 4 angles the same shape.

Count the numbers of rows and columns.

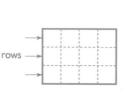

rows

There are 3 rows.

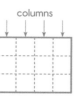

columns

There are 4 columns.

▷ Mr. Rosa's garden has 3 rows and 4 columns of same-size squares.

Support English Language Learners

Many geometry-based words are used in this lesson, such as *quadrilateral, square, rectangle, sides, angles,* and *length.* Draw an example of each of these or find examples in the lesson. Review each word with English language learners to make sure they understand its meaning and how to pronounce it.

Begin by saying each word aloud and having children repeat it. Say the word again, and point to an example. Explain in simple terms what the word means, and ask children to repeat what you say. Then have children take turns pointing to examples and saying the words aloud until you believe they have sufficient understanding to complete the work of the lesson.

Understand: Count to find the number of same-size squares in a rectangle

Find the number of same-size squares in Mr. Rosa's garden.

One way: Add the rows. There are 4 same-size squares in each row. There are three rows.

Use repeated addition to find the number of same-size squares in all three rows.

4 →
4 →
4 →

Add 4 three times: 4 + 4 + 4 = 12

Another way: Add the columns. There are 3 same-size squares in each column. There are four columns.

Use repeated addition to find the number of same-side squares in all four columns.

3 3 3 3
↓ ↓ ↓ ↓

Add 3 four times: 3 + 3 + 3 + 3 = 12

▷ There are __12__ squares in Mr. Rosa's garden.

Understand: Count to find the number of same-size squares in a rectangle

■ This presentation will show children two different ways to add to find the number of same-size squares in a rectangle.

■ After reading the question, ask children how they think they could add to find the number of same-size squares.

■ Remind children that they can check their answer by counting all the squares and comparing that number to their answer. When they use this method, encourage them to number each square as they count it to keep from counting it more than once.

Math-to-Real World Connection

Designing a Garden Explain that people who want to plant a garden may first draw an outline of the garden on paper. They may then draw lines inside the outline to show small garden plots. A garden plan can help the gardener decide which plots to use for planting each type of vegetable, fruit, or flower.

Divide the class into groups. Provide each group with a sheet of grid paper on which you have outlined a large rectangular area. Have children talk about how they could draw small garden plots inside the outline to make a garden plan. Allow groups time to draw their plots. Then tell them to use the words *row* and *column* as they describe their plans to the class.

Guided Instruction

Connect: What you know about same-size squares in a rectangle Use this page to help children extend their understanding of using rows and columns to create same-size squares in a rectangle.

■ Make sure children know that the question is asking for the number of rows and the number of columns, and not the total number of same-size squares.

■ Prior to solving, extend your arms straight out to the sides as you say that rows go across from left to right. Then hold one arm straight up and the other straight down and say that the columns go up and down.

■ Encourage children to number each row and column as they count it.

Connect: What you know about same-size squares in a rectangle

How many rows and columns of same-size squares are in this rectangle?

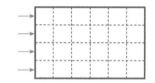

Step I

Count the number of rows.

There are ___4___ rows.

Step 2

Count the number of columns.

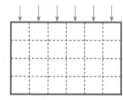

There are ___6___ columns.

▷ There are ___4___ rows and ___6___ columns of same-size squares in the rectangle.

258 Unit 4 ■ Focus on Geometry

Math-to-Games Connection

Board Games Many board games use boards that are divided into same-size squares. A good example of this is the checkerboard, which has rows and columns formed by same-size squares. Display a checkerboard or show a picture of one to the class. Have children count the rows and the columns, and then talk about how to find the total number of squares in the board. Ask children to tell about other board games that they may have played in which the board is made up of same-size squares.

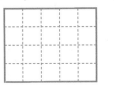

I. **How many same-size squares are in this rectangle?**

Step 1

Count the rows.

There are __4__ rows of same-size squares in the rectangle.

Step 2

Count the number of same-size squares in each row.

There are __5__ same-size squares in each row.

Step 3

Skip count by 5s four times.

__5__ , __10__ , __15__ , __20__

There are __20__ same-size squares in the rectangle.

Think•Pair•Share

MP3 2. Show how to add to find the number of same-size squares in the rectangle.

Answers may vary. Possible answer: Add 5 + 5 + 5 + 5 or add 5 + 5 = 10, 10 + 5 = 15, and 15 + 5 = 20.

Unit 4 ■ Focus on Geometry **259**

Mathematical Practices

Mathematical Practice Standards underline the teaching and understanding of all concepts and skills presented. The emphasis of specific practices is noted throughout the guided and independent practice of this lesson.

MP3	Construct viable arguments and critique the reasoning of others

Item 2: Children use what they know about finding the number of same-size squares in a rectangle to show and explain the procedure.

Observational Assessment

Use page 259 to assess children's understanding of finding the number of same-size squares in a rectangle. Take note of children who are not identifying the rows and columns correctly or who are not counting the squares correctly. These children may need additional practice to strengthen their understanding of rows and columns.

Think•Pair•Share

Peer Collaboration Ask pairs to share their work after they have determined their answers. As they work, ask them questions such as:

• *What information do you need to know before you can add to find the total number of squares?*

• *If you know how many rows and columns there are in any rectangle, how do you find the number of same-size squares in all?*

To summarize, point out that to find the total number of same-size squares in a rectangle, first count the number of rows or columns. Then count the number of squares in one row or column. Finally, write an addition sentence to solve.

Return to the Essential Question

Reread the Lesson 29 Essential Question on page 256: *How do you make same-size squares in rectangles?*

Tell children to think about what they learned in this lesson to answer this question.

(Possible response: I can draw same-size squares in rows that go across the rectangle. Or, I can draw same-size squares in columns that go up and down. After I fill the rectangle with squares, I can count or add to find the total number of squares.)

Concept Application

Children may work independently on these pages in the classroom or at home. They may refer to the first four pages of the lesson to revisit the instruction or to see a worked-out example.

Common Errors and **Teaching Tips** may help you support learning either in the classroom or as a follow-up for work done at home.

Common Errors

Items 7–8

Children may not understand the difference between problems 7 and 8. Clarify that problem 7 is asking for the number of squares in each row and problem 8 is asking for the total number of squares in the rectangle. Have children write an addition sentence to show how they used their answer from problem 7 to answer problem 8.

Teaching Tips

Items 1–4

You may wish to have children draw arrows to indicate the directions of the rows and columns or have them number each row and column to help them find their answers.

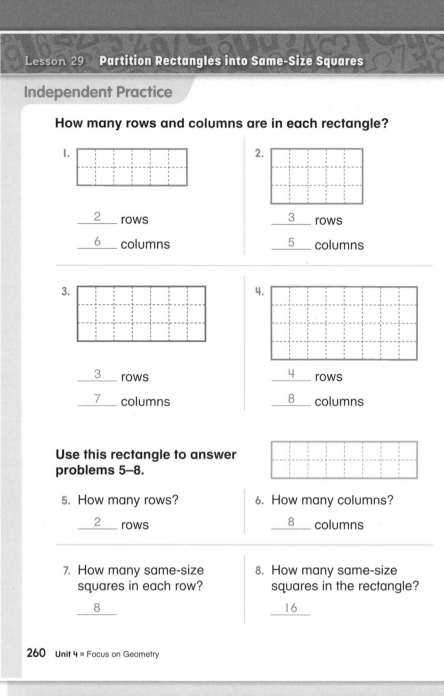

Lesson 29 Partition Rectangles into Same-Size Squares

Independent Practice

How many rows and columns are in each rectangle?

1.
   2 rows
   6 columns

2.
   3 rows
   5 columns

3.
   3 rows
   7 columns

4.
   4 rows
   8 columns

Use this rectangle to answer problems 5–8.

5. How many rows?
   2 rows

6. How many columns?
   8 columns

7. How many same-size squares in each row?
   8

8. How many same-size squares in the rectangle?
   16

260 Unit 4 ■ Focus on Geometry

Talking About Math

Square Properties It is important for children to build a strong foundation of counting the number of same-size squares as this skill will later develop into an understanding of area.

Have children work in pairs to explain why all the rows must be the same length and all the columns must be the same length. Then ask them to explain how the small squares might change if some of the rows or some of the columns were different lengths. You may wish to have children draw a few examples of rectangles in which the rows and columns are not all the same length. By doing this they should see that having rows and columns of different lengths creates small rectangles, and not squares, inside the large rectangle.

Independent Practice

Use this rectangle to answer problems 9–12.

9. How many rows? ___5___ rows

10. How many columns? ___3___ columns

11. How many same-size squares
    in each row? ___3___

12. How many same-size squares
    in the rectangle? ___15___

Use this rectangle to answer problems 13–15.

13. How many rows? ___3___ rows

14. How many same-size squares
    in each row? ___8___

15. How many same-size squares
    in the rectangle? ___24___

Use this rectangle to answer problems 16–18.

16. How many rows? ___4___ rows

17. How many same-size squares
    in each row? ___7___

18. How many same-size squares
    in the rectangle? ___28___

Unit 4 ■ Focus on Geometry **261**

Common Errors

Items 9–18

Make sure children read carefully to find out what each question is asking. Point out that reading a problem too quickly sometimes causes children to make mistakes.

Teaching Tips

Items 9–18

Encourage children to draw arrows to show the directions of the rows and columns of each rectangle or write the number of rows and columns to help them find their answers.

Digital Connection

Interactive Whiteboard Draw a 9 in.-by-3 in. rectangle on the whiteboard. Have children use 1-inch squares to fill the rectangle. Then ask questions about the numbers of rows and columns and how to find the total number of squares inside the rectangle without counting them all. Draw rectangles of other sizes, have children fill them with 1-inch squares, and repeat the questioning for each.

Independent Practice

Common Errors

Item 19–24

Children at this age may confuse *rows* and *columns*. Although this should not make a difference to an answer, make sure children are using the correct words as they explain their answers aloud.

Teaching Tips

Items 19–24

Be sure children show how they determined their answer for each problem.

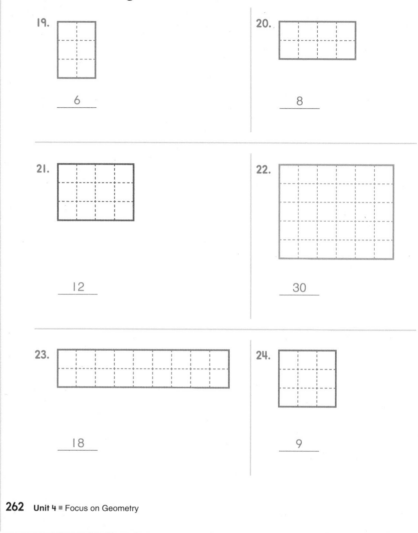

Independent Practice

Write how many same-size squares there are in each rectangle.

19. _____ 6 _____

20. _____ 8 _____

21. _____ 12 _____

22. _____ 30 _____

23. _____ 18 _____

24. _____ 9 _____

262   Unit 4 ■ Focus on Geometry

Math-to-Home Connection

Floor Tiles Explain that many people use square tiles to cover some of the floors in their homes. When people shop for tiles, they must know how many they will need so they do not buy too few tiles or too many. Tell children that a floor plan that shows the size of the room can be used to find the number of tiles needed.

Provide a sample floor plan of a room drawn on grid paper. Have children identify the number of rows, the number of columns, and the total number of tiles needed to cover the floor. To extend the question, tell children that tiles come in boxes of 10. Have them then identify the total number of boxes that someone would need to buy to cover this floor.

Lesson 29

Independent Practice

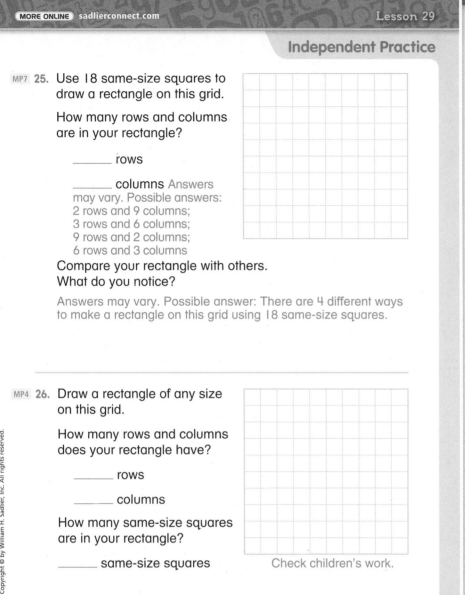

MP7 **25.** Use 18 same-size squares to draw a rectangle on this grid.

How many rows and columns are in your rectangle?

_____ rows

_____ columns Answers may vary. Possible answers: 2 rows and 9 columns; 3 rows and 6 columns; 9 rows and 2 columns; 6 rows and 3 columns

Compare your rectangle with others. What do you notice?

Answers may vary. Possible answer: There are 4 different ways to make a rectangle on this grid using 18 same-size squares.

MP4 **26.** Draw a rectangle of any size on this grid.

How many rows and columns does your rectangle have?

_____ rows

_____ columns

How many same-size squares are in your rectangle?

_____ same-size squares

Check children's work.

Unit 4 ■ Focus on Geometry **263**

Teaching Tips

Item 25

To help children get started, ask them to think about how they would draw 18 squares in 2 rows of the same length. They may need to fill in each square while counting to keep track. If you do provide this guidance, check that children use numbers other than 18 and 2 to solve the problem.

Mathematical Practices

MP4	**Model with mathematics.**

Item 26: Children create their own rectangle on a grid, and then use their knowledge of rows and columns to determine the total number of same-size squares.

MP7	**Look for and make use of structure.**

Item 25: Children determine sets of rows and columns that create a rectangle of a given size.

Common Core Focus:

2.G.3 Partition circles and rectangles into two, three, or four equal shares, describe the shares using the words *halves, thirds, half of, a third of,* etc., and describe the whole as two halves, three thirds, four fourths. Recognize that equal shares of identical wholes need not have the same shape.

OBJECTIVE

Make and recognize equal shares of rectangles, circles, and squares.

ESSENTIAL QUESTION

After reading the Essential Question aloud, ask children to describe what they think *equal shares* means. As an example discuss the concept of sharing treats equally.

PREREQUISITE SKILLS

Use Foundational Skills Handbook page 288, *Equal Shares,* to show partitioning a shape in halves and quarters.

FLUENCY PRACTICE

Fluency practice is available at **sadlierconnect.com**.

Concept Development

Understand: Make equal shares of a rectangle

■ This presentation builds on children's understanding of partitioning rectangles at the same time it introduces the concept of fractional shares of a whole.

■ Lead a discussion about the term *equal shares.* Be sure children understand that the word *shares* in this context means parts or pieces.

■ When defining the word *fourth,* show children the word *four* as the root. This should help them remember that four equal shares are called fourths.

■ Relate the words *quarter* and *fourth* by reminding children of the equivalent values of 4 quarters and 1 dollar.

Lesson
30 Equal Shares

Essential Question:
How do you make and recognize equal shares?
2.G.3

Words to Know
equal shares
fourth
quarter
third
half
halves

Guided Instruction

In this lesson you will learn how to make and recognize equal shares.

Understand: Make equal shares of a rectangle

An artist wants to cut this rectangle into 4 equal shares.

How can she cut the rectangle to make 4 equal shares?

You can break up a whole shape into equal shares.

These drawings show two ways to break up the rectangle. Each way has 4 equal shares.

Each equal share is 1 fourth of the whole rectangle.

The whole rectangle is equal to 4 fourths.

▷ The drawings show two ways that the artist can cut a rectangle into 4 equal shares, or 4 fourths.

A fourth is also called a quarter. Each drawing shows how the rectangle can be cut into 4 quarters.

Words to Know

equal share: one part of an object that has been divided equally

fourth, or quarter: one out of four equal parts of an object

Glossary can be found on pp. 293–304.

Understand: Recognize and describe an equal share

Nick has a pita bread shaped like this circle.

How can he cut the bread into 3 equal shares?

Circle A shows equal shares.

I third

A

Each share is I third of the whole.

The whole circle is equal to 3 thirds.

One of the 3 equal shares of Circle A is I third.

Circle B does not show equal shares.

B

Circle B does not show thirds.

➡ Circle __A__ shows how Nick can cut the pita bread into 3 equal shares.

Understand: Recognize and describe an equal share

■ This presentation shows how one whole circle is marked to show equal shares while another is marked to show unequal shares.

■ Point out that the word *third* starts with *th-* just like the word *three*. This may help children connect the word third to an image of three parts.

■ Have children number each share to ensure that they count them all.

■ Ask children to compare Circles A and B. Make sure they understand that Circle B is not the correct answer because the shares are not the same size.

Words to Know

third: one out of three equal parts of an object

half: one out of two equal parts of an object

halves: two equal parts that make one whole object

Glossary can be found on pp. 293-304.

Guided Instruction

Connect: **What you know about equal shares** Use this page to help children extend their understanding of partitioning a shape into equal shares.

■ If children have trouble understanding why the shares in Square B are equal, provide them with paper squares. Have them fold, and then cut the square into the two parts as shown in Square B. Direct them to place one triangle on top of the other so that they fit exactly. Explain that this shows the shares are equal.

■ Help children relate the definition of *half* to the real world; for example, halftime at a basketball game or half an hour. Children should understand that halftime divides a basketball game in half, just as half-past the hour divides the hour in half.

Guided Instruction

Connect: **What you know about equal shares**

There is more than one way to cut a square into equal shares.

Each of these squares is cut into equal shares.

A   B

Step 1

Look at Square A.

Square A is cut into how many equal shares? __2__

Each share is 1 half of the whole.

How many halves make up the whole? __2__

There are __2__ halves in the whole.

Step 2

Look at Square B.

Square B is cut into how many equal shares? __2__

Each share is ___1 half___ of the whole.

How many halves make up the whole? __2__

There are __2__ halves in the whole.

The drawings show two different ways to cut a square

into ___halves___.

266 Unit 4 ■ Focus on Geometry

Support English Language Learners

The term *share* in this lesson can be confusing to English language learners. They may have learned the word *share* as meaning to let others use something along with them, as in to share a toy. Explain that *share* in this lesson means something very different. Clarify that here, the word *share* means a part or a piece.

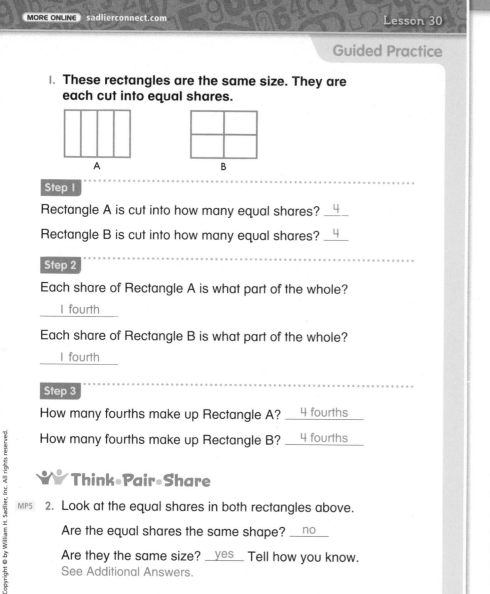

Lesson 30

Guided Practice

I. **These rectangles are the same size. They are each cut into equal shares.**

A   B

Step 1

Rectangle A is cut into how many equal shares? __4__

Rectangle B is cut into how many equal shares? __4__

Step 2

Each share of Rectangle A is what part of the whole?

__1 fourth__

Each share of Rectangle B is what part of the whole?

__1 fourth__

Step 3

How many fourths make up Rectangle A? __4 fourths__

How many fourths make up Rectangle B? __4 fourths__

Think•Pair•Share

MP5 2. Look at the equal shares in both rectangles above.

Are the equal shares the same shape? __no__

Are they the same size? __yes__ Tell how you know.
See Additional Answers.

Unit 4 ■ Focus on Geometry **267**

Mathematical Practices

Mathematical Practice Standards underline the teaching and understanding of all concepts and skills presented. The emphasis of specific practices is noted throughout the guided and independent practice of this lesson.

MP5	Use appropriate tools strategically.

Item 2: Children use illustrations that show two ways to create equal-size shares. They use convenient tools to determine that while the shares are not the same shape, they must be the same size.

Observational Assessment

Use page 267 to assess children's understanding of equal shares. Take note of children who are unsure either of the number of equal shares or that the equal shares are the same size.

☺☺ Think•Pair•Share

Peer Collaboration Ask pairs to share their work after determining their answer. Ask each pair of children questions such as:

- *How do you determine if the shares are the same shape?*

- *If the shares are not the same shape, how can they be the same size?*

Return to the Essential Question

Reread the Lesson 30 Essential Question on page 264: *How do you make and recognize equal shares?*

Tell children to think about what they learned in this lesson to answer this question.
(Possible responses: First, take the shape and break it into equal-size parts. There are different ways to break up the shape, but the shares must be the same size. Then, count the number of shares. If there are two equal shares, the shares are halves. If there are three equal shares, the shares are thirds. If there are four equal shares, the shares are fourths, or quarters.)

Additional Answers

Item 2: The equal shares are not the same shape but they must be the same size because each share of each rectangle is 1 fourth of the whole. The rectangles are the same size, so each fourth must be the same size as every other fourth.

Independent Practice

Concept Application

Children may work independently on these pages in the classroom or at home. They may refer to the first four pages of the lesson to revisit the instruction or to see a worked-out example.

Common Errors and **Teaching Tips** may help you support learning either in the classroom or as a follow-up for work done at home.

Common Errors

Item 8

Children may see this shape and immediately think it is divided into equal shares. Ask them to look at each individual share and compare it to each of the other shares.

Teaching Tips

Items 1–3

Help children recognize equal shares. Tell them to imagine folding the shape along the lines and then unfolding it to compare the size of the shares.

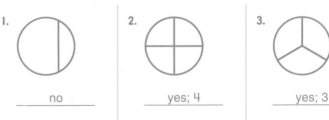

Independent Practice

Tell if each circle shows equal shares. Write *yes* or *no*. If *yes*, write how many equal shares.

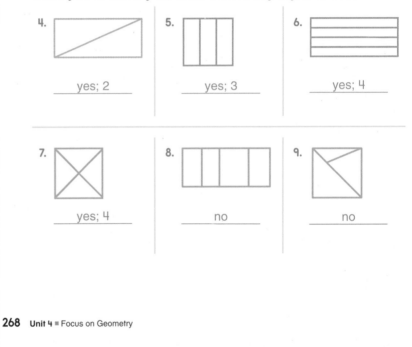

1. _____ no _____

2. _____ yes; 4 _____

3. _____ yes; 3 _____

Tell if each quadrilateral shows equal shares. Write *yes* or *no*. If *yes*, write how many equal shares.

4. _____ yes; 2 _____

5. _____ yes; 3 _____

6. _____ yes; 4 _____

7. _____ yes; 4 _____

8. _____ no _____

9. _____ no _____

Talking About Math

Putting the Pieces Together Cut large rectangles, circles, and triangles from construction paper. Then cut each shape into equal shares. Have children work in pairs with one of each shape's shares putting the pieces back together using what they know about shares. Finally, have children glue the pieces onto paper to show how they reformed the shapes. Ask them to describe the shares and shapes.

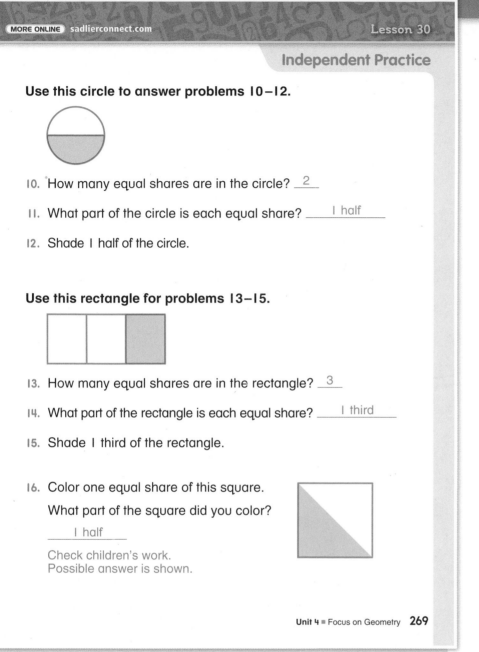

Lesson 30

Independent Practice

Use this circle to answer problems 10–12.

10. How many equal shares are in the circle? __2__

11. What part of the circle is each equal share? ___I half___

12. Shade I half of the circle.

Use this rectangle for problems 13–15.

13. How many equal shares are in the rectangle? __3__

14. What part of the rectangle is each equal share? ___I third___

15. Shade I third of the rectangle.

16. Color one equal share of this square.

    What part of the square did you color?

    ___I half___

    Check children's work.
    Possible answer is shown.

Unit 4 ■ Focus on Geometry **269**

Teaching Tips

Items 10–15
Encourage children to number each equal share to ensure they are counting each share once.

Item 16
After children complete this question, have them share their answers. Point out that there are different ways to correctly show equal shares of a square.

Digital Connection

Online Review Activity Use a computer search engine to find an online review activity that has children identify shapes that are partitioned into equal shares. Have children draw each shape with equal shares in different ways.

Independent Practice

Common Errors

Items 17-22

Children may have difficulty drawing equal shares, especially when trying to show thirds. If rectangular and circular manipulatives are available, encourage children to use them to model the problems.

Independent Practice

**Draw lines to cut each shape into thirds.
Then color 1 third.** Answers may vary. Possible answers are shown. Child should color one of the thirds.

17.

18.

**Draw lines to cut each shape into halves.
Then color 1 half.** Answers may vary. Possible answers are shown. Child should color one of the halves.

19.

20.

**Draw lines to cut each shape into fourths.
Then color 1 fourth.** Answers may vary. Possible answers are shown. Child should color one of the fourths.

21.

22.

Math-to-Sports Connection

Tennis Court Explain to children that courts and fields where a particular kind of sport is played must be designed the same way. Research and display a photo of a tennis court. Tell children that there are rules for the length of the court, where to draw the lines on the court, and where to place the net. Encourage a discussion on why a tennis court would have to be marked in equal parts. Have children draw plans for a new tennis court that is marked in halves, thirds, or fourths.

Independent Practice

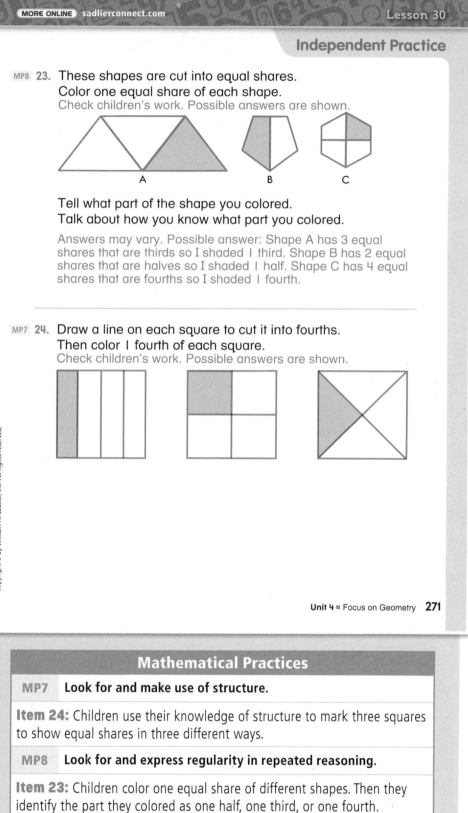

MP8 **23.** These shapes are cut into equal shares.
Color one equal share of each shape.
Check children's work. Possible answers are shown.

A   B   C

Tell what part of the shape you colored.
Talk about how you know what part you colored.

Answers may vary. Possible answer: Shape A has 3 equal shares that are thirds so I shaded 1 third. Shape B has 2 equal shares that are halves so I shaded 1 half. Shape C has 4 equal shares that are fourths so I shaded 1 fourth.

MP7 **24.** Draw a line on each square to cut it into fourths.
Then color 1 fourth of each square.
Check children's work. Possible answers are shown.

Common Errors

Item 24

Remind children that they only need to draw one line on each square to divide that square into fourths. Remind them that all the fourths in one square must be the same size.

Teaching Tips

Item 23

Encourage children to number each equal share within each of the three shapes. This should help children make sure that they are counting all the shares.

Mathematical Practices

MP7	**Look for and make use of structure.**

Item 24: Children use their knowledge of structure to mark three squares to show equal shares in three different ways.

MP8	**Look for and express regularity in repeated reasoning.**

Item 23: Children color one equal share of different shapes. Then they identify the part they colored as one half, one third, or one fourth.

The Common Core Review covers all the standards presented in the unit. Use it to assess your children's mastery of the unit's concepts and skills.

Depth of Knowledge

The depth of knowledge is a ranking of the content complexity of assessment items based on Webb's Depth of Knowledge (DOK) levels. The levels increase in complexity as shown below.

Level 1: Recall and Reproduction
Level 2: Basic Skills and Concepts
Level 3: Strategic Reasoning and Thinking
Level 4: Extended Thinking

Item	Standard	DOK
1	2.G.1	3
2	2.G.1	2
3	2.G.1	1
4	2.G.1	1
5	2.G.2	1
6	2.G.2	1
7	2.G.2	1
8	2.G.3	2
9	2.G.3	2
10	2.G.3	2
11	2.G.3	4

Unit 4 Common Core Review

1. Draw a closed shape that has 6 sides. What is the name of the shape?

Check children's drawings.

Name of shape: ___hexagon___

Identify the shape. If the shape is a special quadrilateral, write its name.

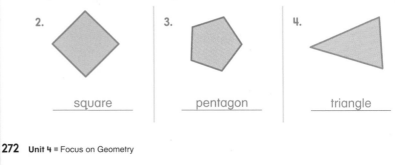

2. square

3. pentagon

4. triangle

Unit 4 Common Core Review

Use this rectangle to answer problems 5–7.

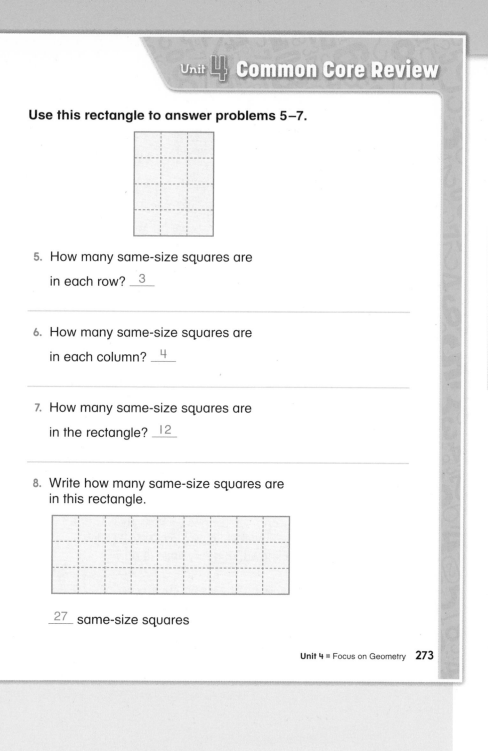

5. How many same-size squares are
   in each row? __3__

6. How many same-size squares are
   in each column? __4__

7. How many same-size squares are
   in the rectangle? __12__

8. Write how many same-size squares are
   in this rectangle.

   __27__ same-size squares

This chart correlates the Common Core Review items with the lessons in which the concepts and skills are presented.

Item	Lesson
1	28
2	28
3	28
4	28
5	29
6	29
7	29
8	29
9	30
10	30
11	30

Unit 4 ■ Focus on Geometry **273**

Talking About Math

Direct children to respond to the Unit 4 Essential Question. (This can also be found on page 247.)

Essential Question:
What are halves, thirds, and fourths?

Possible responses:

- Halves show two equal shares of a whole.
- Thirds show three equal shares of a whole.
- Fourths show four equal shares of a whole.
- You can draw lines to cut whole shapes into 2 equal shares, or halves; 3 equal shares, or thirds; and 4 equal shares, or fourths.

Unit Assessment

- Unit 4 Common Core Review, *pp. 272–274*
- Unit 4 Performance Task ONLINE

Additional Assessment Options

- Performance Task 2, *pp. 275–278*
  ALSO ONLINE

Optional Purchase:

- iProgress Monitor ONLINE
- Progress Monitor Student Benchmark Assessment Booklet

---

9. Draw lines to cut the shape into thirds. Then color 1 third.

Answers may vary. Sample answer is shown. Children should color one of the thirds.

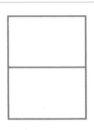

10. Draw lines to cut the shape into halves. Then color 1 half.

Answers may vary. Sample answer is shown. Children should color one of the halves.

MP7 11. Draw a line to finish cutting each circle into 4 fourths in different ways. Color 1 fourth of each circle.

Check children's work. Sample answers are shown. Children should color one of the fourths in each circle.

Explain how you know that each circle is now cut into fourths.

Answers may vary. Sample answer: Fourths are also called quarters. Each circle is cut into 4 fourths, or quarters. Each circle has 4 parts that are the same size.

274 Unit 4 ■ Focus on Geometry

Mathematical Practices

MP7	**Look for and make use of structure.**

Item 11: Children recognize the significance of a line drawn on a shape and draw a second line on that shape to solve a problem.

Performance Task 2

2.OA.1, 2.OA.2, 2.NBT.2, 2.MD.1, 2.MD.3, 2.MD.4, 2.MD.8, 2.MD.10

Performance Tasks

Performance Tasks show your understanding of the math that you have learned.

Beginning This Task

This is the beginning of a Performance Task. The next three pages have problems for you to solve.

As you work, you will:

1. Show that you can use math skills and concepts

2. Decide how to solve a problem

3. Use different ways to model and solve real-world problems

Tips to help you!

- Read each problem carefully.
- Plan how you will solve the problem.
- Check your work.
- Be ready to show your work or explain your thinking.

Performance Task 2 **275**

⟨ONLINE⟩ Customize Performance Task 2

Performance Task 2 in *Common Core Progress Mathematics* also provides children with additional practice. You can use the online items of Performance Task 2 to customize the amount and kind of performance task practice based on your ongoing evaluation of your children. You may choose to challenge some children, to give extra experience with a particular kind of task for other children, or to extend exposure to performance assessment for the entire class.

Go to **sadlierconnect.com** to download the following resources for Performance Task 2.

- Additional Items

- Additional Teacher Support

- Additional Scoring Rubrics

Performance Task 2 Overview

Performance Task 2 in *Common Core Progress Mathematics* provides children with practice for the types of items that may be found on standardized performance assessments.

Various item formats, including short- and extended-response items and technology-enhanced items, are included in the tasks. All items connect mathematical content correlated to the Mathematical Practices.

Items in Performance Task 2 are based on three primary types of tasks:

Type I   Mastery of mathematical concepts, skills and procedures

Type II   Using and explaining mathematical reasoning

Type III Modeling problem situations in a real-world context

Performance Task 2 begins with a collection of three self-contained items in the Student Book and continues with additional items online at **sadlierconnect.com**.

Introduce Performance Task 2 Read page 275 to children. Explain that Performance Task 2 may cover any of the math they have learned in Units 3 and 4. Orient children to each item and communicate helpful reminders that will enable children to approach each item successfully. Once children have completed each item, go over the correct responses with them.

Recommended Pacing Administer Performance Task 2 on Student Book pages 276–278 over three 15-minute sessions.

Teacher Resources For each task, the teacher materials include:

- Item types and purposes

- Correlations to Common Core State Standards for Mathematical Content and Practice, and Depth of Knowledge (DOK) levels

- Suggested administration procedure

- Scoring Rubric

Performance Task 2

Item 1: Summer Camp

Item	Type	Purpose
1.a.	I	Estimate and explain length in centimeters.
1.b.	III	Draw and estimate length in centimeters.
1.c.	III	Use a centimeter ruler to find lengths.
1.d.	III	Draw conclusions about length comparisons in centimeters.

Item	CCSS	MP	DOK
1.a.	2.MD.3	6	Level 2
1.b.	2.MD.3	2	Level 3
1.c.	2.MD.4	2	Level 3
1.d.	2.MD.4	3	Level 4

Administering Item 1 (Pacing: 15 minutes)

Ask a volunteer to read the introductory paragraph. Have others describe the situation in their own words.

Item 1.a. (2 minutes)

Children need to make a reasonable estimate rather than find an exact measurement. To help children who have difficulty with this task, tell them that the length of 1 centimeter is a little longer than a ladybug.

Item 1.b. (5 minutes)

Make sure children understand that the drawing does not need to fill the space or meet a specific size requirement.

Item 1.c. (5 minutes)

Check that children are using centimeter rulers and are aligning the 0-mark on their rulers with the left end of the fish being measured.

Item 1.d. (3 minutes)

Children may need assistance completing this sentence. Have children practice comparing the fish aloud, and then have them transcribe their spoken sentences onto the page.

Additional Answers

Item 1.a.: Possible answer: I estimated the width of my thumb as being about a centimeter. Then I counted how many times my thumb fit across the drawing.

Summer Camp

1. Every morning the children at Blue Lake Camp work on craft projects. Terry drew this fish that he planned to carve from a piece of wood.

a. Estimate the length of Terry's fish drawing in centimeters.

   The drawing is about ___5–9___ centimeters long. Talk about how you estimated the length.
   See Additional Answers.

b. Draw a fish that you would like to carve from a piece of wood. Estimate the length of your drawing in centimeters. Check children's work.

c. Use a centimeter ruler to measure Terry's fish. Then measure your fish to the nearest centimeter.

   Terry's fish is __7__ centimeters long.

   My fish is ___ centimeters long. Check children's work.

d. Compare the lengths. Whose fish is longer? How much longer?

   ___My/Terry's___ fish is _____ centimeters

   ___shorter/longer___ than ___My/Terry's___ fish.

276 Performance Task 2

Scoring Rubric

Item	Points	Student Responses
1.a.	2	Correctly estimates and describes the estimate.
	1	Demonstrates some understanding of estimation.
	0	Writes irrational or no estimate.
1.b.	2	Draws a fish and reasonably estimates its length in centimeters.
	1	Draws a fish but makes an illogical estimate.
	0	Makes no drawing or estimate.
1.c.	2	Adequately measures each fish.
	1	Adequately measures one fish.
	0	Does not measure the fish.
1.d.	2	Writes and quantifies the comparison.
	0	Does not answer or quantify the comparison.

Performance Task 2

At the Camp Store

2. Keesha needs 56¢ to buy a marker.

 a. Draw coins that Keesha could use to pay for the marker.

 Answers may vary. Sample answer:

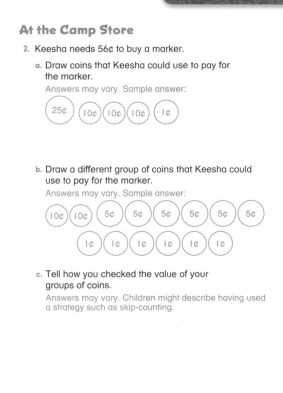

 b. Draw a different group of coins that Keesha could use to pay for the marker.

 Answers may vary. Sample answer:

 c. Tell how you checked the value of your groups of coins.

 Answers may vary. Children might describe having used a strategy such as skip-counting.

Performance Task 2 **277**

Item 2: At the Camp Store

Item	Type	Purpose
2.a.	I	Draw coins to show 56¢.
2.b.	III	Draw 56¢ using different coins.
2.c.	II	Explain solution strategies.

Item	CCSS	MP	DOK
2.a.	2.NBT.2, 2.MD.8	4	Level 2
2.b.	2.NBT.2, 2.MD.8	4	Level 2
2.c.	2.NBT.2, 2.MD.8	4	Level 3

Administering Item 2 (Pacing: 15 minutes)

Ask a volunteer to read the introductory paragraph. Have others describe the situation in their own words.

Item 2.a. (4 minutes)

Explain to children that coin drawings can be circles with 25, 10, 5, or 1 labeled. To help children who have difficulty with this task, provide coin manipulatives or stamps to help them model and then draw their answers.

Item 2.b. (6 minutes)

Children should show the same total coin value using a different combination of coins. If children struggle to complete the task, provide hints such as using skip-counting or drawing all the coins in a row according to their values, from greatest to least.

Item 2.c. (5 minutes)

Have children discuss strategies, comparisons, and how hands-on models or drawings can help solve the problem.

Scoring Rubric

Item	Points	Student Responses
2.a.	2	Correctly draws coins to show 56¢.
	1	Drawing has a calculation error but child is able to explain and correct.
	0	Does not attempt a reasonable drawing.
2.b.	2	Correctly draws another way to show 56¢.
	1	Drawing has a calculation error but child is able to explain and correct.
	0	Does not attempt a reasonable drawing.
2.c.	2	Shows clear understanding of adding and checking coin values.
	1	Shows partial understanding.
	0	Does not show understanding.

Item 3: Blue Lake Art Project

Item	Type	Purpose
3.a.	I	Complete a picture graph.
3.b.	I	Interpret information from a graph.
3.c.	II	Write questions about data shown in a graph.

Item	CCSS	MP	DOK
3.a.	2.MD.10	4	Level 2
3.b.	2.OA.1, 2.OA.2, 2.MD.10	5	Level 3
3.c.	2.OA.1, 2.OA.2, 2.MD.10	2	Level 3

Administering Item 3 (Pacing: 15 minutes)

Ask a volunteer to read the introductory paragraph. Have others describe the situation in their own words.

Item 3.a. (6 minutes)

Make sure children understand that they will use information from the picture graph to complete the other parts of the task. Provide a tip to children that lining up each symbol that they draw below one of the acorns in Judy's row will later help them compare data.

Item 3.b. (3 minutes)

Be sure that children understand that they need to find the sum of three numbers to answer the question. Provide place-value tens and ones models for those who struggle with the computation.

Item 3.c. (6 minutes)

Have children make up at least two questions about the picture graph. For children who need additional help, provide some terms that may prompt thinking such as *compare, join groups, greatest,* and *least.*

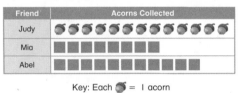

Blue Lake Art Project

3. Three campers collected acorns for an art project. Judy collected 13 acorns. Mia collected 8 acorns. Abel collected 11 acorns.

Friend	Acorns Collected
Judy	🌰🌰🌰🌰🌰🌰🌰🌰🌰🌰🌰🌰🌰
Mia	▪▪▪▪▪▪▪▪
Abel	▪▪▪▪▪▪▪▪▪▪▪

Key: Each 🌰 = I acorn

a. Complete the picture graph. Children should draw 8 symbols in the row for Mia and 11 symbols in the row for Abel.

b. How many acorns did the three campers collect in all?

__32__ acorns

c. Make up your own questions about the data in the graph.

Answers may vary. Sample answer: How many more acorns did Judy collect than Mia? How many acorns did Abel and Mia collect together?

Scoring Rubric

Item	Points	Student Responses
3.a.	2	Correctly completes the picture graph.
	1	Correctly draws symbols in one row of the picture graph.
	0	Does not correctly draw symbols in either row of the picture graph.
3.b.	2	Correctly writes 32 as the sum.
	0	Writes incorrect or no sum.
3.c.	2	Creates at least two valid questions about the data in the graph.
	1	Creates one question.
	0	Does not create a question.

Addition Problems

Tyrone has 4 bananas, 3 apples, and 6 oranges.
How many fruits does he have in all?

| | 4 | + | 3 | + | 6 | = | 13 |

Tyrone has 13 fruits in all.

Solve each problem.

1. Elana put 6 red marbles, 2 blue marbles, and 3 green marbles in a jar. How many marbles are in the jar?

   6 + 2 + 3 = __11__

   There are __11__ marbles in the jar.

2. Joe has 5 green crayons and 4 blue crayons. How many crayons does he have in all?

   __5__ + __4__ = __9__

   Joe has __9__ crayons in all.

3. Ryan has 2 stickers. Julie has 6 stickers and Selene has 9 stickers. How many stickers do they have altogether?

   __2__ + __6__ + __9__ = __17__

   They have __17__ stickers altogether.

The Foundational Skills Handbook: provides review of prerequisite content for the Grade 2 Common Core State Standards for Mathematics.

Addition Problems

Have children read the sample problem and discuss how the picture represents the problem. Make sure children understand the symbols used in the addition equation. Read the concluding sentence of the sample problem and explain that it answers the question that the problem asks. Tell children that on this page they will solve word problems that involve two or three addends.

Children should be fluent enough in adding 1-digit numbers mentally to complete problems 1–3 on their own. Suggest addition strategies such as counting on or grouping addends. Children who need to draw a picture or use counters to solve the problems may need additional practice with addition facts to 20.

Foundational Skills Handbook Contents

Subtraction Problems

Have children read the sample problem and discuss how the picture represents the problem. Suggest that children draw lines to match each of Michelle's apples one-to-one with each of Derrick's apples until no more matches are possible. Make sure children understand the symbols used in the subtraction equation. Read the concluding sentence of the sample problem and explain that it answers the question that the problem asks.

Children should be able to identify all the problems as requiring subtraction. Problems 1 and 3 both use subtraction to take one amount from another. Problem 2 uses subtraction to compare numbers. To help children solve the problems, suggest that they use subtraction strategies such as counting on from the number being subtracted or using a related addition fact. Children who need to draw a picture or use counters to model the problems may need additional practice with subtraction facts within 20.

Subtraction Problems

Michelle picks 8 apples.
Derrick picks 5 apples.
How many more apples did Michelle pick than Derrick?

Michelle's apples

Derrick's apples

$$8 - 5 = 3$$

Michelle picked 3 more apples than Derrick.

Solve each problem.

1. Brandon had 12 toy cars. He gave 5 of them to Luke. How many cars does Brandon have left?

   $12 - 5 = \underline{7}$

   Brandon has $\underline{7}$ cars left.

2. Maria picks 15 strawberries. Nia picks 9 strawberries. How many fewer strawberries did Nia pick than Maria?

   $15 - 9 = \underline{6}$

   Nia picked $\underline{6}$ fewer strawberries than Maria.

3. Jordan's dad gives him 14 pennies. Then Jordan spent some of the pennies. Now he has 9 pennies left. How many pennies did Jordan spend?

   $14 - \underline{5} = 9$

   Jordan spent $\underline{5}$ pennies.

Related Facts

You can write related addition and subtraction facts using the numbers 6, 7, and 13.

6 + 7 = 13	13 − 7 = 6
7 + 6 = 13	13 − 6 = 7

Write the missing numbers to form related addition and subtraction facts.

1. 2 + 7 = 9
   9 − 7 = _2_
   7 + _2_ = 9
   9 − _2_ = 7

2. 4 + _6_ = 10
   10 − _6_ = 4
   _6_ + 4 = 10
   10 − 4 = _6_

3. 9 + _3_ = 12
   12 − _3_ = 9
   3 + _9_ = 12
   12 − _9_ = 3

4. 7 + _8_ = 15
   15 − _8_ = 7
   8 + 7 = _15_
   _15_ − 7 = 8

5. 8 + 6 = _14_
   6 + _8_ = 14
   _14_ − 6 = 8
   14 − _8_ = 6

6. _7_ + 9 = 16
   9 + _7_ = 16
   _16_ − 7 = 9
   16 − _9_ = 7

Related Facts

Read the instructional sample at the top of the page aloud. Explain that each color—blue, red, and green—stands for the same number in all the addition and subtraction problems. Point out that, while the order of the 6 and 7 in the two addition facts differs, the sum for each fact is 13. Ask children to tell how the two subtraction facts are alike and how they differ.

As children complete problems 1–6, tell them to remember that each related fact contains the same three numbers. After children have completed the page, discuss why, for some problems, they wrote the same number on all the lines and why, for other problems, they wrote two different numbers on the lines.

Compare Numbers

Explain to children that each tower of connecting cubes represents 1 ten and that the cubes that are not connected represent ones. Children can count the cubes in a tower to see that 10 ones make 1 ten. Be sure that children understand how the first group of cubes represents 42 and how the second group represents 17.

Read the comparisons under the groups of cubes and review the meaning of the inequality symbols. Have children circle the term *greater than* and the symbol just below it. Then have them circle the term *less than* and the symbol just below it.

For problems 1–8, have the class discuss hints for remembering the direction of the inequality symbols. For example, children may remember that the point of the symbol always indicates the lesser number or that the open part of the symbol is close to the greater number.

Compare Numbers

Compare 42 and 17.

4 tens 2 ones | 1 ten 7 ones

42 | 17

42 is greater than 17
42 > 17

17 is less than 42
17 < 42

Compare the numbers. Write >, <, or =.

1. 13 $<$ 35
2. 46 $<$ 79
3. 58 $=$ 58
4. 91 $>$ 67
5. 83 $>$ 38
6. 47 $<$ 93
7. 21 $=$ 21
8. 65 $>$ 56

282 Foundational Skills Handbook

Add 2-Digit Numbers

26 + 37 = ▇

Add the ones.
   6 ones + 7 ones = 13 ones
You can make a ten.
   13 ones = 1 ten 3 ones.

Add the tens.
   2 tens + 3 tens + 1 ten = 6 tens

26 + 37 = 63

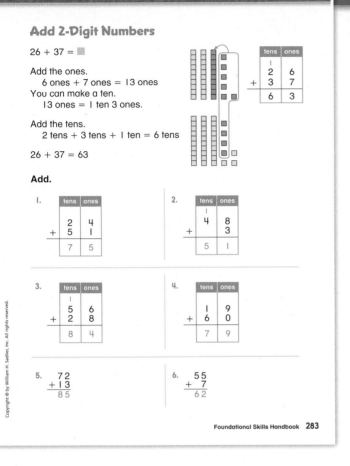

Add.

1.

tens	ones
2	4
+ 5	1
7	5

2.

tens	ones
1	
4	8
+	3
5	1

3.

tens	ones
1	
5	6
+ 2	8
8	4

4.

tens	ones
1	9
+ 6	0
7	9

5.
```
  7 2
+ 1 3
-----
  8 5
```

6.
```
  5 5
+   7
-----
  6 2
```

Add 2-Digit Numbers

Make sure children understand how to make a ten using the model. Children may misinterpret the first group of models by thinking that it shows 36. Explain that this group models the first addend, 26, and that the 6 ones along with 4 of the ones below are grouped to make the 1 new ten. Remind children that they should always add the ones first before adding the tens.

Use the sample place-value chart to be sure children understand how to record 13 ones as 1 ten and 3 ones. Point out that the red 1 at the top of the tens column shows how to record the new ten.

As children complete problems 1–6, remind them to make a new ten only when the sum in the ones column is 10 or more.

Subtract Tens

Explain to children that the model at the top of the page shows that taking 20 away from 50 is the same as taking 2 tens away from 5 tens. Point out that children can use mental math to subtract the tens when there are no ones in both numbers.

Have children use mental math to complete problems 1–12. If they struggle to solve the problems without using models, have them cover the ones, subtract the tens, and then write 0 in the ones place.

Subtract Tens

$50 - 20 = $ ▩

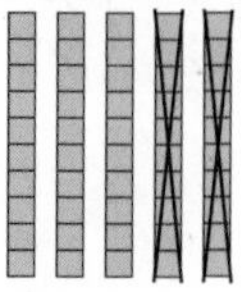

50 = 5 tens   20 = 2 tens

Think of a subtraction fact that uses the tens digit of each number.

$5 - 2 = 3$

5 tens − 2 tens = 3 tens

3 tens = 30

$50 - 20 = 30$

Subtract.

1.	2.	3.	4.
20 − 10 1 0	40 − 30 1 0	30 − 20 1 0	70 − 20 5 0

5.	6.	7.	8.
50 − 10 4 0	60 − 40 2 0	80 − 70 1 0	90 − 40 5 0

9.	10.	11.	12.
40 + 20 2 0	30 − 30 0 0	60 − 30 3 0	90 − 70 2 0

Measure Length

How long is the pencil?

Count how many paper clips fit from one end of the pencil to the other.

The pencil is 5 paper clips long.

How long is each object?

1.

The crayon is __4__ paper clips long.

2.

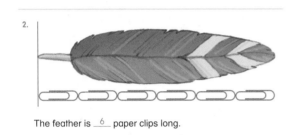

The feather is __6__ paper clips long.

Measure Length

This activity reviews measuring the length of an object with non-standard units of length. Children lay multiple copies of the length unit end to end along the object being measured. Then they count the units and express the length of the object as a number of length units.

Point out the importance of lining up the left end of the object being measured with the left end of the row of paper clips. Have children point to the red line in each pair of pictures to verify the alignment.

If children struggle to count the paper clips accurately, hold up one and point out the two rounded ends that make up one paper clip. Children may also draw a short line between the end of one paper clip and the next to make the separations between the paper clips easier to see and count.

Tell Time

Children learned to tell time to the hour and half hour in Grade 1. Ensure children's fluency with this skill and their understanding of the purpose of each clock hand. Use a demonstration clock, if available, to model the time shown on each of the two sample clocks. Then have children focus on the way each time is written in the samples.

Problems 1 and 2 have children write the time to the hour. Problems 3 and 4 have them write the time to the half hour. Some children may need to cover first one row and then the other to consider these skills separately. Also, for problems 3 and 4, make sure children understand that time to the half hour is "half-past" the hour. Explain that at this time the hour hand points halfway between two numbers and the minute hand points to the 6.

Tell Time

The hour hand points to 1.
The minute hand points to 12.
It is one o'clock.
Write 1:00.

The hour hand is between 5 and 6.
The minute hand points to 6.
It is five thirty.
Write 5:30.

Write the time.

1.

<u>11</u> : <u>00</u>

2.

<u>2</u> : <u>00</u>

3.

<u>4</u> : <u>30</u>

4.

<u>10</u> : <u>30</u>

Tables

Look at this table.

How many votes are there for Fish?

Favorite Pet	
Kind of Pet	**Number of Votes**
Cat	4
Dog	6
Fish	2

There are 2 votes for Fish.

Use the table to answer each question.

1. How many votes are there for Cat? __4__

2. Which kind of pet has the most votes? ____Dog____

3. Which kind of pet has the fewest votes? ____Fish____

4. How many more votes are there for Cat than for Fish? __2__

5. How many fewer votes are there for Fish than for Dog?
   __4__

6. How many votes are there in all? __12__

Tables

Direct children's attention to the table and ask volunteers to describe the column headings. Make sure children understand that the numbers in the *Number of Votes* column tell how many children chose cat, dog, or fish as their favorite pet.

For problems 1–6, children identify and compare data and use addition and subtraction to answer questions about the table. Ask any children who answer incorrectly to explain their thinking. This will help you identify whether the errors were due to using the wrong data, misunderstanding the question, or to miscalculations.

Equal Shares

In Grade 1, children break circles and squares into halves or fourths. They refer to these divisions as equal shares, or equal parts. Use the sample circle and square at the top of the page to review halves and fourths, or quarters, and have children notice that the shares in each shape are equal.

As children consider each shape in the problem, make sure they understand that half of one shape does not have to look the same as half of another shape. Likewise, fourths of two different shapes do not have to look the same.

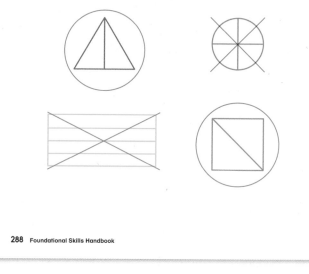

Equal Shares

There are 2 equal parts.
2 equal parts are called *halves*.

There are 4 equal parts.
4 equal parts are called *fourths*, or *quarters*.

Which shapes show halves? Circle them.
Which shapes show quarters? Draw an X on them.

288 Foundational Skills Handbook

Problem-Solving Model

You can use this model to solve problems.

Read

Read the problem.
- What facts do you know?
- What do you need to find?

Plan

Plan how to solve the problem.
- Will you add or subtract?
- Will you draw a picture?
- Is it a one-step or a two-step problem?

Solve

Use your plan to solve the problem.
- Did you answer the question?
- Did you label your answer?

Check

Make sure your answer makes sense.
- How can you solve the problem in a different way?
- Is the answer the same?

Problem-Solving Model **289**

Introducing the Problem-Solving Model

You can use the Problem-Solving Model pages to encourage children to think problems through and solve them successfully.

The Problem-Solving Model is just one way to help children master the art of problem solving. Many children intuitively will see alternative methods or solutions. Their intuitive grasp of the problem situation should not be impeded or slowed by having to use the model. Children should be asked only to demonstrate that they solved a problem using some logical plan, and not necessarily this specific model. Children should be able to explain the method they have used.

Problem-Solving Model

A Fish Problem

Models and drawings provide children with a sense of the size of quantities and the relationship between those quantities.

To find the missing number in A Fish Problem, children refer to the drawing to perceive how the missing number relates to the two given numbers. They write a subtraction equation to find the missing number and then use the related addition fact to check the answer.

A Fish Problem

Read

Carlos has 15 fish.
Kim has 9 fewer fish than Carlos.
How many fish does Kim have?

What facts do you know?
Carlos: 15 fish
Kim: 9 fewer fish than Carlos has

What do you need to find?
How many fish Kim has

Plan

Carlos has more fish than Kim. He has 15 fish.
The missing number and 9 are both less than 15.
Make a drawing to show how the numbers are related.

Subtract to find the missing number.

15	
?	9

number of fish Carlos has → $15 - 9 = \blacksquare$ ← number of fish Kim has

↑ 9 fewer than the number Carlos has

Solve

$15 - 9 = 6$ The missing number is 6.

▷ Kim has 6 fish.

Check

Use a related addition sentence. Start with the number of fish Kim has. Add the number you subtracted. The sum is the number of fish Carlos has.

$6 + 9 = 15$ The answer is correct.

A Tulip Problem

As children learn to add and subtract quantities, they use the equation format to establish the relationship among and between quantities.

In A Tulip Problem, children add to find a sum that represents one quantity and then use that sum to find another quantity. Children use models to check the answer.

A Tulip Problem

Read

Pat has 7 tulips.
Jake has 8 more tulips than Pat.
Ana has 2 more tulips than Jake.
How many tulips does Ana have?

What facts do you know?
Pat: 7 tulips
Jake: 8 more tulips than Pat has
Ana: 2 more tulips than Jake has

What do you need to find?
How many tulips Ana has

Plan

The problem has two steps. First, add to find how many tulips Jake has.
$7 + 8 = \blacksquare$

Then add to that answer to find how many tulips Ana has.
$\blacksquare + 2 = \blacktriangle$

Solve

$7 + 8 = 15 \longrightarrow$ Jake has 15 tulips. $\longrightarrow 15 + 2 = 17$

▷ Ana has 17 tulips.

Check

Use counters to model the problem.

●●●●●●● ●●●●●●●●   ●●

  7   +   8 $= 15$

            $15 + 2 = 17$

The answer is correct.

Common Core State Standards for Mathematical Practice

The Standards for Mathematical Practice, identified here, are an important part of learning mathematics. They are covered in every lesson in this book.

MP1 Make sense of problems and persevere in solving them.

- Analyze and plan a solution
- Relate to a similar problem
- Assess progress
- Use concrete objects or pictures
- Check solutions

MP2 Reason abstractly and quantitatively.

- Pay attention to all mathematical language
- Represent problems using symbols
- Consider units in problem solving
- Use properties of operations and objects

MP3 Construct viable arguments and critique the reasoning of others.

- Analyze a problem situation
- Share reasoning with others
- Explain an approach to a problem
- Construct arguments by using drawings or concrete objects

MP4 Model with mathematics.

- Relate mathematics to everyday problems
- Make assumptions and estimations
- Explain the relationship of quantities
- Use concrete tools to explain operations
- Interpret the solution in the context of a situation

MP5 Use appropriate tools strategically.

- Consider the range of available tools (e.g., place-value charts, graphs, clocks, etc.)
- Decide on appropriate tools to use for each situation
- Use tools carefully and strategically

MP6 Attend to precision.

- Communicate with precision
- Identify the meaning of symbols
- Use measurement units appropriately
- Calculate accurately
- Carefully formulate full explanations

MP7 Look for and make use of structure.

- Search for patterns or structure
- Evaluate the structure or design of a problem
- Discuss geometric shapes in terms of their similarities and differences

MP8 Look for and express regularity in repeated reasoning.

- Make generalizations in computation
- Obtain fluency using patterns
- Look for patterns with shapes and designs
- Use patterns to relate operations
- Evaluate reasonableness of answers

Key: MP = Mathematical Practice

Glossary

A.M. the time from midnight until noon

add to find how many in all

$3 + 2 = 5$

addend the numbers you add

angle where 2 sides meet

array objects arranged in equal rows and equal columns

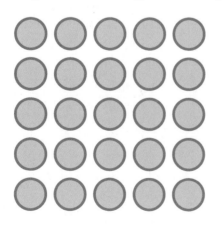

B

bar graph a graph that uses bars to show data

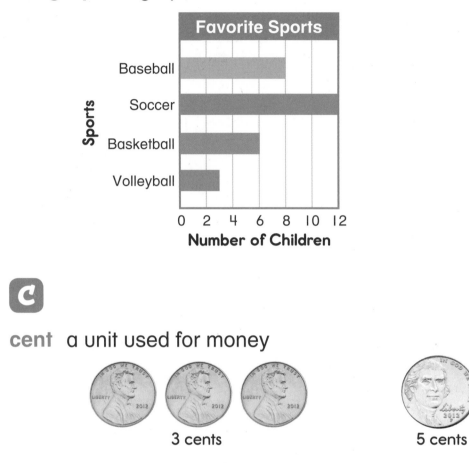

C

cent a unit used for money

3 cents   5 cents

centimeter a unit of measure used to measure length

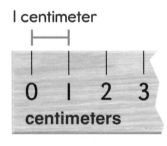

cube

data information sometimes shown in a table or graph

Heights of Tomato Plants	
Height (in inches)	**Number of Plants**
5	3
6	2
7	4

difference the answer in subtraction

$$14 - 5 = 9$$

↑

difference

digit 0, 1, 2, 3, 4, 5, 6, 7, 8, 9 are used to write numbers

24

↑ ↑

digits

dime a coin worth 10 cents, or 10¢

10 cents

dollar a dollar is worth 100 cents, or $1

equal share

Each rectangle shows 4 equal shares.

---

equal sign (=) is equal to

$$1 + 1 = 2$$

is equal to

---

equation a number sentence with an equal sign

$$5 + 6 = 11 \qquad\qquad 8 - 6 = 2$$

---

estimate tells about how long an object is

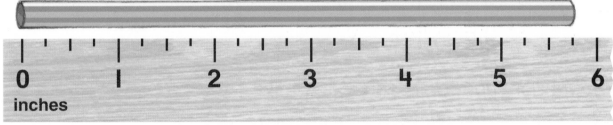

The straw is about 6 inches long.

---

even number even numbers make pairs

An even number has 0, 2, 4, 6, or 8 in the ones place.

---

expanded form

284 in expanded form is $200 + 80 + 4$

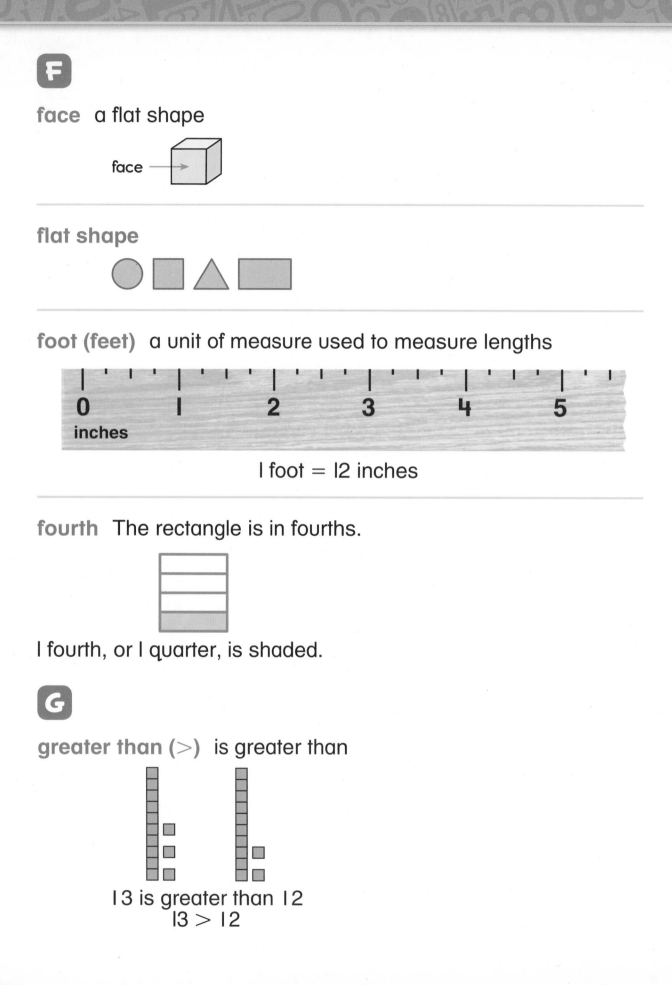

F

face a flat shape

face ⟶

---

flat shape

---

foot (feet) a unit of measure used to measure lengths

0 1 2 3 4 5
inches

1 foot = 12 inches

---

fourth The rectangle is in fourths.

1 fourth, or 1 quarter, is shaded.

G

greater than (>) is greater than

13 is greater than 12
13 > 12

half The rectangle is cut in half.

1 half is shaded.

halves 2 halves make a whole

2 halves are shaded. 1 whole circle is shaded.

hexagon a flat shape with 6 sides and 6 corners

hour

There are 60 minutes in 1 hour.

I

inch a unit of measure used to measure length

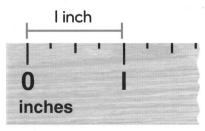

key the part of a picture graph that shows what each picture means

Books Read	
June	☐☐☐☐
July	☐☐☐☐☐☐
August	☐☐☐☐☐

Key: Each ☐ = 1 book

less than (<) is less than

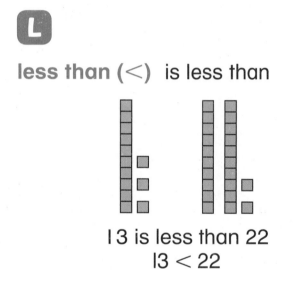

13 is less than 22

13 < 22

line plot a graph that uses a number line and Xs to show data

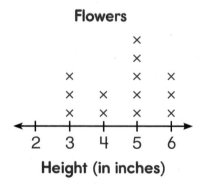

Flowers

Height (in inches)

meter a unit of measure used to measure lengths

1 meter = 100 centimeters

midnight 12 A.M.

minute There are 60 minutes in 1 hour.

nickel a coin worth 5 cents, or 5¢

5 cents

noon 12 P.M.

number line

0 1 2 3 4 5 6 7 8 9 10 11 12 13 14 15 16 17 18 19 20

odd number odd numbers of objects make pairs with 1 left over

An odd number has 1, 3, 5, 7, or 9 in the ones place.

P.M. the time from noon until midnight

penny a coin worth 1 cent, or 1¢

1 cent

pentagon flat shape with 5 sides and 5 angles

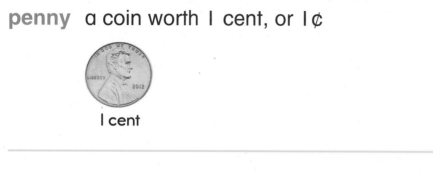

picture graph

Books Read	
June	☐☐☐☐
July	☐☐☐☐☐☐
August	☐☐☐☐☐

Key: Each ☐ = 1 book

place-value chart a chart that shows the value of each digit

tens	ones
6	4

64 has 6 tens and 4 ones.

quadrilateral flat shape with 4 sides and 4 angles

quarter a coin worth 25 cents, or 25¢

25 cents

rectangle a flat shape with 4 sides and 4 corners

regroup use 10 ones to make 1 ten or make 1 ten from 10 ones

14 ones = 1 ten 4 ones

2 tens 3 ones = 23 ones

related facts facts that have the same numbers

$$7 + 6 = 13 \qquad 13 - 6 = 7$$
$$6 + 7 = 13 \qquad 13 - 7 = 6$$

These 4 facts are related facts.

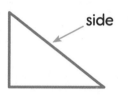

side

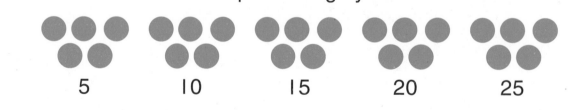

skip-count when you count by a number other than 1

skip-counting by 5s

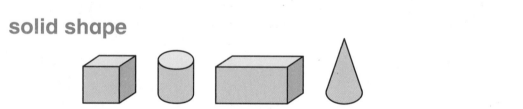

| 5 | 10 | 15 | 20 | 25 |

solid shape

square a flat shape with 4 equal sides and 4 corners

subtract to find how many after taking apart, taking away from, or comparing

sum the answer in addition

$$4 + 3 = 7$$

↑
sum

T

third The rectangle is in thirds. I third is shaded.

triangle flat shape that has 3 sides and 3 corners

Y

yard a unit of measure used to measure lengths

One yard is the same length as 3 feet, or 36 inches.

Notes